THE BLUEPRINT LANGUAGE

OF THE MACHINE INDUSTRIES

HENRY CECIL SPENCER, M. S. PROFESSOR OF TECHNICAL DRAWING, CHAIRMAN OF DEPARTMENT, ILLINOIS INSTITUTE OF TECHNOLOGY

HIRAM E. GRANT, B. S. ASSOCIATE PROFESSOR OF ENGINEERING DRAWING, CHAIRMAN OF DEPARTMENT, WASHINGTON UNIVERSITY

NEW YORK — THE MACMILLAN COMPANY — 1947

PREFACE

World War II brought a host of new and untrained workers into industry, many of these being women without any mechanical experience. There has always been a need for training in blueprint reading, but now this need is greater than ever before. It is the aim of this book to provide fundamental training in blueprint reading with the necessary emphasis upon the visualization of views of objects. Worksheets after each chapter are provided to give the student "training by doing."

We have set out to provide a thoroughly practical book which will adequately meet the requirements of industry. With this in mind we have obtained the cooperation of over a hundred major industrial companies in the development of problems and illustration material. We have personally inspected over 150,000 original tracings in these plants and have selected the basic material for the required illustrations and problems. Thus, there are no "classroom" problems, no theoretical cutaway blocks, and no "trick" exercises; every drawing has been taken from an actual commercial blueprint.

The "completion problem" idea has been adopted to make it possible to cover a very wide range of problems in a relatively limited time. Special "easy-sketching" cross-section grids are provided, in order that students without any marked ability in sketching may proceed easily with the work. These problems are designed to bring out principles, and are sufficiently difficult to make the student think.

A considerable number of facsimile reproductions of commercial prints are included at the end of the book. These have been carefully selected to provide a broad view of the practices of various companies, and to cover fundamental principles. Worksheets, with questions, and grids for sketching, accompany the blueprints.

We wish to acknowledge the encouragement and help of many engineers and professional associates, too numerous to list here. A list of industrial concerns which cooperated in this undertaking is given on page x. Without their whole-hearted collaboration this book would not be possible in its present form. The authors also wish to express appreciation for the use of several illustrations from *Technical Drawing* by Giesecke, Mitchell and Spencer, and from *Engineering Preview* by Grinter, et al.

The problem sheets in this book have been used repeatedly in blueprint-reading classes conducted both at the University of Wisconsin and at the Illinois Institute of Technology, and their appropriateness in teaching the principles of the subject has been thoroughly established.

It is hoped that those in the schools and in industry who use this book will feel free to write the authors concerning the work covered and it is hoped in particular they will make suggestions for improvement of the text as ideas suggest themselves through class experience.

H. C. SPENCER
H. E. GRANT

CONTENTS

CONTENTS

NAMES OF CONTRIBUTING COMPANIES

Allis-Chalmers Mfg. Co.
American Can Company
American Tool Works Co.
Avey Drilling Machine Co.

Baker Bros., Inc.
Baldwin Locomotive Works
Bauer Bros. Co.
Baush Machine Tool Co.
Beloit Iron Works
Boston Gear Works
Boulder Dam — Canyon Outlet Works
Brown & Sharpe Mfg. Co.
Bucyrus Erie Co.
Butterworth, H. W. & Sons Co.

Case, G. I. Co.
Caterpillar Tractor Co.
Chain Belt Co.
Chevrolet Motor Co.
Chicago Ordnance District
Cincinnati Milling Machine Co.
Cincinnati Planer Co.
Cincinnati Shaper Co.
Cleveland Automatic Machine Co.
Cleveland Twist Drill Co.
Cleveland Universal Jig Co.
Consolidated Machine Tool Corp.
Consolidated Packaging Machine
  Corp.
Crown Can Co.
Cullen Friestedt Co.

Davis & Thompson Co.
Defiance Machine Works
Drever Mfg. Co.

Eclipse Counterbore Co.

Farnham Mfg. Co.
Fosdick Machine Tool Co.

Gairing Tool Co.
General Engineering Co.
General Motors Corp., Frigidaire Div.
Giddings & Lewis Machine Tool Co.
Gisholt Machine Co.
Gorton, Geo., Machine Co.
Gray, G. A., Co.
Greenfield Tap & Die Corp.
Greenlee Bros. & Co.

Haskins, R. G., Co.
Hunter Mfg. Co.
Hydraulic Press Mfg. Co.

Illinois Tool Works
Industrial Gear Co.
Ingersoll Milling Machine Co.

Journal Co., The

Kearney & Trecker Co.
Kelley Reamer Co.
Koehring Co.

Lamson & Sessions Co.
LeBlond, R. K., Machine Tool Co.
Liquid Carbonic Corp.
Lodge & Shipley Co.

Machinery (Magazine)
Madison-Kipp Corp.
Mattison Machine Works
Meyer, Geo. J., Mfg. Co.
McCullock Engineering Co.
Miehle Printing Press & Mfg. Co.
Milwaukee Foundry Equipment Co.
Monarch Machine Tool Co.
Murphy Diesel Co.

National Broach & Machine Co.
National-Superior Co.
Niagara Machine & Tool Works
Nordberg Mfg. Co.
Northwest Engineering Co.

Oilgear Co.

Package Machinery Co.
Packard Motor Car Co.
Pease, C. F. & Co.
Poloroid Corp.
Pontiac Motor Corp.

Reed-Prentice Corp.
Rock Island Arsenal
Rosenthal Thresher Co.

Sidney Machine Tool Co.
Smith Engineering Works
Starrett, L. S., Co.
Stephan National Adv. Co.
Stokes & Smith Co.
Stover Lock Nut and Machinery Corp.

Sundstrand Machine Tool Co.

Taylor Mfg. Co.
Thompson Products, Inc.

U. S. Dept. of Interior
Universal Power Shovel Corp.

Vilter Mfg. Co.

Warner & Swasey Co.
Watertown Arsenal
Western Austin Co.
Western Electric Co.

Yoder Co.
York Ice Machinery Corp.

FOREIGN COUNTRIES

Canada
  Bertram, J., & Sons; Dundas,
  Ontario
  Brown-Boggs Co. Ltd.; Hamilton,
  Ontario
  Canada Machinery Corp.; Galt,
  Ontario
  McDougal, R., Co. Ltd.; Galt,
  Ontario

Czechoslovakia
  Dra. E. Beneše, Vysoké Školy
  Technické; Brne

Finland
  Suomen Sähkö O. Y. Gottfred
  Strömberg; Helsinki
  Techniska Läroverket; Helsinki
  Technical University; Helsinki

France
  Ecole Nationale Professionnelle;
  Metz

Great Britain
  Alfred Herbert, Ltd.; Coventry

Sweden
  A.–B. Gerh. Arehns M. V.; Stockholm

Switzerland
  Ateliers des Charmilles S. A.;
  Geneva

Tasmania
  University of Tasmania; Hobart

THE BLUEPRINT LANGUAGE

CHAPTER I

INDUSTRIAL PRINTS

1. Value of Blueprint Reading. Since World War I practically all of the basic older industries have grown enormously, and in recent years numberless new industries have come into existence as a result of new inventions and scientific discoveries. Others, such as the aircraft and shipbuilding industries, were expanded greatly as a result of the needs of the War Machine in World War II. In consequence of this terrific industrial expansion, we are no longer an agricultural nation but a nation of industrial workers who must understand machines and processes.

Every industrial worker knows that in these industries mechanical information is recorded and transmitted from one person to another largely by means of blueprints; and it follows that no worker can be effective if he does not possess the ability to read and understand clearly the information conveyed by these prints. The term *blueprints* has by common usage come to designate roughly all kinds of industrial prints made from engineering drawings or tracings, and is used in this broad sense throughout this book.

There are two distinct classes of individuals who are concerned with blueprints: the draftsman, or engineer, who prepares the original drawing and the worker who *reads*, or interprets, the meaning of the print made from that drawing. The draftsman must possess a complete theoretical understanding of the geometry of his craft and also a definite amount of skill in drawing. In addition to this, he or the engineer under whose direction he works must above all have a thorough knowledge of the principles of design, involving mathematics, mechanics, machine design, physics, and chemistry.

On the other hand the industrial worker is charged with the responsibility of carrying out the instructions shown on the prints. He need not have the complete theoretical training and skill in drawing which the draftsman must possess; indeed, it might be a waste of time for the worker to train himself

extensively as a draftsman in order to learn to read industrial prints.

In normal times most workers knew how to read blueprints. During the war, however, there was an enormous influx of new workers into the plants, and relatively few of them could read blueprints. In order to speed up production these people were grouped under *lead men* who could read blueprints; then the workers performed the specific tasks assigned them, without following the instructions directly from the print.

Obviously, promotion would depend largely upon the acquirement of the ability to read the prints directly and not through some superior. Every worker in mechanical industries should therefore learn at the earliest possible moment the principles involved in the reading of blueprints.

It is the purpose of this book to provide complete training in reading prints, and not in making the original mechanical drawings.

On the other hand, we do not believe that a complete understanding of prints can be obtained through the mere inspection of prints and answering questions regarding them.

Of prime importance in reading industrial prints is the ability to visualize the three-dimensional object from the views shown on the print. We feel that previous books on blueprint reading have, by and large, failed in this respect, and we propose to emphasize this phase of the subject far beyond previous treatises. In addition to questions relating to blueprints, freehand sketching and drawing with the aid of a straightedge, which can be executed by the average lay worker without training, will be used extensively to provide training in the various phases of the subject. The only materials needed by the student will be a pencil, an eraser, and a small celluloid rule. In short, we feel that a thorough understanding of the subject can be obtained not alone by inspecting drawings but by *doing* as well. However,

1

skill is not an objective, and the drawing is limited to providing certain missing lines to drawings already made.

2. Blueprinting. Today a number of different processes are used to reproduce drawings to provide exact copies at low cost. Of these, blueprinting is still the most widely used. Discovered by Sir John Herschel in 1840, it is essentially a photographic process in which the original tracing is the negative.

Blueprint paper is prepared by coating, or sensitizing, one surface with a chemical preparation which is affected by the action of light. The sensitized side of unexposed paper is light green in color. When such paper is exposed to natural sunlight or to brilliant electric light with the original tracing arranged so that the light must pass through the tracing to reach the sensitized paper, a chemical reaction occurs in all parts of the paper except in those protected by the opaque lines of the tracing.

When this process was first employed, a *sun frame* was used, Fig. 1; later electric machines, Fig. 2, were developed and are now exclusively used in commercial blueprinting rooms.

The time of exposure varies from about 20 seconds to several minutes, depending upon the "speed" of the paper and the intensity of light used.

After exposure the paper is washed for a few minutes in clear water, followed usually by a solution of potassium dichromate or other solution, then washed again in clear water and dried in the open air or in a special dryer.

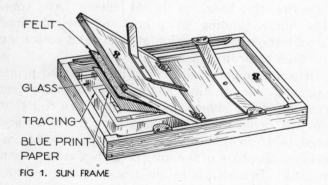

FIG 1. SUN FRAME

FELT
GLASS
TRACING
BLUE PRINT PAPER

The majority of prints are made from penciled *tracings*, drawn with a relatively soft pencil. If the draftsman produces lines of sufficient darkness, satisfactory blueprints may be obtained. The clearest prints are made from inked tracings on tracing cloth or vellum, but these tracings are more expensive to make and hence are not used where penciled tracings will suffice.

A number of typical commercial blueprints, made from ink tracings, are shown in Chapter XVI.

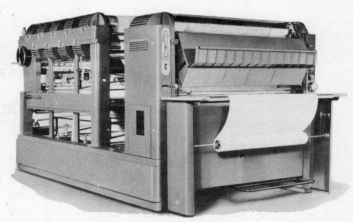

FIG. 2. CONTINUOUS BLUEPRINTING, WASHING, AND DRYING MACHINE

3. Blue-Line Prints. During the last ten years there has been a definite trend toward the use of prints with dark lines on a light background. *Blue-line* prints are used to some extent, but their use is limited by the fact that they cannot be made directly from the original tracing. First, a *brown print*, or *vandyke* print, must be made, and this is then used as a negative to produce the blue-line print. The vandyke print has white transparent lines on a dark brown opaque background, and, when used with blueprint paper the light penetrates the transparent line areas, thus exposing the blueprint paper in those areas and producing blue lines on a white background. All the problem sheets in this book are replicas of blue-line prints.

4. Ozalid Prints. The *Ozalid* method is coming into wider use daily. Ozalid paper is exposed in the same manner as blueprint paper, but instead of being washed, it is exposed to the action of ammonia vapors in a special *developer*. Ozalid prints are "positive" when made directly from the original tracing, having dark maroon or purple lines on a near-white background. Ozalid prints, having a light background, may be marked upon with an ordinary pencil if necessary, but are easily soiled in the shop. They are not subject to the shrinkage resulting from washing in water and other baths, and do not fade in sunlight as readily as do blueprints.

5. Black-and-White Prints. Several types of paper are made under different trade names in which black lines appear on white backgrounds, and these have the same general advantages and disadvantages as Ozalid prints. As yet, their use is not very extensive.

6. Handling of Blueprints. The space between the border line and the edge of the sheet is provided for "thumb room" in handling prints with soiled hands in the shop. If this rule is followed, there should be no smudging of important notes or dimensions on the print. Obviously, prints with white backgrounds should be handled with particular care.

Blueprints, which are subject to considerable shrinkage and distortion as a result of washing and drying, should never be scaled (measured with a rule) by the workman to obtain dimensions. On a small print the margin of error might be $\frac{1}{16}$″ to $\frac{1}{8}$″ and on a large print could be even more. A dimension which is obviously incorrect should be called to the attention of the foreman or other superior so that the correction can be made at the source.

So far as possible, blueprints should not be left for extended periods in sunlight, as all kinds of prints are subject to some fading.

Prints placed in the hands of the workman constitute his official instructions, and he should not mark upon them, as such marks may have the effect of authenticity. Foremen and others who are properly authorized may mark upon blueprints with a special pencil made for the purpose. These are available in silver, white, yellow, orange, and other colors.

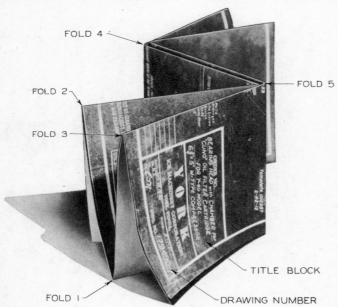

FIG. 3. ACCORDION FOLDING

The sizes of prints and system of folding depend upon the filing system and equipment employed. There is a strong trend toward the basic 8½″ × 11″ size and multiples thereof, such as 11″ × 17″, 17″ × 22″, and so on, which may be folded into a size 8½″ × 11″, or standard letter size. This is a convenient size for filing in standard letter-file drawers and for mailing in standard envelopes.

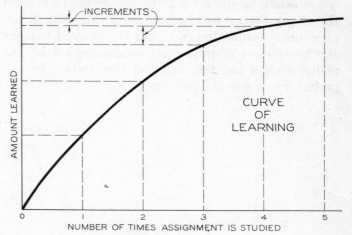

FIG. 4. CURVE OF LEARNING

The user of the print should observe how it is folded and take care to refold it in the same manner. The most common method of folding is the "accordion" style shown in Fig. 3.

Prints should not, of course, be taken from the shop by the workman without first obtaining proper authorization, for these prints may carry information relative to recent designs which should not be allowed to fall into the hands of outsiders. In war production plants such matters were rigidly controlled, and a violator might face criminal prosecution.

7. How to Study Blueprint Reading. Subject matter such as that included in the following pages requires study, not merely casual reading, and should be read several times. First, the assignment should be read over with the objective of grasping the general ideas and flow of argument. Then the same material should be carefully studied at least two more times and an effort made to obtain a thorough understanding of every point, however unimportant it may seem.

The diagram shown in Fig. 4 illustrates in graphic form approximately the additional amounts learned through successive readings of an average assignment. It will be noted that after the third time the increment in the amount learned becomes very small, approaching zero, or satisfactory understanding.

It should be remembered that illustrations, particularly in a book of this kind, are given for study and not for casual inspection. The student should be just as sure that he understands the illustrations as he does the typed matter.

While studying, the student should make written notes of those items of printed matter or illustrations which do not seem clear, and at his earliest convenience he should ask the instructor to explain those questions. Requests for over-all general explanations usually indicate that the student has not given sufficient effort to the assignment; if he has really studied the text-material thoroughly, he can probably ask specific questions.

In the solution of problems, the student should make full use of the text and other references at his disposal before asking for help, and in no case should he ask his fellow students for assistance of any kind. Students usually supply the answer (often wrong), but do not teach. Only the instructor is qualified to do that, and his usual method is not to supply the answer but to help the student reach an understanding through his own mental processes.

CHAPTER II

VIEWS OF OBJECTS

8. Views of Objects. In the mechanical industries it is necessary to have an accurate method of representing parts to be manufactured. An exact scheme must be used to convey the ideas of the designer to the worker in the shop, and the designer himself needs a method of representation which can be built up progressively as his ideas are developed. It is important also that different workers, possibly in different localities, working on the same part or mating parts in the same mechanism, have identical instructions from the designer. Finally, the manufacturer for many reasons needs a perfect record for his files of all parts he manufactures.

The natural vehicle of design is drawing, and the universal method of representing parts for manu-facturing purposes is and always has been that of drawing *views, systematically arranged.*

A photograph or an artist's pictorial drawing shows an object as it appears to the observer, but not as it actually is. Such a picture does not describe the object fully, because it does not show the exact sizes and shapes of the several parts, and in fact does not show at all those parts rendered invisible because they are on the side of the object away from the observer, or are inside the object.

A *view* of an object is obtained by the observer looking directly (perpendicularly) toward one side or face of the object, Fig. 5. The observer is theoretically at an infinite distance from the object. The *front view* is usually obtained first, and then the other

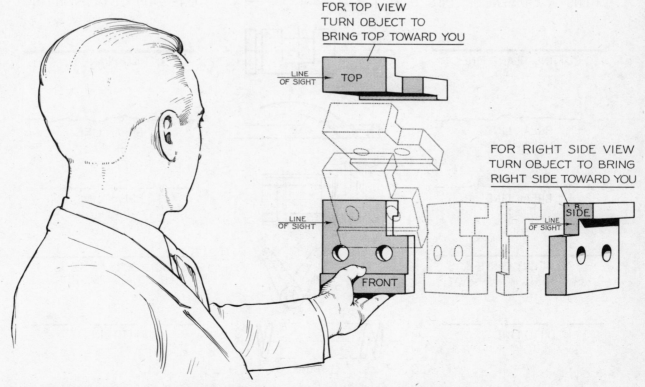

FIG. 5. OBTAINING THE THREE VIEWS OF BLADE CLAMP HOLDER FOR AUTOMATIC SCREW MACHINE

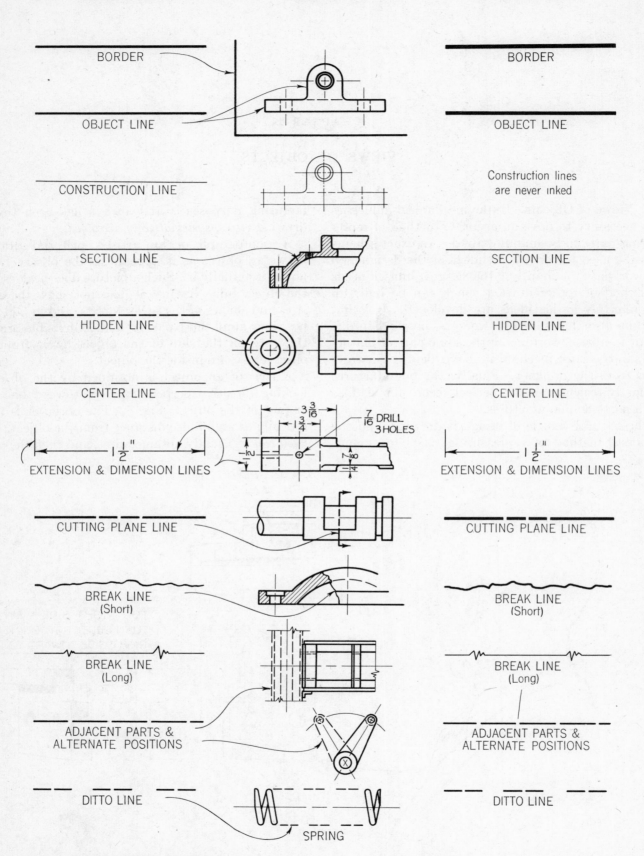

PENCIL LINES	APPLICATIONS	INK LINES
BORDER		BORDER
OBJECT LINE		OBJECT LINE
CONSTRUCTION LINE		Construction lines are never inked
SECTION LINE		SECTION LINE
HIDDEN LINE		HIDDEN LINE
CENTER LINE		CENTER LINE
EXTENSION & DIMENSION LINES		EXTENSION & DIMENSION LINES
CUTTING PLANE LINE		CUTTING PLANE LINE
BREAK LINE (Short)		BREAK LINE (Short)
BREAK LINE (Long)		BREAK LINE (Long)
ADJACENT PARTS & ALTERNATE POSITIONS		ADJACENT PARTS & ALTERNATE POSITIONS
DITTO LINE		DITTO LINE

3 3/16

1 3/4

7/16 DRILL 3 HOLES

1/2

7/8

1/4

1 1/2"

1 1/2"

SPRING

FIG. 6. THE GRAPHIC ALPHABET (FULL SIZE)

principal faces of the object are viewed. Note, in Fig. 5, how the object is revolved upward to obtain the *top view*, so that the top of the object then faces

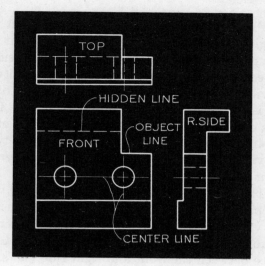

FIG. 7. THREE VIEWS OF BLADE CLAMP HOLDER

the observer, and how the object is revolved to the right so as to bring the right side of the object toward the observer to obtain the *right side view*.

These three common views are shown in their standard relative positions in Fig. 7: the top view directly above the front view and the right side view directly to the right of the front view.

9. Conventional Lines. The three most common

line-symbols are also illustrated in Fig. 7: the *object line* denoting visible edges, *hidden lines* indicating invisible edges, and *center lines* marking centers of holes and indicating symmetry, as will be shown later. An object line or hidden line represents the intersection of two surfaces or a contour. Object lines are usually heavy so that the outlines of the view will stand out clearly. Hidden lines are usually of medium weight. Other types of lines used on blueprints are shown, and their applications illustrated, in Fig. 6.

10. Possible Views. Any object can have as many as six regular views when viewed in the standard manner from the six possible directions, Fig. 8. In addition to the front view, top view, and right side view, already explained in Figs. 5 and 7, the *left side view, bottom view,* and *back view* are included. This is the American Standard arrangement of views, and while only two or three views are usually sufficient to describe completely most objects, those views which are shown will always be arranged in this manner (except as explained in § 13).

11. Observer at Infinity. The thoughtful student may observe that from a strictly scientific point of view the observer must be at an infinite distance from the object when obtaining any given view, and not close to the object as in Fig. 5. Only in this way can the *lines of sight* be parallel to each other, Fig. 9(a), thus enabling the observer to see *as points*

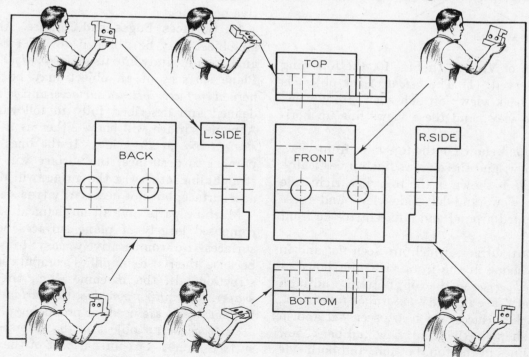

FIG. 8. SIX VIEWS OF A BLADE CLAMP HOLDER

those edges of the object which are perpendicular to the face being viewed.

For example, in Fig. 9(a) the line AB in the pictorial when viewed for the front view appears as a point, as shown in the front view (b). Likewise, line CD appears as a point in the same view, but if the observer were actually near the object he could not view both lines AB and CD as points at the same time without shifting his position. If the observer is considered to be an infinite distance from the object, the lines of sight would be parallel, and a true view of the object would be obtained, as shown.

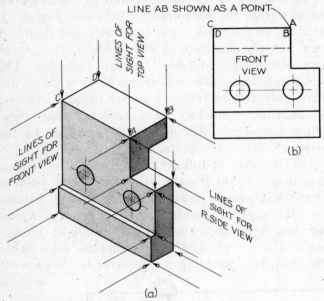

FIG. 9. OBSERVER AT INFINITY

12. Analysis of Views. In Fig. 10, the following should be observed: (1) The *height* of the object is shown in the back view, left side view, front view, and right side view, and these views line up horizontally.

(2) The *width* is shown in the top view, front view, and bottom view, and these views line up vertically.

(3) The *depth* is shown in the top view, right side view, bottom view, and left side view, and these views are grouped around and adjacent to the front view.

(4) The front surfaces which are seen *flat* and in true size and shape in the front view are shown as lines, that is *edgewise*, in the top, bottom, and both side views, and "face inward" *toward the front view.*

(5) The back surfaces which are seen *flat* and in true size and shape in the front view and back view are shown as lines in the top, bottom, and both side views, and "face outward" *away from the front view.*

(6) Every object line or hidden line represents a line of intersection of two surfaces of the object, or a *contour*, as in the side view of a cylinder (i.e., a hole).

(7) *Adjacent views are reciprocal.* If the front view is imagined to be the object itself, the right side view is obtained by looking toward the right side of the object in the direction of the upper arrow between these views. Likewise, if the right side view of the object is imagined to be the object itself, the front view is obtained by looking toward the front of the object in the direction of the lower arrow between these views. This relationship exists *between all adjacent views*, regardless of the combination.

(8) The distance between any two adjacent views is independent of the distances between other adjacent views; for example, the distance between the front and top views is not necessarily equal to the distance between the front and right side views.

13. Side View beside Top View. Frequently the draftsman, in order to save space on the drawing of a wide, flat object, where the height is small compared to the width and depth, places the side view horizontally across from the top view instead of the front view, Fig. 11.

It should be observed that the side view is exactly the same size and shape whether placed beside the front view or beside the top view, and has the same visibility of lines. The only difference is in the relative positions.

14. Surfaces, Edges, and Corners. Any rectangular object may be "broken down" for purposes of analysis and study into its *surfaces, edges,* and *corners.* Plane surfaces of an object may be classified as *normal surfaces, inclined surfaces,* and *oblique surfaces,* defined and described fully in following chapters. A plane surface will show either as a *surface* or *a straight line* in any view. If the lines of sight are parallel to a surface, the surface will appear as a straight line; otherwise the surface will always appear as a surface, but not necessarily true size and shape.

Machine parts and all mechanical structures are composed largely of plane surfaces because plane surfaces are comparatively easy to produce and because their use simplifies computation and construction. In the machine shop, the *planer*, the *shaper*, the *milling machine*, the *surface grinder*, and the *power saw* are used for producing plane surfaces.

An *edge* of an object is the intersection of two surfaces, and is of course a part of the boundary of each of the two surfaces. *Objects are represented on*

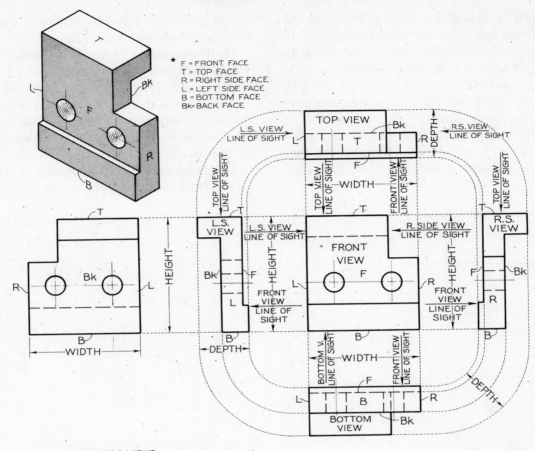

* F = FRONT FACE
T = TOP FACE
R = RIGHT SIDE FACE
L = LEFT SIDE FACE
B = BOTTOM FACE
Bk = BACK FACE

FIG. 10.   ANALYSIS OF VIEWS

blueprints by views of the visible edges (object lines) *and invisible edges* (hidden lines) of the object.

If the lines of sight are parallel to an edge, the edge will appear as a point; otherwise the edge will appear as a line, but not necessarily in true length.

A *corner* is the common intersection of three or more surfaces or edges. A typical example is the corner of a room where the ceiling and two walls meet at a common point. A corner will always appear as a point in any view.

15. Reading of Views. Up to this point we have seen how a given object is viewed by the observer, and how the views of the object are obtained and systematically arranged on the drawing or blueprint. The blueprint reader, however, is faced with the reverse process: he must start with the drawing showing the views of the object and *visualize* the object from those views. He must, in short, think back through the process by which the views were obtained to the point where he can visualize the three-dimensional object in space just as the draftsman did before he started to draw.

The blueprint-reading student has two very useful

aids in developing his ability to visualize an object from its views. The first is to make a pictorial sketch on plain paper or on specially ruled isometric paper.

The latter, obtainable at drafting supply stores, has ruled lines at 30° with the horizontal, and vertical

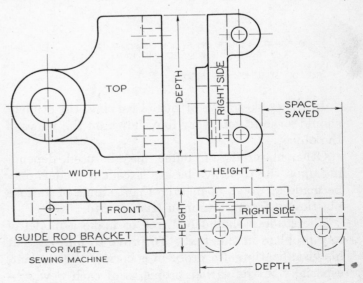

FIG. 11.   SIDE VIEW BESIDE TOP VIEW (GUIDE ROD BRACKET)

lines, as shown in Fig. 12(b). Along these lines the student sketches the main rectangular edges of the object, each equal in length to those shown on the given views. For example, in Fig. 12(a) and (b), lines *AB*, *AC*, and *AD* are each sketched along the isometric lines, full length, and the remaining edges are added in similar manner.

The second and perhaps best aid is to carve a model of the object from white laundry soap (highest grade) or from children's modeling clay, Fig. 12(c), (d), and (e).

of the problem. Several excellent examples of soap carving are shown in Fig. 13.

16. Problems — Views of Objects. The problem sheets to follow are to be removed from the book carefully along the perforated edges, and all required lines are to be drawn freehand or with the aid of a small rule, using a soft pencil. The student's name may be written or lettered in the title strip as required by the instructor.

All problems and illustrations in this book are taken from actual prints used in industry. The

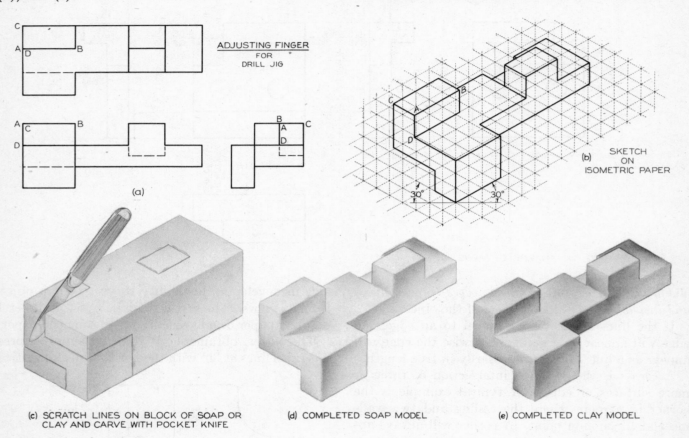

ADJUSTING FINGER
FOR
DRILL JIG

(a)

(b) SKETCH ON ISOMETRIC PAPER

(c) SCRATCH LINES ON BLOCK OF SOAP OR CLAY AND CARVE WITH POCKET KNIFE

(d) COMPLETED SOAP MODEL

(e) COMPLETED CLAY MODEL

FIG. 12. SKETCHES AND MODELS

In either sketching or model carving, the student should account for every line shown on the views of the object.

Other materials, of course, may be used, depending upon the tools available. Excellent models may be made of wood, of metal, of soft stone, of various plastics, or from a common Irish potato.

The student should feel free to make a model of any problem in this text. To prove to himself that his visualization of a problem is correct the student, especially in the earlier problems of each new subject, should make either a pictorial sketch or a model

authors personally have selected from the files of over a hundred industrial concerns more than five thousand prints from over 150,000 original tracings inspected. A number of problems were also taken from prints from eleven foreign countries, including universities and industrial firms. In the United States the War Department, the Department of Interior, and the Chicago Ordnance District cooperated in supplying problems of current interest.

In the early problems to follow, fillets and rounds, Art. 102, have been omitted to simplify the solutions. All later problems, however, contain all fillets and

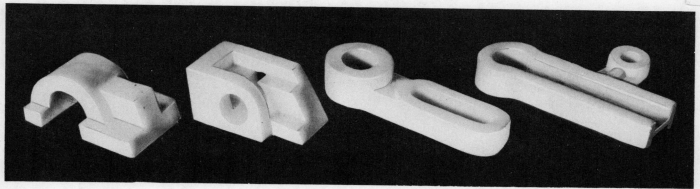

FIG. 13. SOAP MODELS

rounds as well as other characteristics of actual industrial representation.

In a few cases slight changes were made by the authors in the design of various parts to make them suitable for the purpose, but in the vast majority of cases no change whatever has been made. Accordingly the student may recognize a number of the parts shown and be able to identify them in particular machines or structures. It is hoped that full advantage will be taken of this possibility, as a complete understanding of the function of a part promotes understanding of the drawing and increases the interest of the student.

At suitable points in the problems various *shop notes* are given with *leaders* pointing to portions of the drawings representing certain *operations*. If the student will carefully study these explanatory notes in addition to solving the problems, he will obtain considerable familiarity with typical shop instructions on blueprints. See Appendixes V and VI for definitions and abbreviations of common shop terms needed in the reading of blueprints.

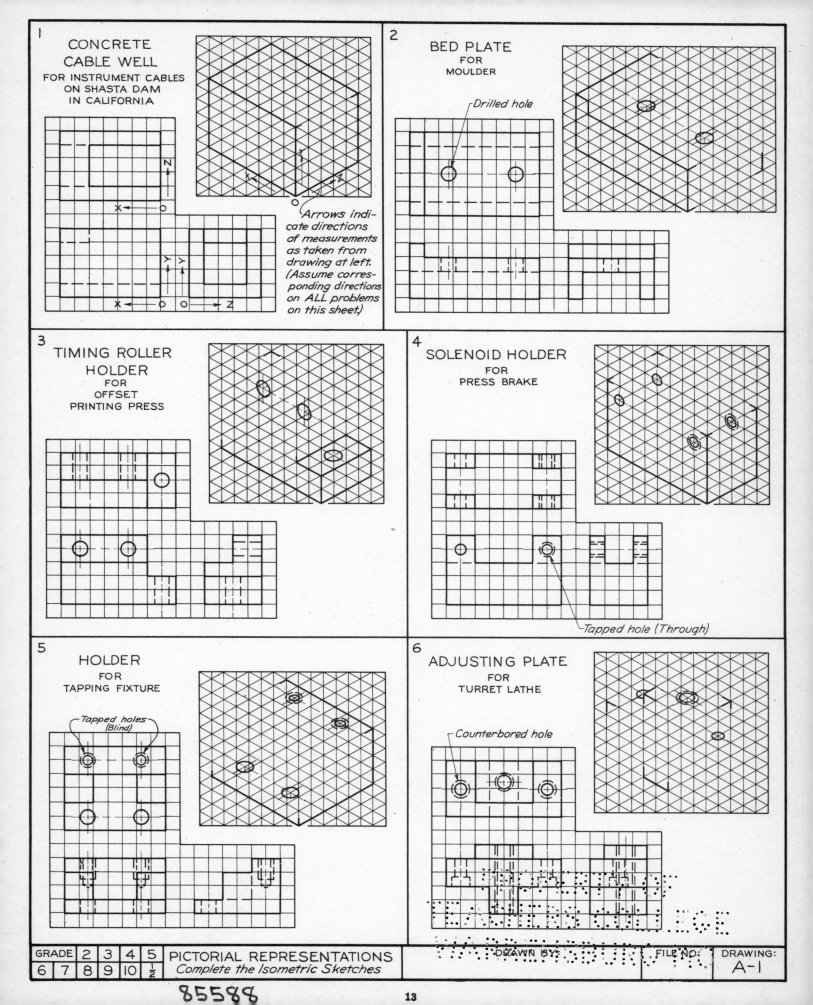

1

CONCRETE CABLE WELL
FOR INSTRUMENT CABLES ON SHASTA DAM IN CALIFORNIA

Arrows indicate directions of measurements as taken from drawing at left. (Assume corresponding directions on ALL problems on this sheet.)

2

BED PLATE
FOR MOULDER

Drilled hole

3

TIMING ROLLER HOLDER
FOR OFFSET PRINTING PRESS

4

SOLENOID HOLDER
FOR PRESS BRAKE

Tapped hole (Through)

5

HOLDER
FOR TAPPING FIXTURE

Tapped holes (Blind)

6

ADJUSTING PLATE
FOR TURRET LATHE

Counterbored hole

GRADE	2	3	4	5	PICTORIAL REPRESENTATIONS
6	7	8	9	10	½	*Complete the Isometric Sketches*

DRAWN BY

FILE NO.

DRAWING: A-1

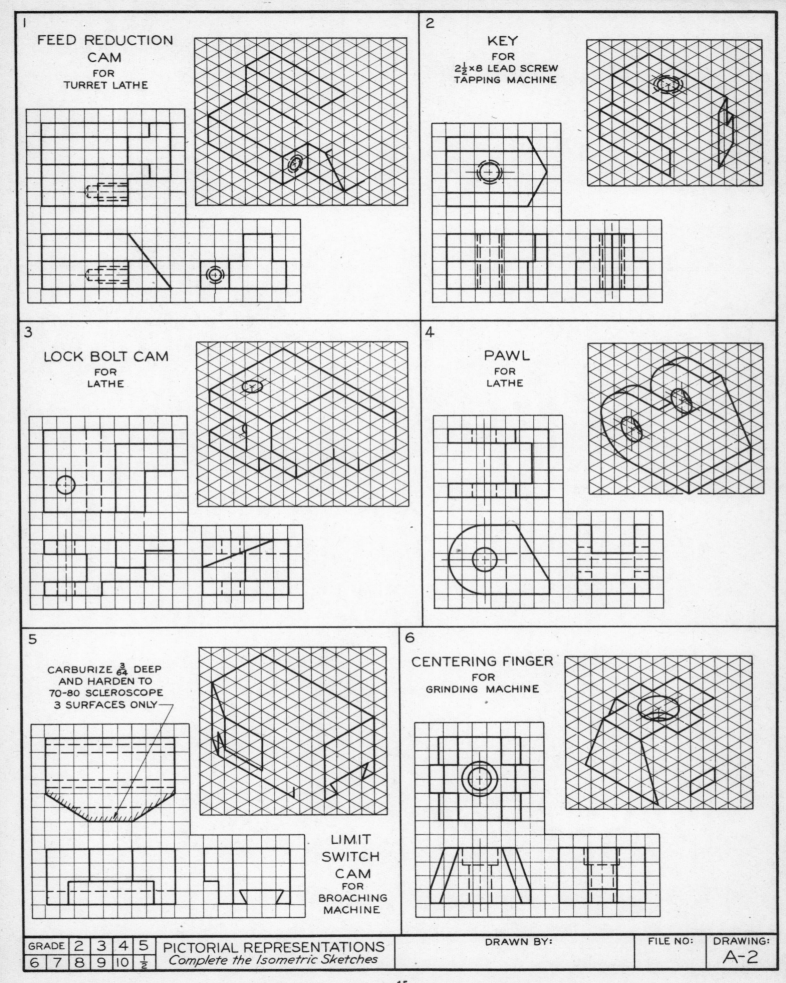

1

FEED REDUCTION
CAM
FOR
TURRET LATHE

2

KEY
FOR
2½×8 LEAD SCREW
TAPPING MACHINE

3

LOCK BOLT CAM
FOR
LATHE

4

PAWL
FOR
LATHE

5

CARBURIZE 3/64 DEEP
AND HARDEN TO
70-80 SCLEROSCOPE
3 SURFACES ONLY

LIMIT
SWITCH
CAM
FOR
BROACHING
MACHINE

6

CENTERING FINGER
FOR
GRINDING MACHINE

GRADE	2	3	4	5	PICTORIAL REPRESENTATIONS	DRAWN BY:	FILE NO:	DRAWING:
	6	7	8	9	10	½	*Complete the Isometric Sketches*			A-2

15

CHAPTER III

NORMAL SURFACES AND EDGES

17. Normal Surfaces. A normal surface is a plane surface of an object which is perpendicular to the lines of sight for one of the regular views. A plane surface perpendicular to the line of sight for any one of the three regular views (front, top, and side) will appear in its true size and shape in that view and as a vertical or horizontal line in each of the other two views.

For example, in Fig. 14(a), the line of sight for the front view is perpendicular to surface *A*; hence surface *A* is shown as a surface, true size, in the front view, as a horizontal line in the top view, and as a vertical line in the side view. The same relationship holds when the surface is perpendicular to the line of sight for the side view, Fig. 14(b), or for the top view, Fig. 14(c). A combination of normal surfaces is shown at (d).

A summary of normal surfaces is given in Table 1. An example of how the table is read is as follows: "*If a normal surface appears as a surface in the front view, it will show as a horizontal line in the top view, and as a vertical line in either side view.*" All the possible combinations in the table should be studied and stated in this manner.

18. Normal Edges. A normal edge is an edge of an object which is parallel to the line of sight for any one of the three regular views. In any such view, the edge appears as a point, and in the other two views it appears as a line in *true length*.

For example, in Fig. 15(a) the line of sight for the front view is parallel to edge *A*; hence edge *A* is shown as a point in the front view, and as a line in its true length in the other two views. The same relationship holds when the edge is parallel to the line of sight for the side view, Fig. 15(b), or for the top view, Fig. 15(c).

A summary of normal edges is also given in Table I. An example of how the table is read is as follows: "*If*

an edge appears as a point in the front view, it will appear as a vertical line in true length in the top view and as a horizontal line in true length in either side view."

19. "Machining Method" of Studying Normal Surfaces. In Figs. 16–22 inclusive are shown progressive cuts made in the machine shop from a rectangular block of cold-rolled steel to produce a Master Jaw, L. H. (Left Hand), for a "Centering Vise for a 2″ Threading Machine." Many machine parts are formed directly from such stock material, and, unlike working from castings or forgings, the workman must visualize the part from the blueprint alone. The different cuts alter the original surfaces into various shapes as L shape, T shape, U shape, O shape, and so on. All surfaces are *normal* surfaces except the cylindrical holes.

Each cut should first be observed in the pictorial drawing for each operation; then, in the three-view drawing, the way the cut is shown in each view should be carefully studied.

Fig. 21 shows the finished jaw and Fig. 22 shows how it fits in the assembly. The student should study the pictorial assembly to determine the reason for each cut made on the jaw block.

20. Breakdown of an Object into Its Edges and Surfaces. In Fig. 23 is illustrated the method of breaking down an object into its principal component edges and surfaces. The student will find it very helpful to study carefully each three-view drawing of lines or planes and identify them with the given three-view drawing of the object and its corresponding pictorial drawing. Also, the views of surfaces and edges should be "read" in the manner of Table 1, p. 18. For example, surface *A* shows in the top view as surface 3, 5, 16, 15 (read clockwise, starting at upper left), in the side view as the horizontal line 50, 51, and in the front view as the horizontal line 20, 21.

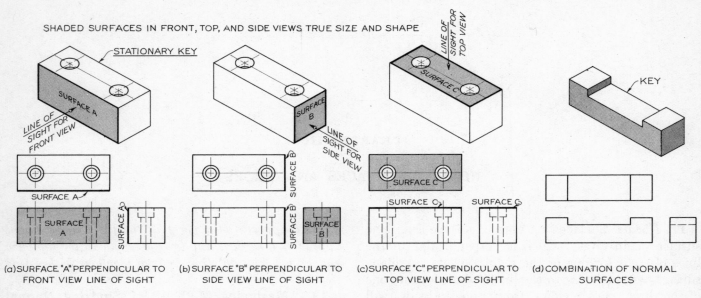

SHADED SURFACES IN FRONT, TOP, AND SIDE VIEWS TRUE SIZE AND SHAPE

(a) SURFACE "A" PERPENDICULAR TO FRONT VIEW LINE OF SIGHT

(b) SURFACE "B" PERPENDICULAR TO SIDE VIEW LINE OF SIGHT

(c) SURFACE "C" PERPENDICULAR TO TOP VIEW LINE OF SIGHT

(d) COMBINATION OF NORMAL SURFACES

KEYS FOR DIE CASTING DIE FOR CRADLE TELEPHONE

FIG. 14. NORMAL SURFACES

TABLE I

NORMAL SURFACES**			
TOP	FRONT	EITHER SIDE VIEW	EXAMPLE
HORIZONTAL LINE *	SURFACE	VERTICAL LINE	
SURFACE	HORIZONTAL LINE	HORIZONTAL LINE	
VERTICAL LINE	VERTICAL LINE	SURFACE	

*THE DIRECTIONS "HORIZONTAL" AND "VERTICAL" ARE BASED ON THE BOTTOM OF THE PAGE AS HORIZONTAL.

NORMAL EDGES**			
HORIZONTAL LINE (TRUE LENGTH)	HORIZONTAL LINE (TRUE LENGTH)	POINT	
VERTICAL LINE (TRUE LENGTH)	POINT	HORIZONTAL LINE (TRUE LENGTH)	
POINT	VERTICAL LINE (TRUE LENGTH)	VERTICAL LINE (TRUE LENGTH)	

**AS THEY APPEAR IN REGULAR VIEWS.

A CORNER SHOWS AS A POINT ONLY IN ALL VIEWS.	

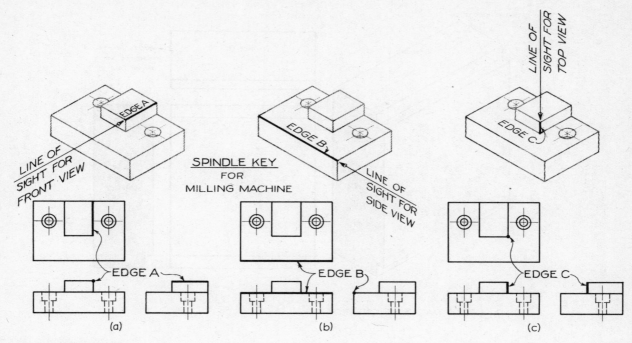

FIG. 15. NORMAL EDGES

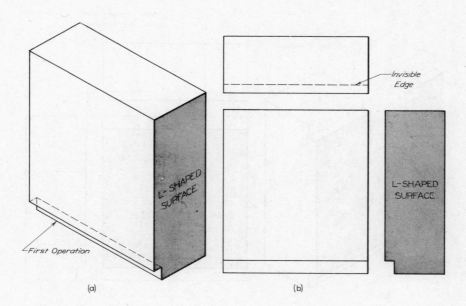

FIG. 16. FIRST MACHINING OPERATION

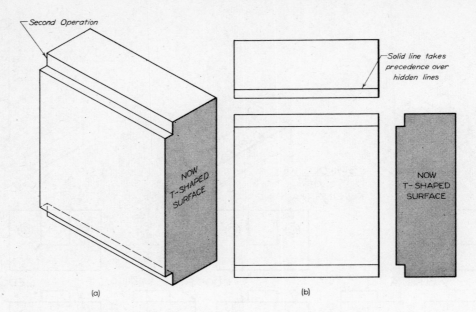

FIG. 17. SECOND MACHINING OPERATION

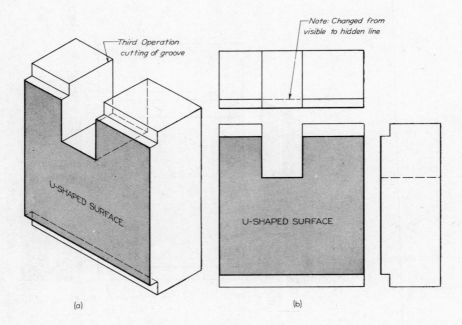

FIG. 18. THIRD MACHINING OPERATION

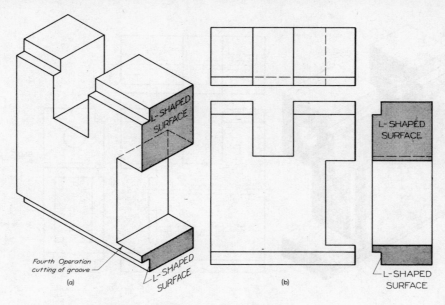

FIG. 19. FOURTH MACHINING OPERATION

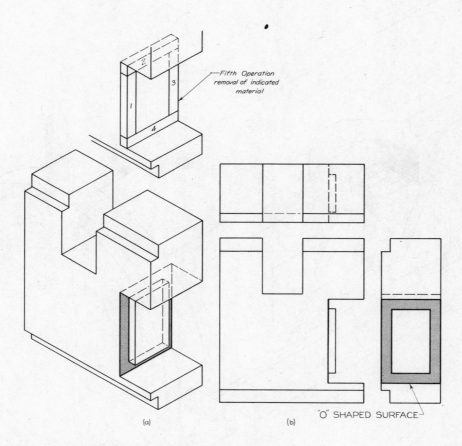

FIG. 20. FIFTH MACHINING OPERATION

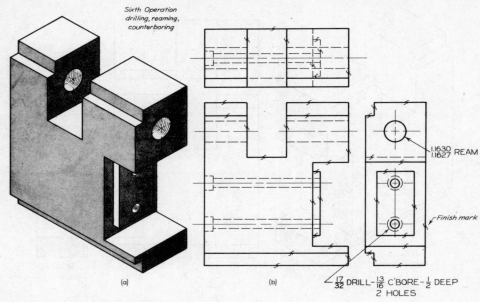

*Sixth Operation
drilling, reaming,
counterboring*

(a)

(b)

1.1630
1.1627 REAM

Finish mark

$\frac{17}{32}$ DRILL—$\frac{13}{16}$ C'BORE—$\frac{1}{2}$ DEEP
2 HOLES

FIG. 21. SIXTH MACHINING OPERATION

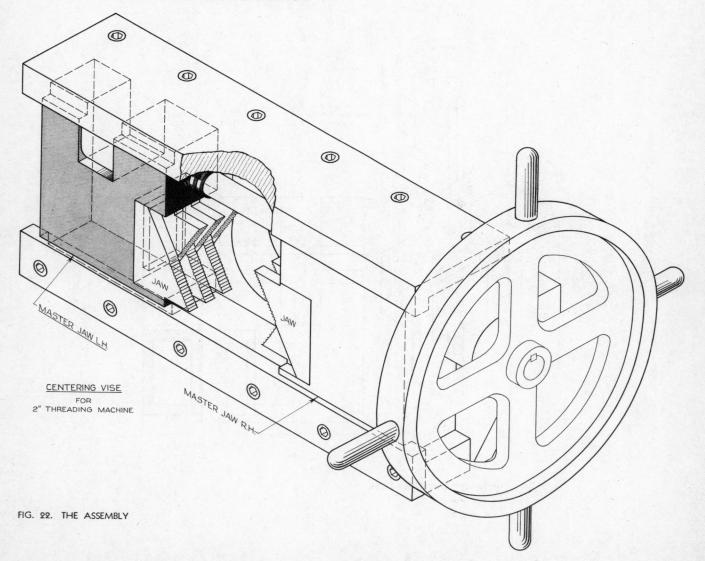

JAW

JAW

MASTER JAW L.H.

CENTERING VISE
FOR
2" THREADING MACHINE

MASTER JAW R.H.

FIG. 22. THE ASSEMBLY

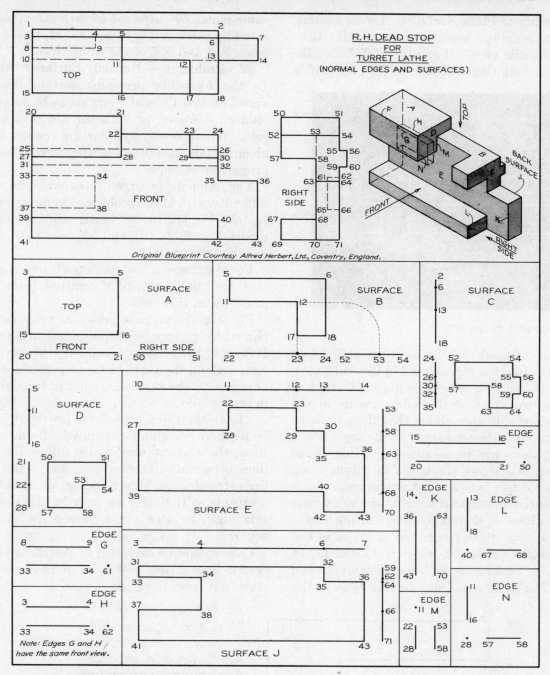

Original Blueprint Courtesy Alfred Herbert, Ltd., Coventry, England.

FIG. 23. BREAKDOWN INTO EDGES AND SURFACES

21. Continuity of Plane Surfaces. Let us assume, Fig. 24, that a solid line was drawn from point 12 to point 14 in the side view. It can be proved that the line does not belong there. The area 11, 12, 14, 13 is

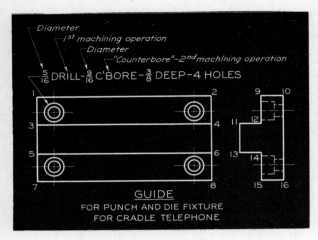

FIG. 24. CONTINUITY OF SURFACES

represented in the front view by the vertical line 4, 6. The area 9, 10, 16, 15 is represented in the front view by the vertical line 2, 8. Since the lines 4, 6 and 2, 8 coincide, the two areas of the side view lie in the same plane. The side view shows that the two areas are adjacent. With the two areas in the same plane and adjacent there can be no line separating them, because a line indicates a change of direction or an edge and none exists between the two areas.

There are three rectangular areas in the front view with the two lines 3, 4 and 5, 6 separating them. The area 3, 4, 6, 5 of the front view is 11, 13 in the side view, parallel to the side views 9, 12 and 14, 15 of areas 1, 2, 4, 3 and 5, 6, 8, 7, respectively, in the front view. The latter areas may be seen to be in the

same plane, not adjacent to each other, but are separated by surfaces 11, 12 and 13, 14, thus creating the edges 3, 4 and 5, 6 of the front view.

22. Problems — Normal Surfaces and Edges. In the following problems certain missing lines, views, and portions of views are to be supplied by the student *freehand*, or with the aid of a 6″ celluloid rule. Where necessary, starting corners or lines are given to aid in obtaining the correct location and proportion of views.

The student is urged, whenever he encounters difficulty with these problems, to make an isometric sketch, Fig. 12(b), or better still, to carve out a model, Fig. 12(c), (d), and (e), from soap, clay, wood, or other materials.

For purposes of instruction all fillets and rounds (see Art. 102) have been omitted from the earlier problems in this book.

Pictorial drawings of problems not already accompanied by pictorials will be found in Appendix IX. However, the student should try to solve the problems without the aid of pictorials, when none are given adjacent to the problems, since industrial blueprints never include such aids.

"Easy-sketching grids" are provided on all problems where sketching is required. By means of these lines, the student may easily follow the projection lines between adjacent views, and make his sketch lines straight. As shown in Fig. 25, the *depth* measurements in the top view may be transferred to the side view, or vice versa, merely by counting the squares.

Care should be exercised in sketching to make the sketch lines black and bold so that the lines will stand out from the grids.

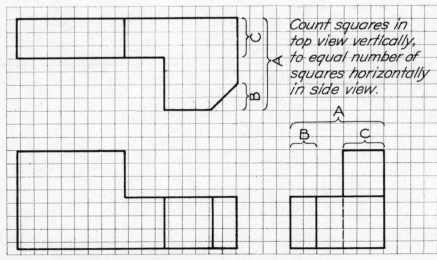

Count squares in top view vertically, to equal number of squares horizontally in side view.

FIG. 25. TRANSFERRING DISTANCES

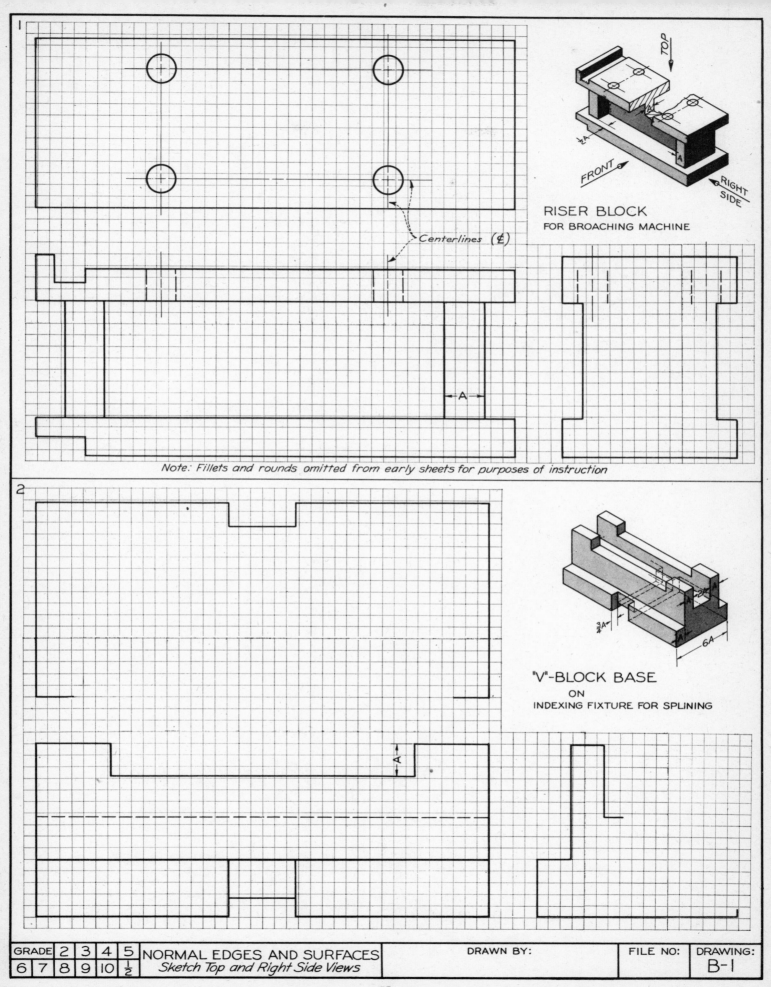

1

Centerlines (℄)

RISER BLOCK
FOR BROACHING MACHINE

A

Note: Fillets and rounds omitted from early sheets for purposes of instruction

2

"V"-BLOCK BASE
ON
INDEXING FIXTURE FOR SPLINING

A

GRADE	2	3	4	5	NORMAL EDGES AND SURFACES	DRAWN BY:	FILE NO:	DRAWING:
	6	7	8	9	10	½	*Sketch Top and Right Side Views*			B-1

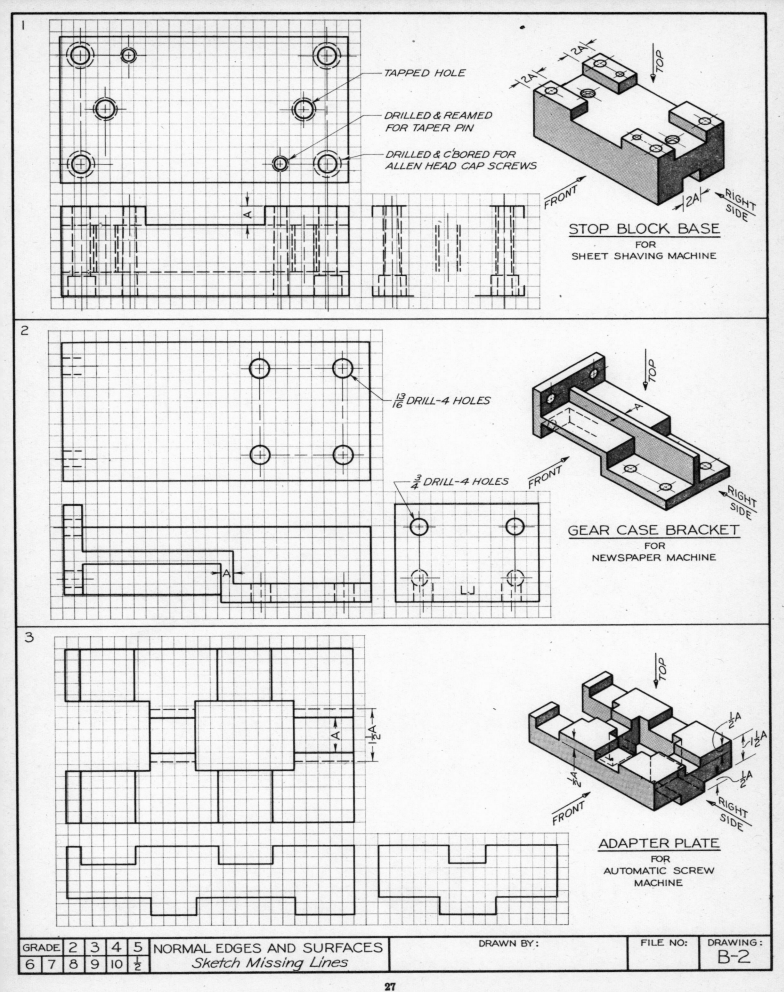

1

TAPPED HOLE

DRILLED & REAMED
FOR TAPER PIN

DRILLED & C'BORED FOR
ALLEN HEAD CAP SCREWS

TOP

2A 2A

2A

FRONT

RIGHT
SIDE

A

STOP BLOCK BASE
FOR
SHEET SHAVING MACHINE

2

$\frac{13}{16}$ DRILL-4 HOLES

$\frac{3}{4}$ DRILL-4 HOLES

A

LJ

TOP

A

FRONT

RIGHT
SIDE

GEAR CASE BRACKET
FOR
NEWSPAPER MACHINE

3

A

$1\frac{1}{2}$A

TOP

$\frac{1}{2}$A

$1\frac{1}{2}$A

$\frac{1}{2}$A

$\frac{1}{2}$A

FRONT

RIGHT
SIDE

ADAPTER PLATE
FOR
AUTOMATIC SCREW
MACHINE

GRADE	2	3	4	5	NORMAL EDGES AND SURFACES	DRAWN BY:		FILE NO:	DRAWING:
	6	7	8	9	10	$\frac{1}{2}$	*Sketch Missing Lines*			B-2

27

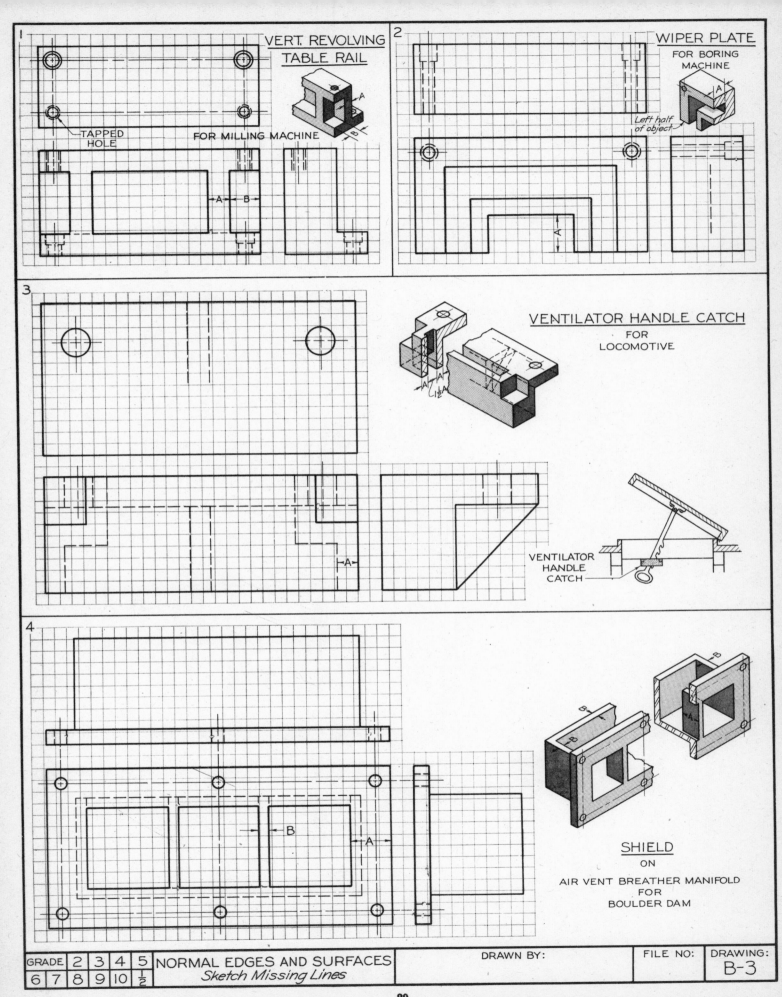

1

VERT. REVOLVING
TABLE RAIL

TAPPED
HOLE

FOR MILLING MACHINE

A B

2

WIPER PLATE

FOR BORING
MACHINE

A

*Left half
of object*

A

VENTILATOR HANDLE CATCH
FOR
LOCOMOTIVE

3

A

VENTILATOR
HANDLE
CATCH

A

B

4

B

SHIELD

ON

AIR VENT BREATHER MANIFOLD
FOR
BOULDER DAM

GRADE	2	3	4	5	NORMAL EDGES AND SURFACES	DRAWN BY:	FILE NO:	DRAWING:
6	7	8	9	10	½	*Sketch Missing Lines*			B-3

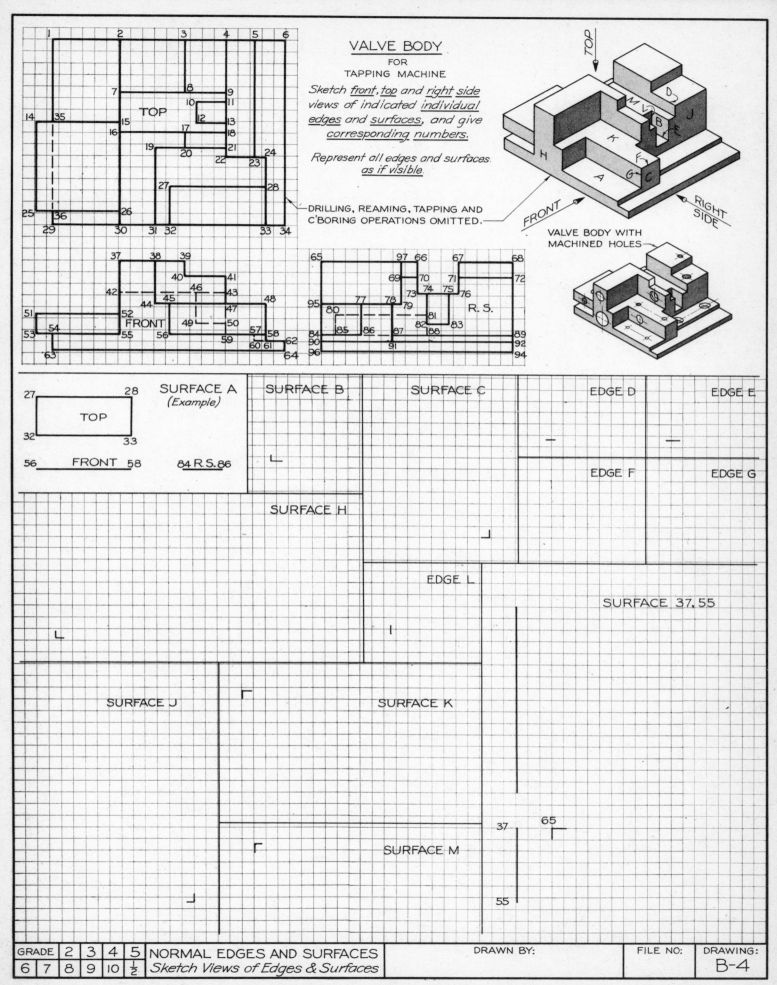

VALVE BODY
FOR
TAPPING MACHINE

*Sketch front, top and right side
views of indicated individual
edges and surfaces, and give
corresponding numbers.*

*Represent all edges and surfaces
as if visible.*

DRILLING, REAMING, TAPPING AND
C'BORING OPERATIONS OMITTED.

TOP

FRONT

R. S.

VALVE BODY WITH
MACHINED HOLES

SURFACE A
(Example)

SURFACE B

SURFACE C

EDGE D

EDGE E

EDGE F

EDGE G

SURFACE H

EDGE L

SURFACE 37, 55

SURFACE J

SURFACE K

SURFACE M

GRADE	2	3	4	5	NORMAL EDGES AND SURFACES	DRAWN BY:	FILE NO:	DRAWING:
6	7	8	9	10	½	*Sketch Views of Edges & Surfaces*			B-4

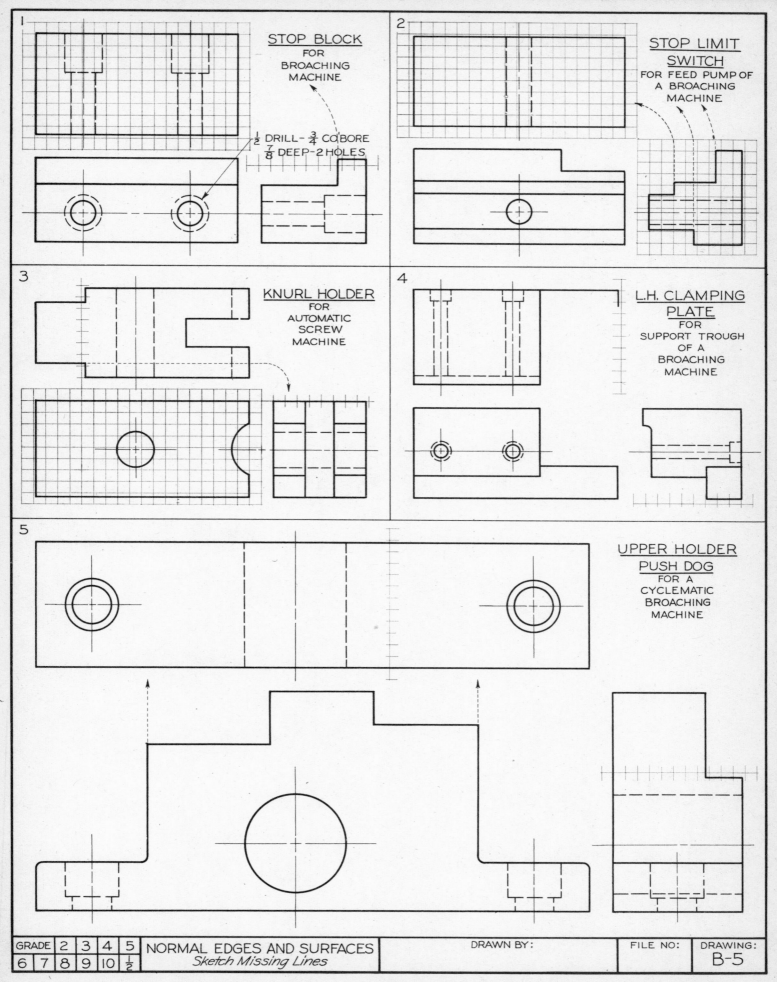

1 STOP BLOCK
FOR
BROACHING
MACHINE

½ DRILL - ¾ C'BORE
⅞ DEEP - 2 HOLES

2 STOP LIMIT
SWITCH
FOR FEED PUMP OF
A BROACHING
MACHINE

3 KNURL HOLDER
FOR
AUTOMATIC
SCREW
MACHINE

4 L.H. CLAMPING
PLATE
FOR
SUPPORT TROUGH
OF
A BROACHING
MACHINE

5 UPPER HOLDER
PUSH DOG
FOR A
CYCLEMATIC
BROACHING
MACHINE

GRADE	2	3	4	5	NORMAL EDGES AND SURFACES	DRAWN BY:	FILE NO:	DRAWING:
	6	7	8	9	10 ½	*Sketch Missing Lines*			B-5

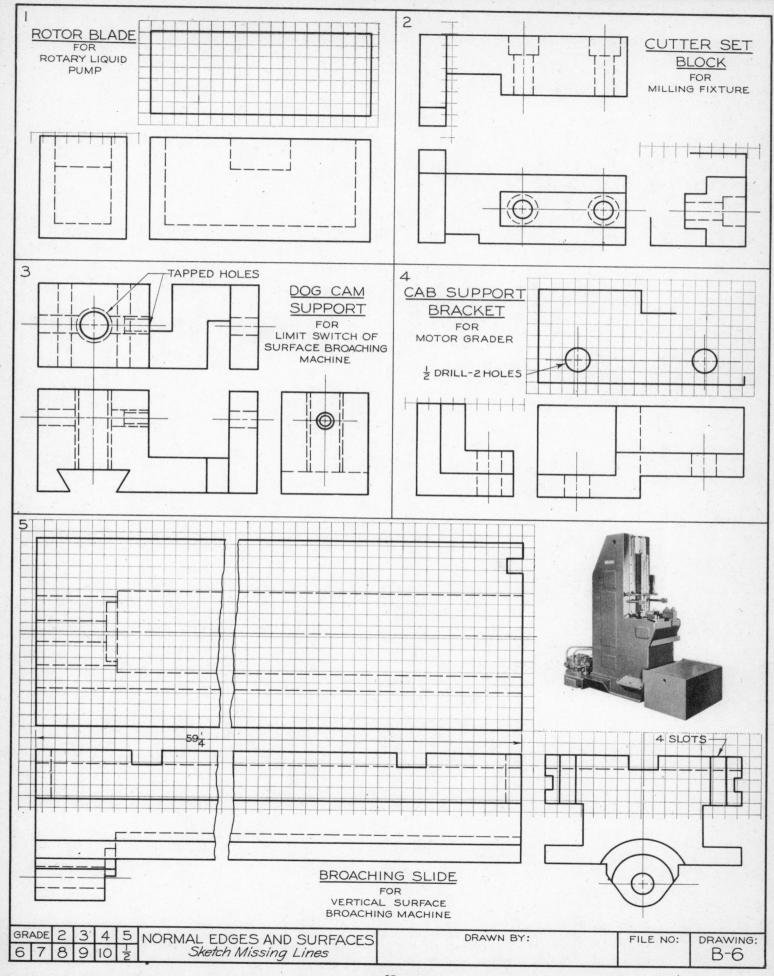

1 ROTOR BLADE
FOR
ROTARY LIQUID
PUMP

2 CUTTER SET
BLOCK
FOR
MILLING FIXTURE

3 TAPPED HOLES
DOG CAM
SUPPORT
FOR
LIMIT SWITCH OF
SURFACE BROACHING
MACHINE

4 CAB SUPPORT
BRACKET
FOR
MOTOR GRADER

½ DRILL-2 HOLES

5

59¼

4 SLOTS

BROACHING SLIDE
FOR
VERTICAL SURFACE
BROACHING MACHINE

GRADE	2	3	4	5	NORMAL EDGES AND SURFACES	DRAWN BY:	FILE NO:	DRAWING:
6	7	8	9	10	½	*Sketch Missing Lines*			B-6

CHAPTER IV

INCLINED AND OBLIQUE SURFACES AND EDGES

23. Inclined Surfaces. An inclined surface is a plane surface which is parallel to the lines of sight for one view, but makes an angle with the respective lines of sight for the other two of the three regular views.

Such an inclined surface will appear as an inclined line in the view where the lines of sight are parallel to it, and as a *foreshortened* surface in each of the other two regular views. A foreshortened surface is one which appears shorter in one dimension and true length in the other dimension. For example,

in Fig. 26(a) the line of sight for the front view is parallel to surface A; hence surface A is shown as a line in the front view, and as foreshortened surfaces in the other two regular views. The same relationship holds when the surface is parallel to the lines of sight, respectively, for the top view, Fig. 26(b), or for the side view, Fig. 26(c). A combination of inclined surfaces is shown at (d).

A summary of inclined surfaces is given in Table II. An example of how the table is read is as follows: "*If a surface shows as an inclined line in the top view,*

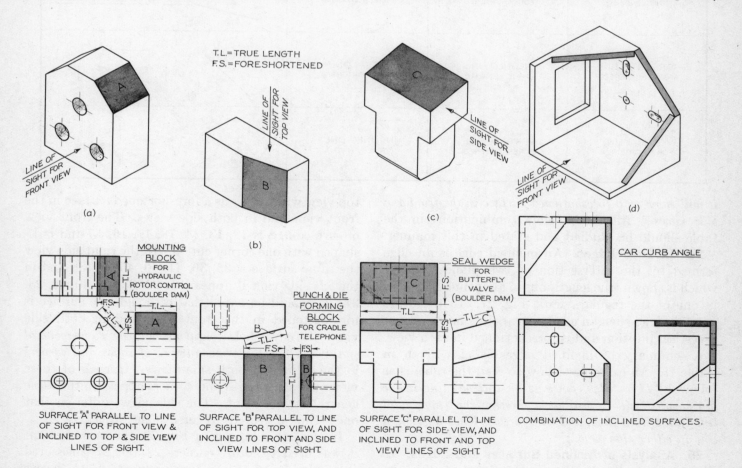

T.L.= TRUE LENGTH
F.S.= FORESHORTENED

LINE OF SIGHT FOR FRONT VIEW

(a)

LINE OF SIGHT FOR TOP VIEW

(b)

LINE OF SIGHT FOR SIDE VIEW

(c)

LINE OF SIGHT FOR FRONT VIEW

(d)

MOUNTING BLOCK
FOR HYDRAULIC ROTOR CONTROL
(BOULDER DAM)

SURFACE "A" PARALLEL TO LINE OF SIGHT FOR FRONT VIEW & INCLINED TO TOP & SIDE VIEW LINES OF SIGHT.

PUNCH & DIE FORMING BLOCK
FOR CRADLE TELEPHONE.

SURFACE "B" PARALLEL TO LINE OF SIGHT FOR TOP VIEW, AND INCLINED TO FRONT AND SIDE VIEW LINES OF SIGHT.

SEAL WEDGE
FOR BUTTERFLY VALVE
(BOULDER DAM)

SURFACE "C" PARALLEL TO LINE OF SIGHT FOR SIDE VIEW, AND INCLINED TO FRONT AND TOP VIEW LINES OF SIGHT.

CAR CURB ANGLE

COMBINATION OF INCLINED SURFACES.

FIG. 26. INCLINED SURFACES

TABLE II

it will show as a foreshortened surface in the front and side views." All the possible combinations in the table should be studied and stated in this manner.

24. Inclined Edges. An inclined edge is an edge formed by the intersection of two plane surfaces, which is shown true length but in an inclined position in one of the regular views, Fig. 27. In the other regular views such an edge appears in a horizontal or a vertical position and is foreshortened in each view.

A summary of inclined edges is also given in Table II. An example of how to read the table is as follows: "*If an edge shows as an inclined line in the top view, it will appear as a foreshortened horizontal line in the front view, and as a foreshortened horizontal line in either side view.*"

25. Analysis of Inclined Surfaces and Edges. In Fig. 28 the inclined surface appearing as 5, 8 in the top view will appear as a foreshortened surface in the front view and in both side views. The front view of surface 5, 8 is 12, 13, 14, 18, 17, 16, 15 and is L-shaped with one corner cut off. In the right side view the same surface is 35, 36, 41, 40, 45, 44, 38 and in the left side view it appears as 22, 23, 25, 30, 29, 28, 27. It should be noted that although the surface is foreshortened in the front view and in both side views, it nevertheless appears in the *same general shape and has the same number of edges and corners* in the front and both side views. In each of these views the same edges and corners appear in the same general arrangement. The side views differ in that one is the "mirrored" reverse of the other.

In the left side view of Fig. 29, the measurement d_1 was used to locate corners 22 and 27 (measured from the front face); measurement d_2 to locate

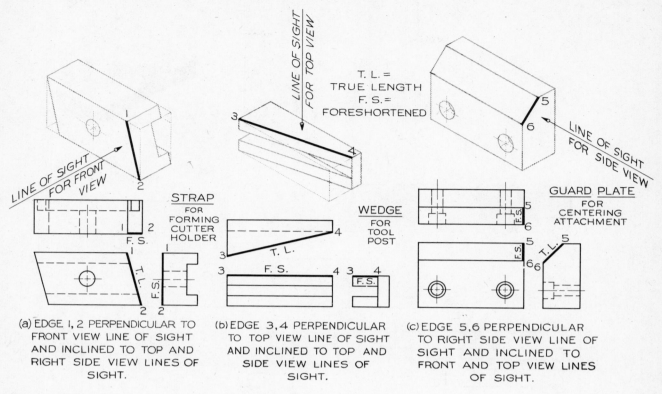

T. L. = TRUE LENGTH
F. S. = FORESHORTENED

STRAP
FOR FORMING CUTTER HOLDER

WEDGE
FOR TOOL POST

GUARD PLATE
FOR CENTERING ATTACHMENT

(a) EDGE 1, 2 PERPENDICULAR TO FRONT VIEW LINE OF SIGHT AND INCLINED TO TOP AND RIGHT SIDE VIEW LINES OF SIGHT.

(b) EDGE 3, 4 PERPENDICULAR TO TOP VIEW LINE OF SIGHT AND INCLINED TO TOP AND SIDE VIEW LINES OF SIGHT.

(c) EDGE 5, 6 PERPENDICULAR TO RIGHT SIDE VIEW LINE OF SIGHT AND INCLINED TO FRONT AND TOP VIEW LINES OF SIGHT.

FIG. 27. INCLINED EDGES

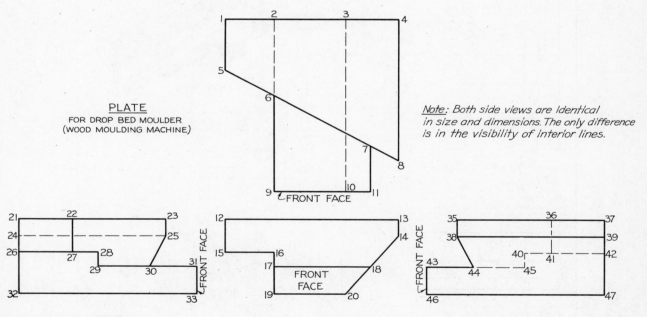

PLATE
FOR DROP BED MOULDER
(WOOD MOULDING MACHINE)

Note: Both side views are identical in size and dimensions. The only difference is in the visibility of interior lines.

FIG. 28. INCLINED SURFACES

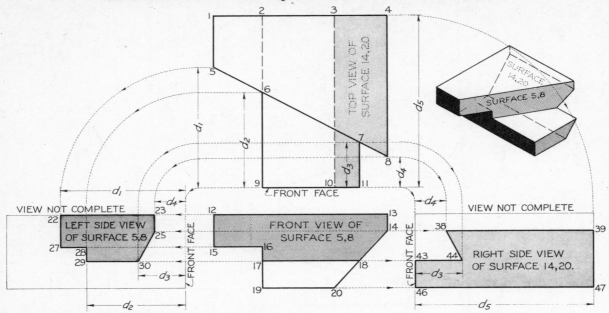

FIG. 29. METHOD OF LOCATING INCLINED SURFACES

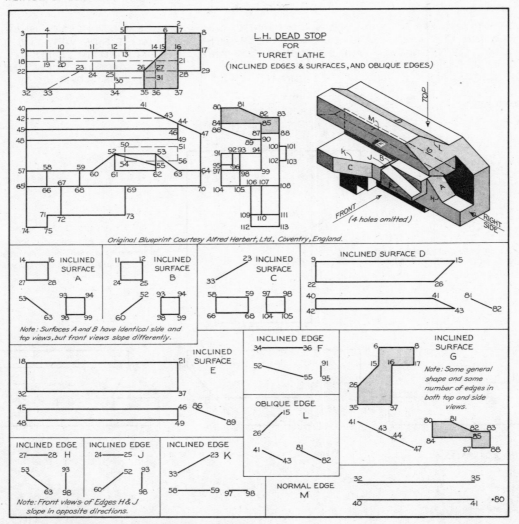

FIG. 30. BREAKDOWN INTO EDGES AND SURFACES

corners 28 and 29; measurement d_3 to locate corner 30; measurement d_4 to locate corners 23 and 25. The various heights were projected from the front view. By connecting these corners with lines representing edges in the same order as shown in the front view, the surface is seen to have the same *general shape and to have the same number of corners and edges.*

Note that all depth measurements (d_1, d_2, etc.) are set off in the top and side views in a direction *away from* the front view.

The inclined surface 14, 20 in the front view may be determined in the top view by projecting points 14, 18 and 20 to the top view where the surface appears foreshortened as 3, 4, 8, 7, 11, 10, the general shape being similar to the letter J or like a fishhook.

It is as important to project point 18 as the two ends of the inclined line 14 and 20 for determining the shape of the surface in the top view and for locating the surface in the side view. Point 18 is the front view of line 7, 11 in the top view and line 43, 44 in the right side view.

In the right side view the measurement d_5 was used to locate corners 39 and 47; measurement d_3 to locate corner 44; measurement d_4 to locate corner 38. By connecting these corners with lines representing edges in the same order as shown in the top view the surface is seen to have the same general shape; that is, a J or "fishhook."

Generalization: When an inclined surface shows as a surface, it must have the same number of corners and edges and the same general shape as the surface has on the object itself.

26. Breakdown of an Object into Its Inclined Surfaces and Edges. In Fig. 30 is shown a "breakdown" of a drawing of an "L. H. Dead Stop for a Turret Lathe," composed largely of inclined surfaces and edges, into its component parts. The student should carefully identify each three-view drawing of the individual surfaces or edges with the given drawings at the top and should note which edges and surfaces are shown in true size and shape and which are foreshortened. Also the surfaces and edges should be "read" in the manner of Table II, page 38. For example, surface G (see pictorial) appears in the top view as a surface 6, 8, 17, 16, 37, 35, 26, 15; in the front view as a line 41, 47; and in the right side view as a surface 80, 81, 82, 83, 88, 87, 85, 84.

27. Oblique Edges. An *oblique edge* is a straight edge which occupies an oblique position such that it does not appear horizontal, vertical, or as a point, in any view. Neither does the line appear in its true length in any view.

For example, in Fig. 30, edge L is an oblique edge, represented in the top view as 26, 15; in the front view as 41, 43; and in the right side view as 81, 82; and edge L does not appear horizontal, vertical, or as a point, in any view.

In Fig. 31(a) the inclined cut from the rectangular bar stock of high-speed steel has intersected the top and bottom *parallel surfaces,* and created two *parallel* inclined edges 1, 2 and 4, 3; hence:

Rule 1: If two parallel plane surfaces are intersected by a third plane surface, the two lines of intersection will be parallel.

The inclined surface is also parallel to *AB,* the line of intersection of the front and left end surfaces of the object, creating *parallel* normal edges 1, 4 and 2, 3; hence:

Rule 2: If two intersecting plane surfaces are intersected by a third plane surface which is parallel to the line of intersection of the first two, all three lines of

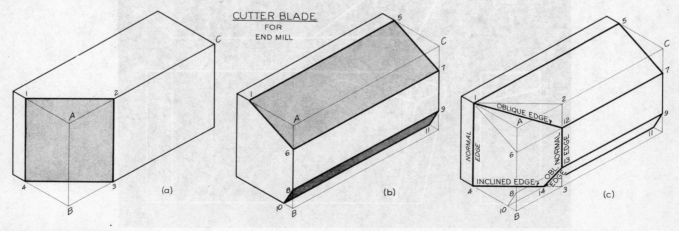

FIG. 31. OBLIQUE EDGES

intersection will be parallel. The most common example in machine work is the *chamfer*, in which a cut is made parallel to the edge that is removed.

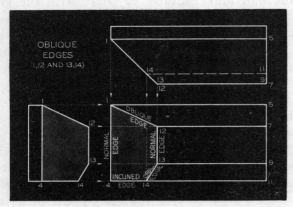

FIG. 32. CUTTER BLADE FOR END MILL

In Fig. 31(b), the two inclined cuts shown create four normal edges 1, 5; 6, 7; 8, 9; 10, 11; and four inclined edges 1, 6; 5, 7; 8, 10; and 9, 11. Note the application of Rules 1 and 2 here also.

In Fig. 31(c), showing the combined cuts of (a) and (b) on the piece of bar stock, it will be seen that the normal edge 2, 3 has been decreased in length to 12, 13; inclined edges 1, 2; 1, 6; and 8, 10 have been completely eliminated; and inclined edge 4, 3 has been shortened to 4, 14. Edges 1, 12 and 14, 13 are new oblique edges, and not parallel to any of the rectangular main surfaces of the object.

In the finished cutter blade, Fig. 32, oblique edges 1, 12 and 13, 14 are not horizontal or vertical or

shown as a point, in any view, and do not appear in true length in any view. An *auxiliary view*, Arts. 54–61, would be required of each oblique edge, to show the true lengths.

Each end of the oblique edges 1, 12 and 13, 14 is obtained in the front view by projecting from their respective top and side views as indicated by the dotted lines and the arrows.

It should also be noted that the inclined surface 1, 12, 13, 14, 4 is five-sided (pentagonal) and appears in similar shape in both the front and side views.

A summary of oblique edges is given in Table III, which follows.

28. Oblique Surfaces. An *oblique surface* is a plane surface which is not parallel to the line of sight for any of the regular views. *Such a surface will not appear as a line in any view but as a surface (never true size) in all regular views.* For example, Fig. 33 (front view), the surfaces 9, 7, 8, 10 and 9, 10, 12, 11 are oblique surfaces and are not shown true size and shape in any view. Notice that neither of these surfaces appears *as a line* in any view, showing that they are not parallel to the line of sight for any view. On the other hand, surface 19, 20 (top view) is an *inclined* surface, not an oblique surface, since it appears as a line in one view.

In Fig. 33 there are eight inclined edges, one oblique edge, and the remainder are normal edges; the student should identify each.

A summary of oblique surfaces is given in Table III.

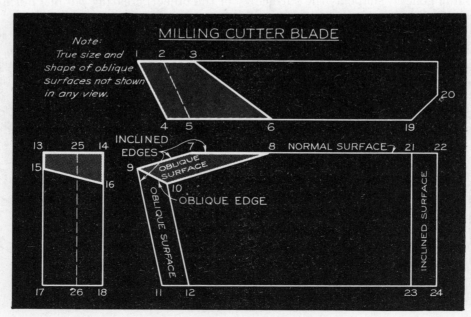

FIG. 33. OBLIQUE SURFACES

TABLE III

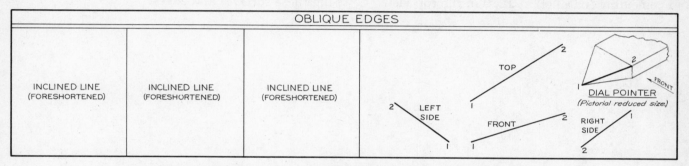

TOP	FRONT	EITHER SIDE VIEW	EXAMPLE

OBLIQUE SURFACES

| SURFACE (NOT TRUE SIZE OR SHAPE) | SURFACE (NOT TRUE SIZE OR SHAPE) | SURFACE (NOT TRUE SIZE OR SHAPE) | |

NOTE:
1. Parallel edges are parallel in all views (also in pictorial).
2. Shapes of surfaces in all views are similar in outline.

CENTERING BLOCK FOR DRILL JIG

(ALL EDGES ON THIS OBLIQUE SURFACE ARE INCLINED EDGES)

OBLIQUE EDGES

| INCLINED LINE (FORESHORTENED) | INCLINED LINE (FORESHORTENED) | INCLINED LINE (FORESHORTENED) | |

DIAL POINTER
(Pictorial reduced size.)

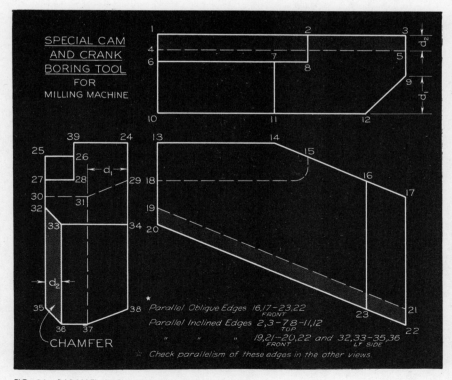

SPECIAL CAM AND CRANK BORING TOOL FOR MILLING MACHINE

CHAMFER

* Parallel Oblique Edges 16,17–23,22
FRONT
Parallel Inclined Edges 2,3–7 8–11,12
TOP
"   "   "   19,21–20,22 and 32,33–35,36
FRONT   LT SIDE
☆ Check parallelism of these edges in the other views.

FIG. 34. PARALLEL INCLINED AND OBLIQUE EDGES

In the example shown in this table it will be observed that inclined edges 3, 2 and 4, 5 are parallel on the object, that is, *in space* (see pictorial drawing) and also that *they appear parallel respectively in all views*.

Similarly, Fig. 33, the parallel edges 9, 7 and 10, 8 (front view) are parallel in space, and also in the three views. The same can also be said of all other parallel lines on the object, regardless of the kinds of lines. On the other hand, oblique edge 9, 10 and inclined edge 7, 8 (front view) are not parallel in any view, and are not, therefore, parallel in space.

In Fig. 34, inclined surface 9, 12 of the top view intersects the *parallel* inclined *surfaces* 14, 17 and 20, 22 of the front view, creating the *parallel oblique edges* 16, 17 and 23, 22 (front view). These edges appear parallel in the side view at 31, 29 and 37, 38 and coinciding (parallel) at 12, 9 in the top view.

The oblique surface shown in the side view as 32, 33, 36, 35 is a parallelogram. Its inclined parallel edges 32, 33 and 35, 36 were formed by the intersection of the parallel normal planes 13, 20 and 17, 22 of the front view with the oblique plane. The front view of these parallel edges is 19, 20 and 21, 22, respectively, their top views being 1, 4 and 3, 5, respectively. The parallel inclined edges 19, 21 and 20, 22 in the front view appear as parallel edges 32, 35 and 33, 36, respectively, in the side view, and as parallel edges 1, 3 and 4, 5, respectively, in the top view.

29. Problems — Inclined and Oblique Surfaces and Edges. The student should study each problem carefully and identify the inclined surfaces and oblique surfaces. Reference should be made to Table II, page 38, and Table III, page 43, in analyzing these surfaces and edges.

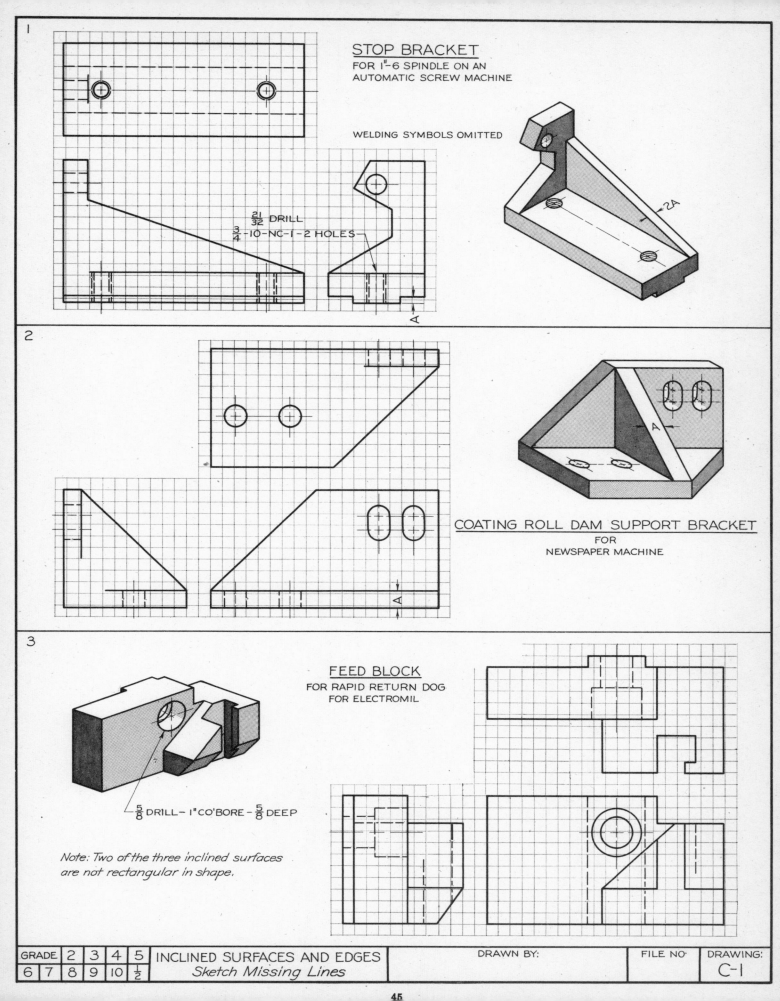

1

STOP BRACKET
FOR 1"-6 SPINDLE ON AN
AUTOMATIC SCREW MACHINE

WELDING SYMBOLS OMITTED

$\frac{21}{32}$ DRILL
$\frac{3}{4}$-10-NC-1-2 HOLES

2A

A

2

COATING ROLL DAM SUPPORT BRACKET
FOR
NEWSPAPER MACHINE

A

A

3

FEED BLOCK
FOR RAPID RETURN DOG
FOR ELECTROMIL

$\frac{5}{8}$ DRILL—1"CO'BORE—$\frac{5}{8}$ DEEP

*Note: Two of the three inclined surfaces
are not rectangular in shape.*

GRADE	2	3	4	5	INCLINED SURFACES AND EDGES	DRAWN BY:	FILE NO·	DRAWING:
6	7	8	9	10	$\frac{1}{2}$	*Sketch Missing Lines*			C-1

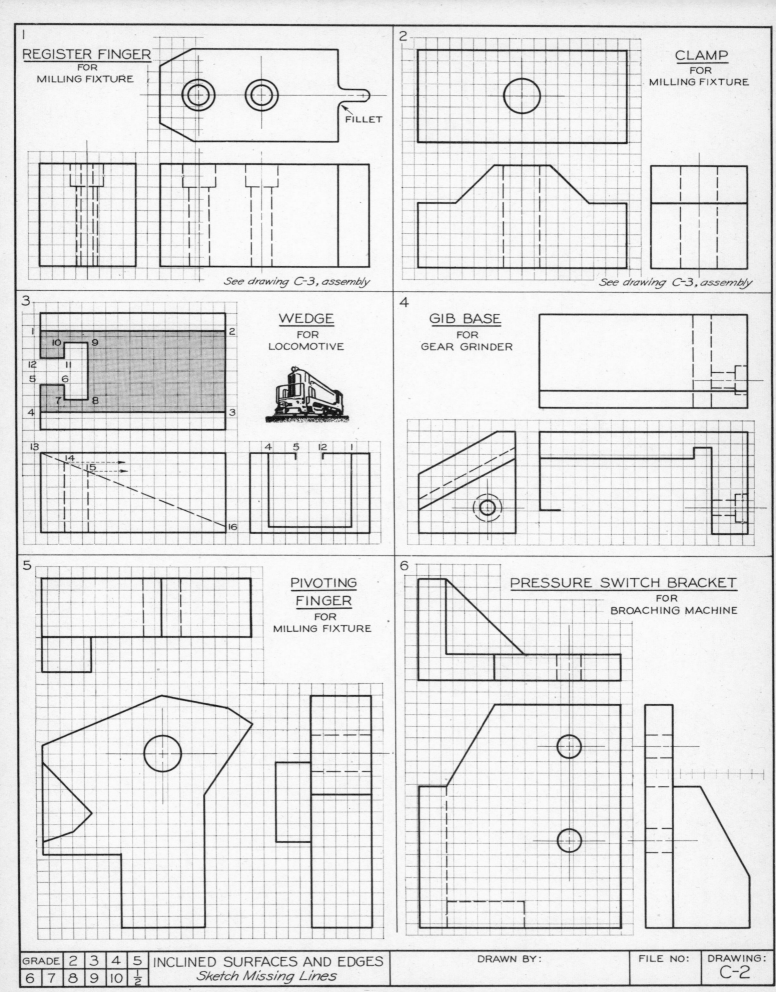

1 **REGISTER FINGER**
FOR
MILLING FIXTURE

FILLET

See drawing C-3, assembly

2 **CLAMP**
FOR
MILLING FIXTURE

See drawing C-3, assembly

3 **WEDGE**
FOR
LOCOMOTIVE

1 10 9 2
12 11
5 6
7 8
4 3

13 14 15 16

4 5 12 1

4 **GIB BASE**
FOR
GEAR GRINDER

5 **PIVOTING FINGER**
FOR
MILLING FIXTURE

6 **PRESSURE SWITCH BRACKET**
FOR
BROACHING MACHINE

GRADE	2	3	4	5	INCLINED SURFACES AND EDGES	DRAWN BY:	FILE NO:	DRAWING:
6	7	8	9	10	½	*Sketch Missing Lines*			C-2

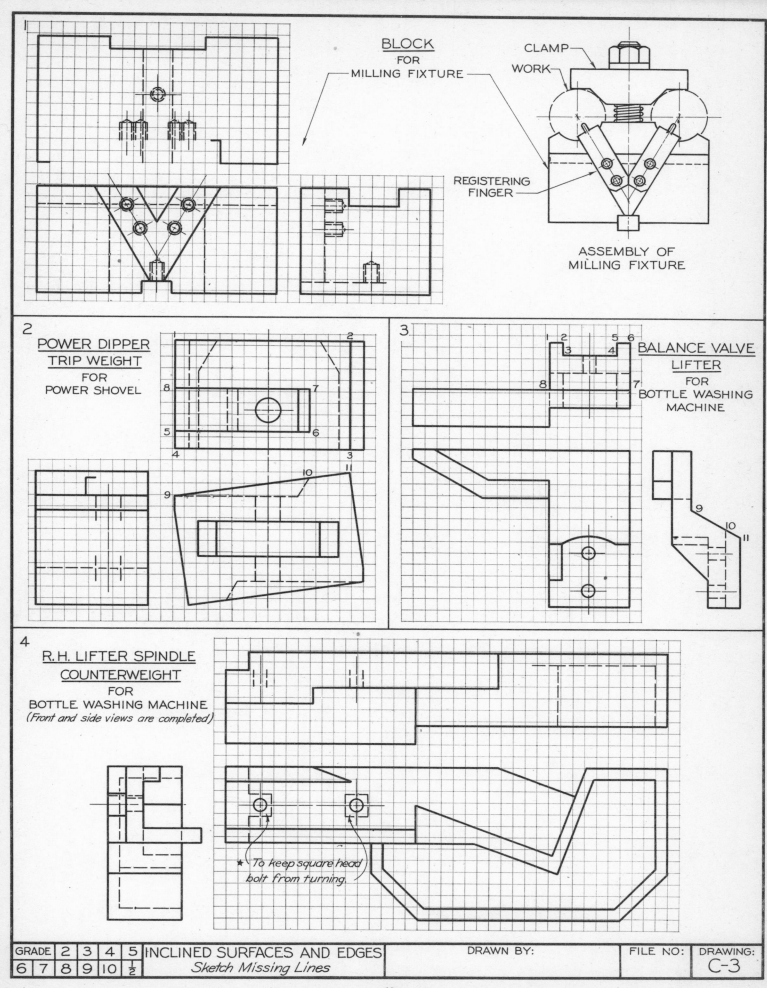

BLOCK
FOR
MILLING FIXTURE

CLAMP

WORK

REGISTERING
FINGER

ASSEMBLY OF
MILLING FIXTURE

1

2

POWER DIPPER
TRIP WEIGHT
FOR
POWER SHOVEL

3

BALANCE VALVE
LIFTER
FOR
BOTTLE WASHING
MACHINE

4

R.H. LIFTER SPINDLE
COUNTERWEIGHT
FOR
BOTTLE WASHING MACHINE
(Front and side views are completed)

★ *To keep square head
bolt from turning.*

GRADE	2	3	4	5	INCLINED SURFACES AND EDGES	DRAWN BY:	FILE NO:	DRAWING:
	6	7	8	9	10	1/2	*Sketch Missing Lines*			C-3

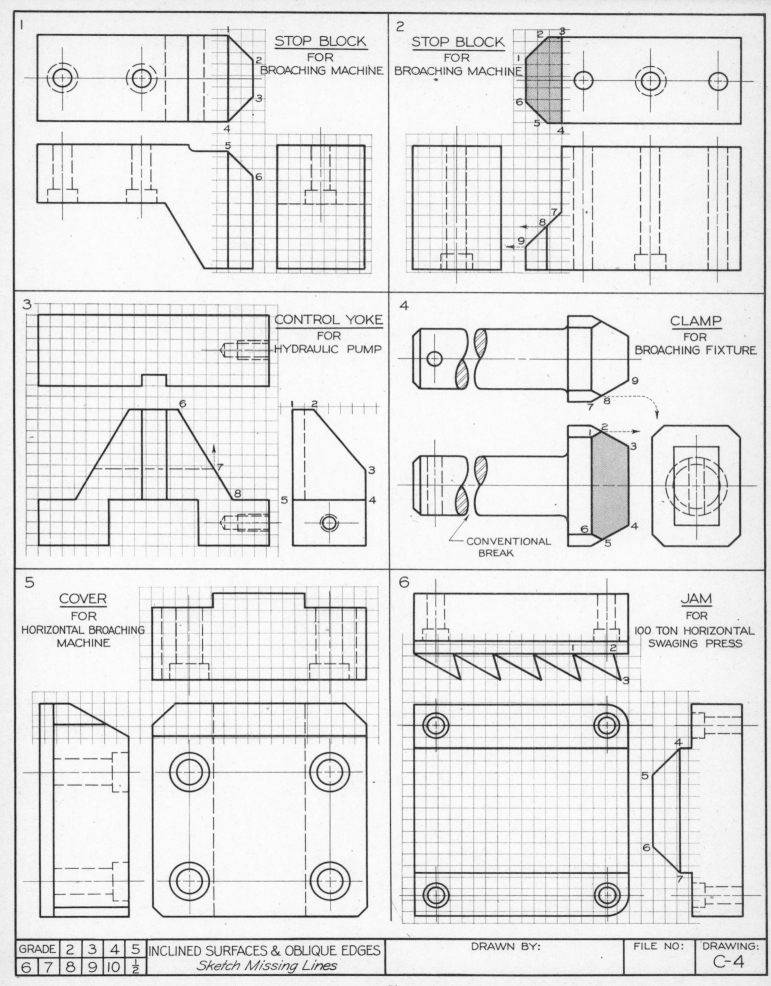

1

STOP BLOCK
FOR
BROACHING MACHINE

2

STOP BLOCK
FOR
BROACHING MACHINE

3

CONTROL YOKE
FOR
HYDRAULIC PUMP

4

CLAMP
FOR
BROACHING FIXTURE

CONVENTIONAL
BREAK

5

COVER
FOR
HORIZONTAL BROACHING
MACHINE

6

JAM
FOR
100 TON HORIZONTAL
SWAGING PRESS

GRADE	2	3	4	5	INCLINED SURFACES & OBLIQUE EDGES	DRAWN BY:		FILE NO:	DRAWING:
	6	7	8	9	10	$\frac{1}{2}$	*Sketch Missing Lines*			C-4

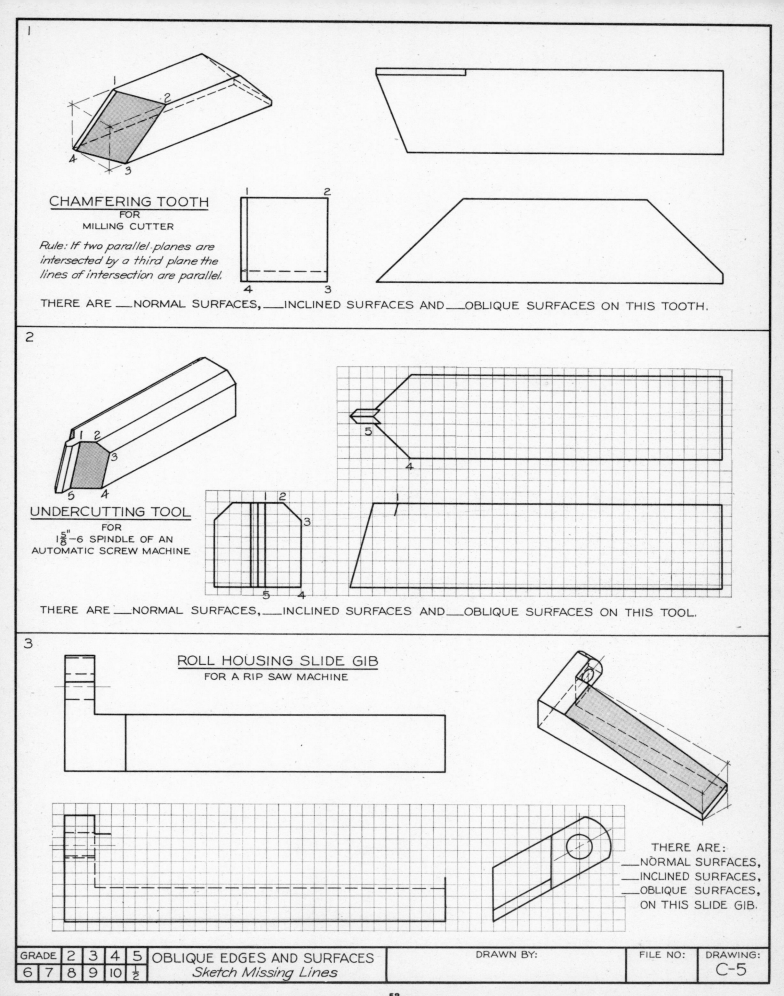

1

CHAMFERING TOOTH
FOR
MILLING CUTTER

Rule: If two parallel planes are intersected by a third plane the lines of intersection are parallel.

THERE ARE ___ NORMAL SURFACES, ___ INCLINED SURFACES AND ___ OBLIQUE SURFACES ON THIS TOOTH.

2

UNDERCUTTING TOOL
FOR
$1\frac{5}{8}"-6$ SPINDLE OF AN
AUTOMATIC SCREW MACHINE

THERE ARE ___ NORMAL SURFACES, ___ INCLINED SURFACES AND ___ OBLIQUE SURFACES ON THIS TOOL.

3

ROLL HOUSING SLIDE GIB
FOR A RIP SAW MACHINE

THERE ARE:
___ NORMAL SURFACES,
___ INCLINED SURFACES,
___ OBLIQUE SURFACES,
ON THIS SLIDE GIB.

GRADE	2	3	4	5	OBLIQUE EDGES AND SURFACES	DRAWN BY:	FILE NO:	DRAWING:
	6	7	8	9	10	$\frac{1}{2}$	*Sketch Missing Lines*			C-5

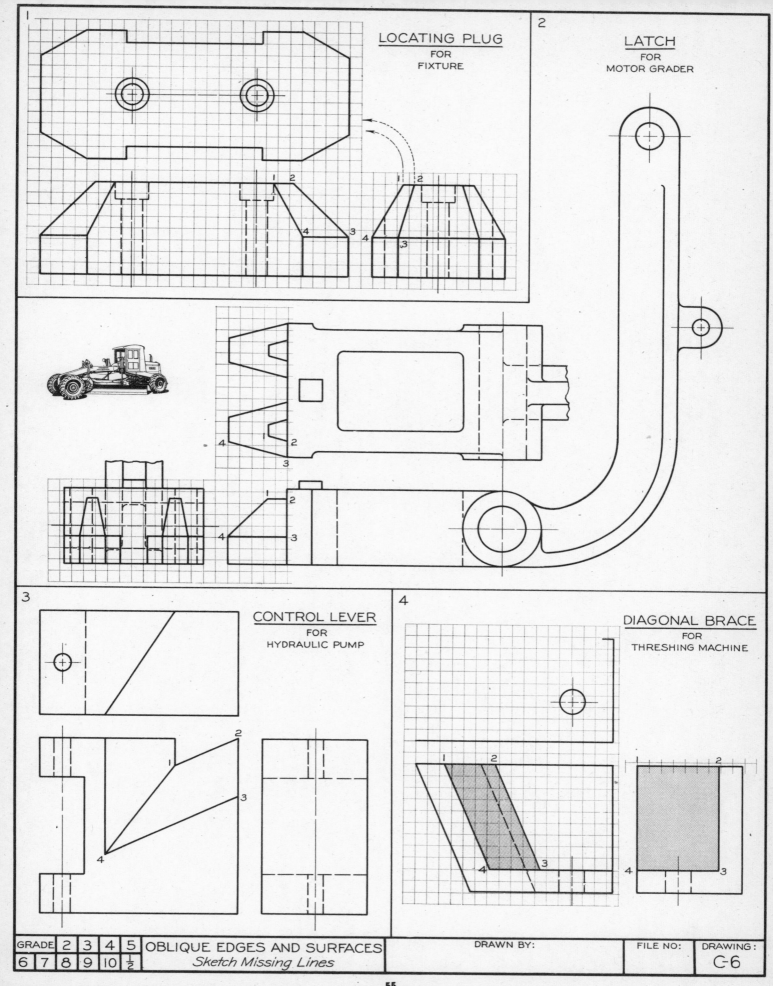

1   LOCATING PLUG
FOR
FIXTURE

2   LATCH
FOR
MOTOR GRADER

3   CONTROL LEVER
FOR
HYDRAULIC PUMP

4   DIAGONAL BRACE
FOR
THRESHING MACHINE

GRADE	2	3	4	5	OBLIQUE EDGES AND SURFACES	DRAWN BY:	FILE NO:	DRAWING:
6	7	8	9	10	½	*Sketch Missing Lines*			C-6

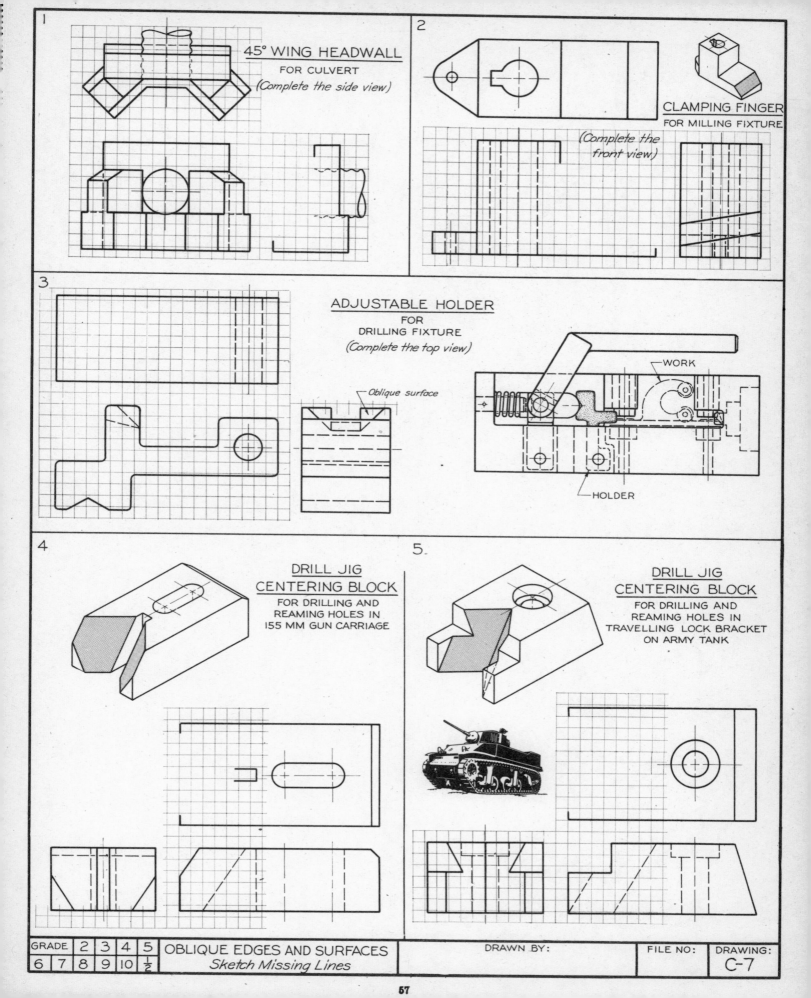

1

45° WING HEADWALL
FOR CULVERT
(Complete the side view)

2

CLAMPING FINGER
FOR MILLING FIXTURE

(Complete the front view)

3

ADJUSTABLE HOLDER
FOR
DRILLING FIXTURE
(Complete the top view)

Oblique surface

WORK

HOLDER

4

DRILL JIG
CENTERING BLOCK
FOR DRILLING AND
REAMING HOLES IN
155 MM GUN CARRIAGE

5.

DRILL JIG
CENTERING BLOCK
FOR DRILLING AND
REAMING HOLES IN
TRAVELLING LOCK BRACKET
ON ARMY TANK

GRADE	2	3	4	5	OBLIQUE EDGES AND SURFACES	DRAWN BY:	FILE NO:	DRAWING:
6	7	8	9	10	½	*Sketch Missing Lines*			C-7

CHAPTER V

CYLINDRICAL SURFACES AND EDGES

30. Cylinders in Production. In engineering work the "right circular" cylinder is a very common form because of the facility with which it may be produced in the shop. Cylindrical patterns are easily cut on the wood lathe, and in this way *cast* cylindrical surfaces are produced. Likewise, metals of all kinds

32. Representation of a Cylinder. A cylinder is represented on a drawing by views of its *edges*, in this case, circular edges, and of *contour elements*, Fig. 35(a) and (b). An element is a straight line lying on a cylindrical surface parallel to the axis. In Fig. 35(a) and (b) the top and bottom circular

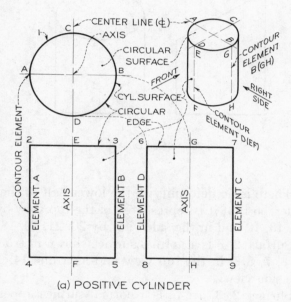

(a) POSITIVE CYLINDER

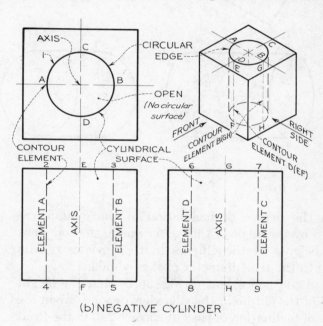

(b) NEGATIVE CYLINDER

FIG. 35. CYLINDERS

may be turned to cylindrical shapes on the metal-cutting lathe. The drill press is a common tool for producing "negative" cylinders, or holes. Other operations used to produce cylindrical surfaces include reaming, boring, and grinding. Deformities of cylinders are produced by these and other operations, and will be described later.

31. Cylindrical Surfaces and Circular Edges. The cylinder has one cylindrical surface, Fig. 35(a), intersected by two plane surfaces. The line of intersection of the curved surface with a plane surface is a *circular edge*. The surface, or "end," contained within the circular edge is called a *circular surface*.

edges are shown as circles in the top views, as horizontal lines 2, 3, and 4, 5 in the front views, and as horizontal lines 6, 7 and 8, 9 in the side views. The contour elements shown as points *A* and *B* in the top views are shown as 2, 4 and 3, 5 in the front views to complete the outline of the cylinders in the front views. The contour elements shown as points *C* and *D* in the top views are shown as 6, 8 and 7, 9 in the side views to complete the outline of the side views of both figures.

33. Ellipses. In Fig. 36(a) the axis of the cylinder is an inclined line, shown true length only in the top view. The circular edges *AB* and *DC* in the top view will appear as ellipses 5 and 6 in the front view and as "fatter" ellipses 7 and 8 in the side view.

In Fig. 36(b) the top end of the cylinder is formed by an inclined plane, producing an ellipse. This ellipse appears as a circle 1 in the top view, as a straight line 2, 3 in the front view, and as an ellipse 4 in the side view.

It should be observed in Fig. 36(a) that the widths of the ellipses in the front and side views depend below the deformity. All of the elements from 2 to 3 in a clockwise direction touching arc 5 will be equal to element *C* as shown by 16, 17 in the side view. All of the elements from 2 to 3 in a counterclockwise direction touching arc 4 will be equal to element *D* as shown by 18, 19 in the side view. The *upper half* of cylindrical surface 1 (front view) is 10, 11, 13, 8, 7, 6, 9, 12 in the top view and 20, 14, 15, 16, 17, 21 in the side view.

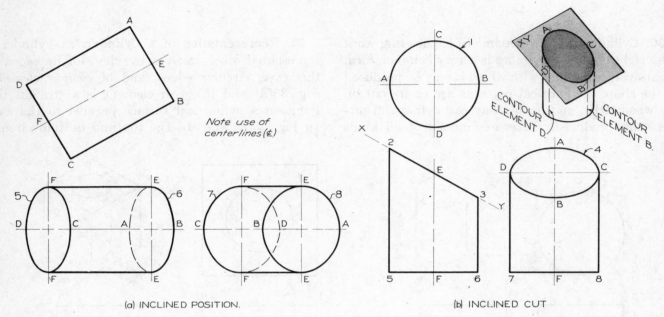

(a) INCLINED POSITION.

FIG. 36. ELLIPSES

(b) INCLINED CUT

upon the degree of inclination of the cylinder as shown by the angle of the center line in the top view. The heights of the ellipses in these views remain equal to the true diameter of the cylinder.

It should be evident in Fig. 36(b) that the height *A*, *B* of the ellipse in the side view depends upon the angle of inclination of the cut surface 2, 3 in the front view, and that the circle 1 in the top view will remain constant regardless of the inclination of the cut surface. When the angle of inclination is 45° the ellipse will appear as a circle in the side view.

34. Deformities of a Cylinder — Example 1. When a cylinder is *deformed*, some of the elements are shortened or portions cut away. The bases may or may not be changed in shape.

In Fig. 37, a milling cut has been made in a bar of cold-rolled steel, producing a deformity 6, 7, 8, 9 in the top view; 2, 3, arc 5 in the front view; and 16, 15, 14 in the side view.

As a result of the cut, the elements above the deformity in the front view will be shorter than those

There is no deformity in the lower half of the cylinder, so that it is represented in the top view by 10, 11, 13, 12 and in the side view by 20, 21, 19, 18.

Surface 2, 3 is a normal surface shown in true size as 6, 7, 8, 9 in the top view and as a line 14, 15 in the side view.

Surface 2, 3, arc 5, is a normal surface appearing in the top view as 6, 7 and in the side view as 16, 15.

The front base is 2, 3, arc 4, shown in true size in the front view and appears in the top view as line 12, 13 and in the side view as line 14, 18.

The rear base is the circular surface 1 shown in true size in the front view, and appears in the top view as line 10, 11, and in the side view as line 17, 19.

35. Deformities of a Cylinder — Example 2. A common student error is to assume that elements *C* and *D*, Fig. 38 (side view), are the same length. Element *D* is in the back half of the cylinder not affected by a deformity; hence it appears in true length in the front view as 18, 21, and in the top view as 4, 5. The middle portion of element *C* is cut away by the deformity so that it shows in two segments in the front view as 18, 19 and 20, 21; and in the top view as 10, 11 and 12, 13. All elements from 2 to 3 (side view) in a counterclockwise direction are deformed in the same manner as element C. All elements from 2 to 3 in a clockwise direction are not touched by the deformity and appear in their original true length in the top and front views.

The *front half* of the cylindrical surface is shown in the top view as 6, 7, 13, 12, 9, 8, 11, 10, in the front view as 14, 15, 25, 24 with a rectangular hole 16, 17, 23, 22, and in the side view as A, C, B. The *back half* of the cylindrical surface is not deformed and is shown in the top view as 4, 5, 7, 6, in the front view as 14, 15, 25, 24 and in the side view as B, D, A.

Surface 2, 3 (side view) is a normal surface represented in the top view as 8, 9 and in the front view (true size) as 16, 17, 23, 22.

Surfaces 8, 11 and 9, 12 in the top view are normal surfaces showing in the front view as 16, 22 and 17, 23, and in the side view as a surface in true size 3, C, 2.

The left end is a circular surface shown true size in the right side view, and as lines 4, 10 and 14, 24 in the top and front views respectively.

The right end of the large cylindrical portion is a circular surface with a round hole 26 removed and shown true size in the side view. The same surface appears as 5, 13 in the top view and 15, 25 in the front view.

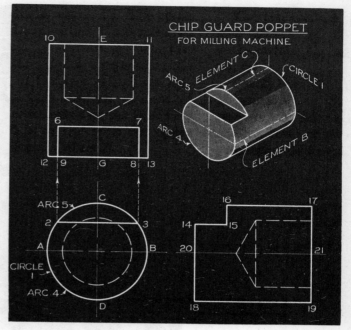

FIG. 37. DEFORMITIES OF A CYLINDER

36. Intersections. The *thread attachment cam* in Fig. 39 was turned down on the lathe to produce cylindrical surfaces 1 and 2. Then a hole 32 in the center was bored and chamfered at 45° at the front end. Finally, two horizontal slots were cut, producing intersections which merit some study.

The upper slot appears in the side view as 33, 35, 36, 38, and in the front view as 24, 27, arc 6, 31, 28, arc 5. Surface 38, 36 (side view) is a normal surface

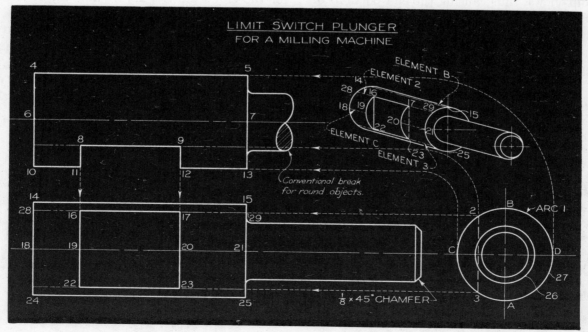

FIG. 38. DEFORMITIES OF A CYLINDER

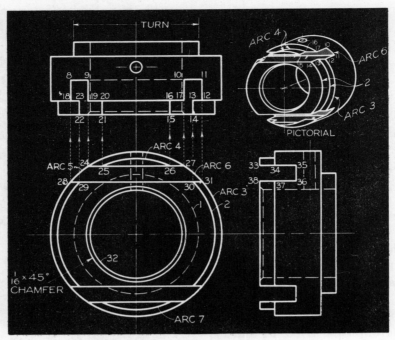

FIG. 39. THREAD ATTACHMENT CAM FOR TURRET LATHE

showing in the front view as 28, 31 and in the top view as 8, 11, 12, 13, 14, 22, 23, 18. Surface 35, 36 (side view) is a normal surface showing in the front view as 24, 27, arc 6, 31, 28, arc 5 and in the top view as 8, 11. Surface 33, 35 (side view) is a normal surface showing in the front view as 24, 27 and in the top view as 9, 10, 17, 16, 15, 21, 20, 19. It should be observed that this surface is not as long as surface 28, 31 (front view), thus causing the end portions of the slot to be visible in the top view at 8, 9, 19, 20, 21, 22, 23, 18 and 10, 11, 12, 13, 14, 15, 16, 17.

In the top view edge 15, 16 was projected from 26 in the front view; edge 17, 10 from 27; edge 12, 11 from 31; and 13, 14 from 30, as indicated by the dotted projection lines.

Arc 6 in the front view shows as line 10, 11 in the top view, and arc 5 shows as 8, 9 in the top view, and both as 35, 36 in the side view. Lines 26, 27 and 30, 31 in the front view account for lines 16, 17 and 13, 12 respectively in the top view, and lines 24, 25 and 28, 29 account for lines 19, 20 and 18, 23 respectively in the top view. Line 29, 30 (front view) is shown in the top view as 22, 14, thus accounting for the end segments 22, 21 and 15, 14 which close the figures of intersection.

37. Cutaway Study of a Roller Support for an Automatic Screw Machine. The order of machining a part varies from factory to factory chiefly because of the variations in machines. The quantity of like parts needed frequently determines the machines to

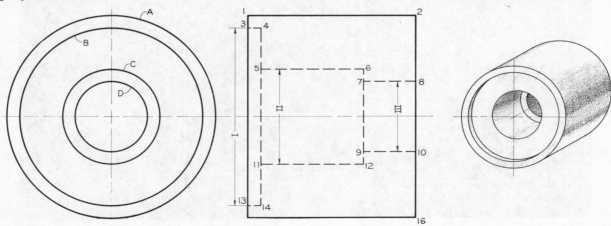

FIG. 40. 1ST STEP IN MACHINING OF ROLLER SUPPORT

be used and the order of machining. If the quantity is large enough, special automatic machines may be built which will combine several operations into one.

Second Operation. The assembly requires three rollers, the design specifying the machining of three cylindrical surfaces E, F, and G of diameter IV,

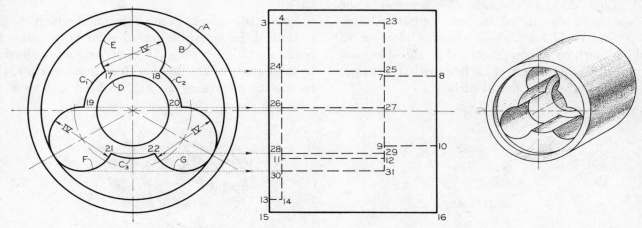

FIG. 41. 2ND STEP IN MACHINING OF ROLLER SUPPORT

A progressive series of operations on a piece of carburizing steel stock has been shown in Figs. 40 to 43 which lend themselves well to the purposes of visualization of cylindrical shapes.

First Operation. First, the three cylindrical surfaces B, C, and D of diameters I, II, and III, of Fig. 40, are machined to their respective depths as shown in the side view; they appear as circles in the front view and as rectangles 3, 4, 14, 13; 5, 6, 12, 11; and 7, 8, 10, 9 in the side view.

Fig. 41. These holes are machined to the same depth as surface C in Fig. 40 and the three cuts create intersections with cylindrical surface C of Fig. 40, which in turn loses much of its original surface, being divided into three cylindrical segments C_1, C_2, and C_3.

In the front view cylindrical surface E intersects C at 17 and 18, which are elements common to both cylinders. Edges 17 and 18 appear in the side view as 24, 25; 19 and 20 as 26, 27; and edges 21 and 22 as 28, 29. Line 11, 12 in the side view is the lower

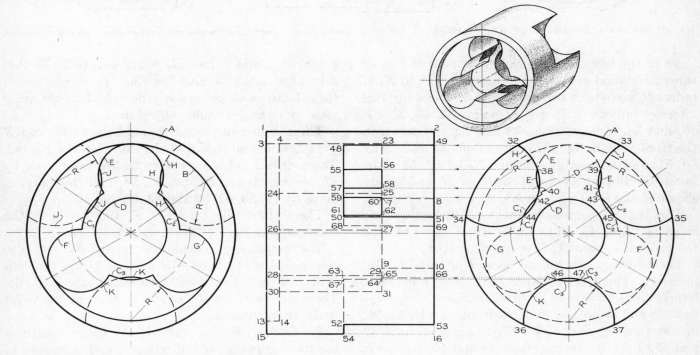

FIG. 42. 3RD STEP IN MACHINING OF ROLLER SUPPORT
Note the three cuts of radius R.

contour element of cylindrical surface C_3. The upper contour element of cylindrical surface C was removed when the upper roller cavity (surface E) was machined. Line 30, 31 in the side view represents the lower contour elements of the two cylindrical surfaces F and G. The highest contour element of cylindrical surface E is represented in the side view by the line 4, 23, which is in line with the upper contour element of cylindrical surface B.

The top contour element of surface K is a short one because of the intersection of this surface with surface C_3, and shows in the front view as 65, 66.

Fourth Operation. Some objects, of which this one is typical, have visible features on both sides, and require both side views. In such cases it is customary to omit most of the hidden lines in each view, thus promoting clearness. In Fig. 43 both side views are

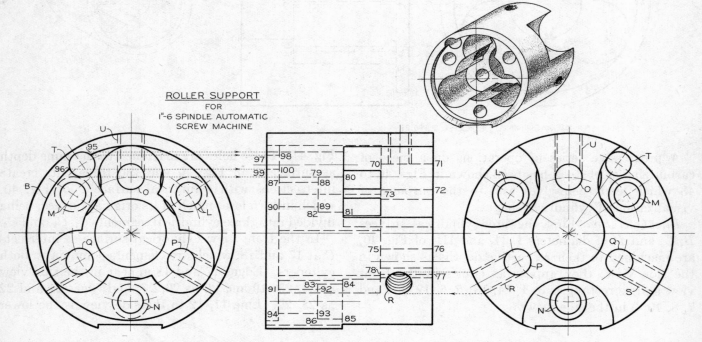

FIG. 43. 4TH STEP IN MACHINING OF ROLLER SUPPORT   NOTE: In accordance with conventional practice some hidden edges are omitted from each side view.

Third Operation. In the right side view of Fig. 42 three additional cylindrical recesses H, J, and K, of radius R, have been machined. These three surfaces intersect outside surface A at points 32, 33, 35, 37, 36, and 34. Intersections 32 and 33 are shown in the front view as 48, 49; intersections 34 and 35 by 50, 51; and intersections 36 and 37 by 52, 53. The lower contour elements of surfaces H and J are shown in the front view by 68, 69.

The bottom contour element of surface A was shortened from 15, 16 to 15, 54 (front view) but the top contour element 1, 2, was not affected.

The three cylindrical surfaces H, J, and K also intersect cylindrical surfaces C_1, C_2, C_3, and E at intersections numbered 38 to 47 inclusive. Intersections 38 and 39 are shown in the front view by 55, 56; intersections 40 and 41 by 57, 58; intersections 42 and 43 by 59, 60; intersections 44 and 45 by 61, 62; and intersections 46 and 47 by 63, 64.

given with many invisible edges omitted. Neither side view includes invisible line representation of those features already clearly described in the other view by means of visible object lines.

Three drilled and counterbored holes L, M, and N were next cut as shown in the side views of Fig. 43. These drilled holes are shown in the front view by 87, 88, 89, 90 and 91, 92, 93, 94, and the counterbores by 79, 80, 81, 82 and 83, 84, 85, 86.

Three plain drilled holes O, P, and Q show in the front view as 70, 71, 72, 73 and 75, 76, 77, 78.

The remaining machining operations are also shown in Fig. 43. Holes R, S, and U are the conventional representations of threaded holes, Art. 68. These are used for set screws to prevent the roller shafts from turning.

The reamed hole T extends the entire length of the roller support for a dowel pin, and is reamed in assembly. Hole T intersects cylindrical surface B at elements 95 and 96 in the left side view, shown in the front view at 97, 98 and 99, 100.

The keyway at the bottom is produced by a milling operation.

A pictorial view and a sectional view of the completed roller support are shown in Figs. 49 and 50, and an assembly drawing of the roller support rest, which shows how the roller support fits into the assembly, is shown in Fig. 64.

38. Continuity of Cylindrical Surfaces. Students often overlook the continuity of cylindrical surfaces and imagine lines where edges do not exist. For example, Fig. 44, a solid line cannot join points 7 and 4 in the top view, because areas 1, 2, 3, 8 and 7, 4, 5, 6 are adjacent areas, and are both represented by arc 16 in the front view, showing that they are one surface and not two.

39. Problems — Cylindrical Surfaces and Edges, and Plotted Curves. In solving the problems that follow, each object should be analyzed or broken up mentally into its component circular surfaces, circular edges, cylindrical surfaces, and the various new surfaces and edges created by any deformities. The solutions will be greatly simplified if each such detail is considered separately in its relation to the problem at hand.

Models will always be helpful in cases of difficulty, and the student is urged to build such models of

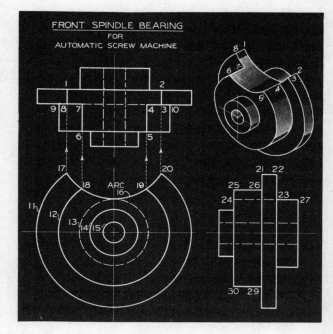

FIG. 44. CONTINUITY OF CYLINDRICAL SURFACES

wood, soap, or other materials at any time where a model is necessary for a complete understanding.

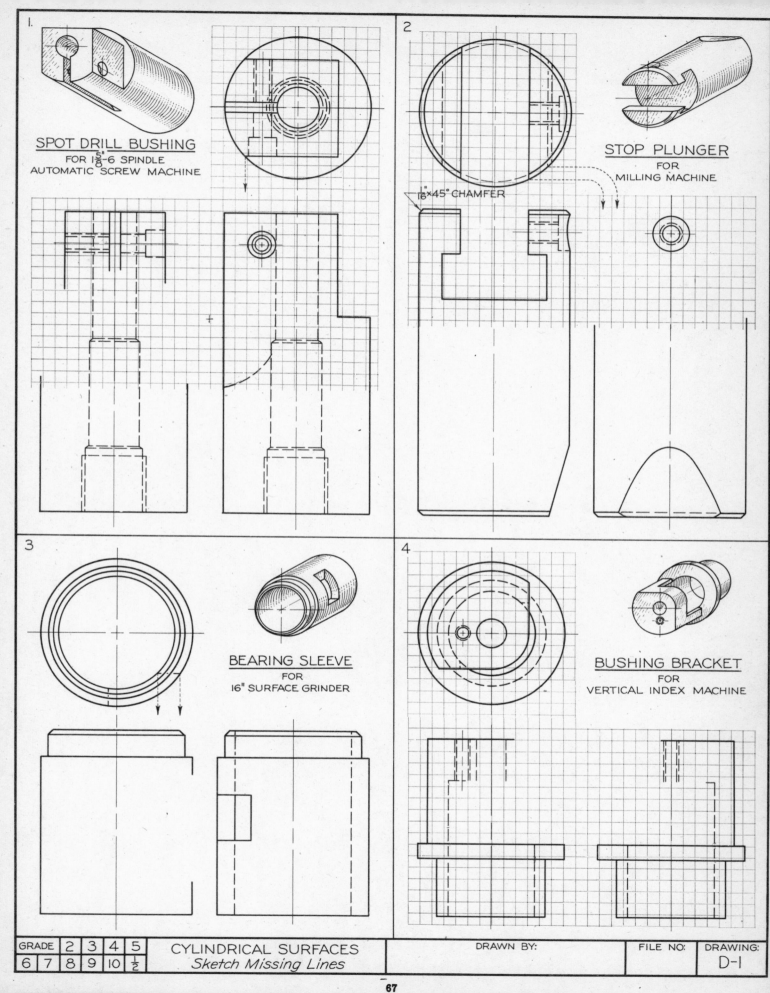

1. SPOT DRILL BUSHING
FOR 1⅝"-6 SPINDLE
AUTOMATIC SCREW MACHINE

2. STOP PLUNGER
FOR
MILLING MACHINE

1/16"×45° CHAMFER

3. BEARING SLEEVE
FOR
16" SURFACE GRINDER

4. BUSHING BRACKET
FOR
VERTICAL INDEX MACHINE

GRADE	2	3	4	5	CYLINDRICAL SURFACES	DRAWN BY:	FILE NO:	DRAWING:
6	7	8	9	10	½	*Sketch Missing Lines*			D-1

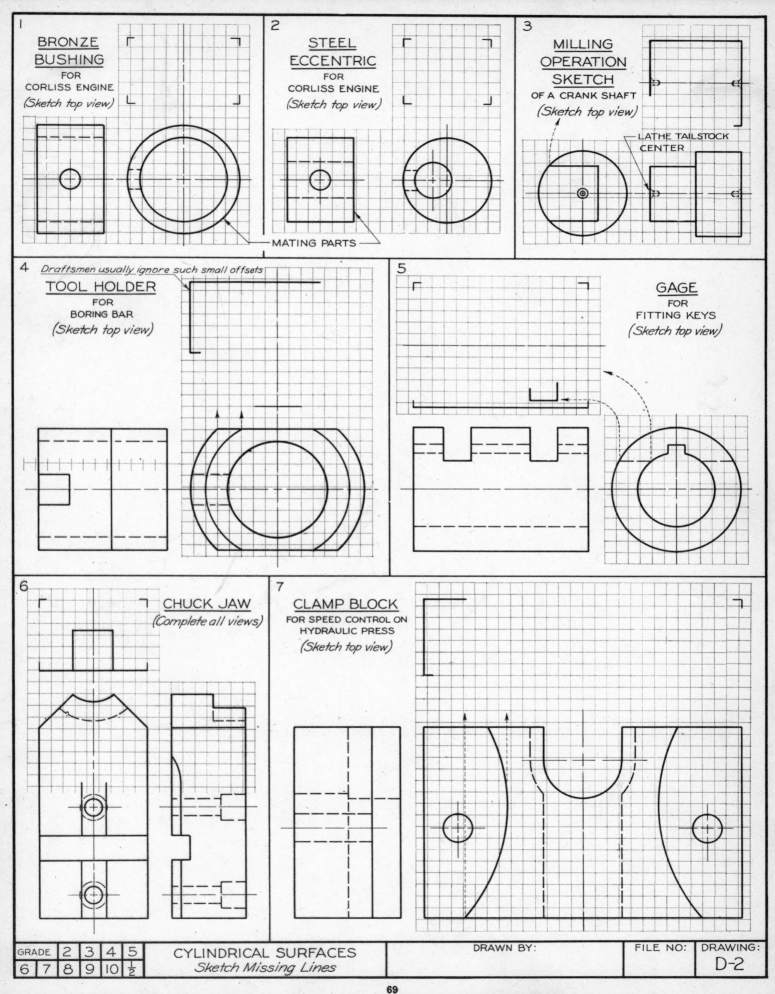

1 BRONZE BUSHING FOR CORLISS ENGINE *(Sketch top view)*

2 STEEL ECCENTRIC FOR CORLISS ENGINE *(Sketch top view)*

MATING PARTS

3 MILLING OPERATION SKETCH OF A CRANK SHAFT *(Sketch top view)*

LATHE TAILSTOCK CENTER

4 *Draftsmen usually ignore such small offsets*

TOOL HOLDER FOR BORING BAR *(Sketch top view)*

5 GAGE FOR FITTING KEYS *(Sketch top view)*

6 CHUCK JAW *(Complete all views)*

7 CLAMP BLOCK FOR SPEED CONTROL ON HYDRAULIC PRESS *(Sketch top view)*

GRADE	2	3	4	5
6	7	8	9	10	½

CYLINDRICAL SURFACES *Sketch Missing Lines*

DRAWN BY:

FILE NO: DRAWING: D-2

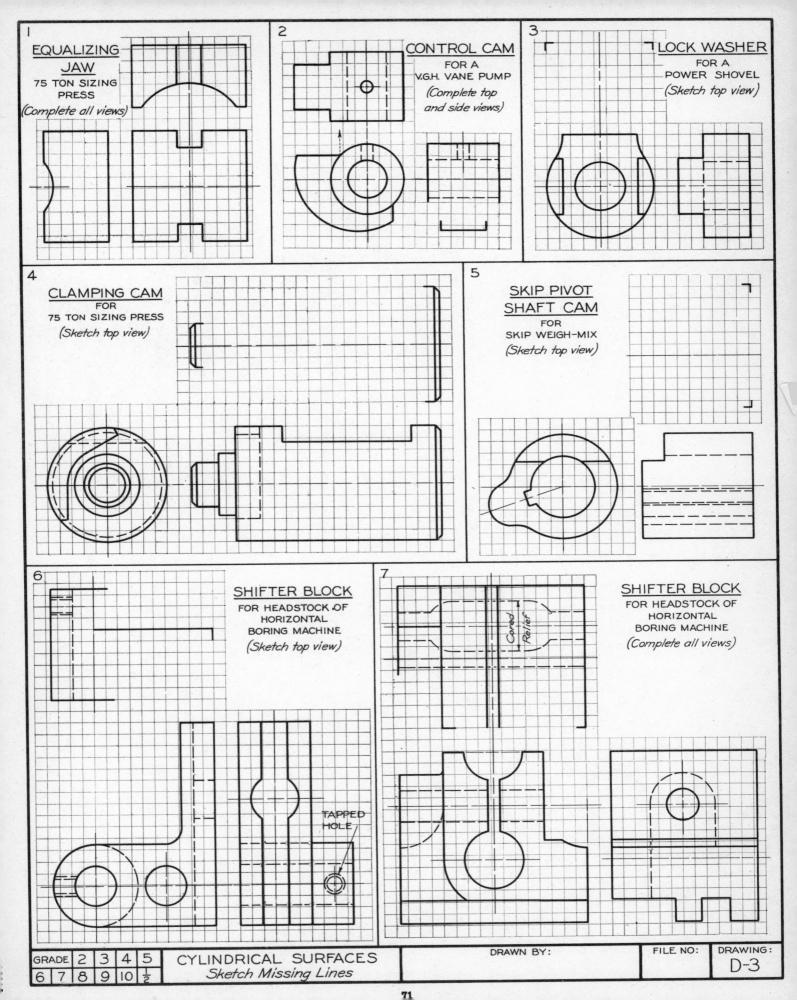

1 EQUALIZING JAW
75 TON SIZING PRESS
(Complete all views)

2 CONTROL CAM
FOR A
V.G.H. VANE PUMP
(Complete top
and side views)

3 LOCK WASHER
FOR A
POWER SHOVEL
(Sketch top view)

4 CLAMPING CAM
FOR
75 TON SIZING PRESS
(Sketch top view)

5 SKIP PIVOT
SHAFT CAM
FOR
SKIP WEIGH-MIX
(Sketch top view)

6 SHIFTER BLOCK
FOR HEADSTOCK OF
HORIZONTAL
BORING MACHINE
(Sketch top view)

TAPPED HOLE

7 SHIFTER BLOCK
FOR HEADSTOCK OF
HORIZONTAL
BORING MACHINE
(Complete all views)

Cored Relief

GRADE	2	3	4	5	CYLINDRICAL SURFACES	DRAWN BY:	FILE NO:	DRAWING:
	6	7	8	9	10	½	*Sketch Missing Lines*			D-3

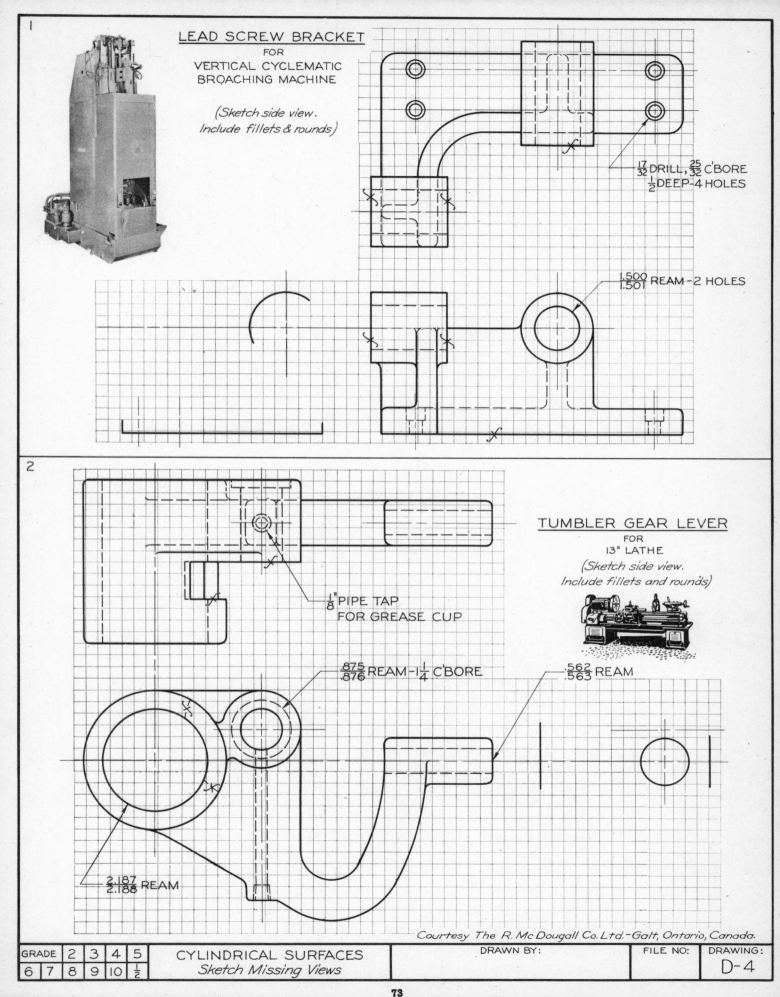

LEAD SCREW BRACKET
FOR
VERTICAL CYCLEMATIC BROACHING MACHINE

(Sketch side view.
Include fillets & rounds)

$\frac{17}{32}$ DRILL, $\frac{25}{32}$ C'BORE
$\frac{1}{2}$ DEEP-4 HOLES

$\frac{1.500}{1.501}$ REAM-2 HOLES

TUMBLER GEAR LEVER
FOR
13" LATHE
(Sketch side view.
Include fillets and rounds)

$\frac{1}{8}$" PIPE TAP
FOR GREASE CUP

$\frac{.875}{.876}$ REAM-$1\frac{1}{4}$ C'BORE

$\frac{.562}{.563}$ REAM

$\frac{2.187}{2.188}$ REAM

GRADE	2	3	4	5
6	7	8	9	10	$\frac{1}{2}$

CYLINDRICAL SURFACES
Sketch Missing Views

DRAWN BY:

FILE NO:

DRAWING:
D-4

CHAPTER VI

SECTIONAL VIEWS

40. Sections. Many objects, especially those which have complicated interiors, may be represented more clearly by assuming the object to be cut apart so as to expose the interior parts to view. This is called *sectioning*, and by means of it most, if not all, hidden lines may be omitted.

section; if it is assumed crosswise, the section is called a *cross section*. If the cutting plane is assumed to cut entirely through the object, the resulting section is a *full section*, Arts. 43–44; otherwise it may be a *half section*, Art. 45, or a *broken section*, Art. 46, as explained below.

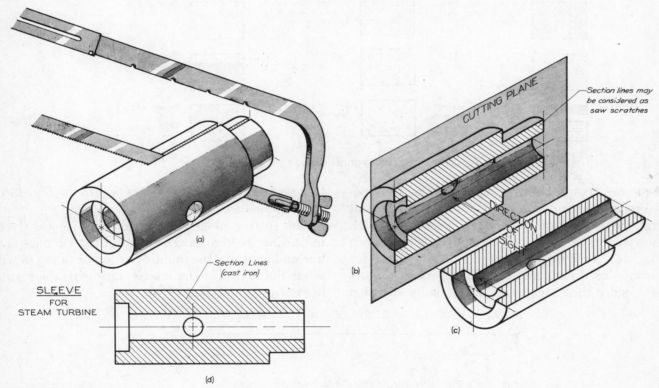

FIG. 45. FULL SECTION

First, the object is "sawed" apart, Fig. 45(a); or, more technically, a *cutting plane* is passed through the object (b) and the portion of the object in front of the plane (c) is removed so as to expose the interior parts in a *sectional view* or *section* (d). Figure 45(b) shows the direction of sight for the sectional view.

If the cutting plane is assumed lengthwise of the object, as in this case, the section is a *longitudinal*

41. Section Lining. The parallel lines across the cut surface in Fig. 45(d) called *section lines*, or *cross-hatching*, are used for two purposes: (1) to define clearly the cut surface or surfaces produced by the cutting plane so that the solid portions may be readily distinguished, and (2) to indicate the kind of material of which the object is made. The section lines in Fig. 45 are the standard symbol for cast iron. They are extremely fine lines spaced at approximately $\frac{1}{16}''$ to $\frac{1}{8}''$ apart, depending upon the size of the sectioned area, and usually slope at 45°.

All sectioned areas of the same part are sectioned in the *same direction and at the same angle.* For example, Fig. 48(e), in the right side view, the upper and lower sectioned areas are section-lined in the same direction because the object is actually one

42. The Cutting Plane. The cutting plane used in sectioning is indicated in the view in which it appears as a line, or "edgewise," by a heavy line composed of alternate long and short dashes. See Figs. 47(a) and 48(c). Arrowheads indicate the direction in which the section is viewed. The line of sight for viewing the section is perpendicular to the cut-

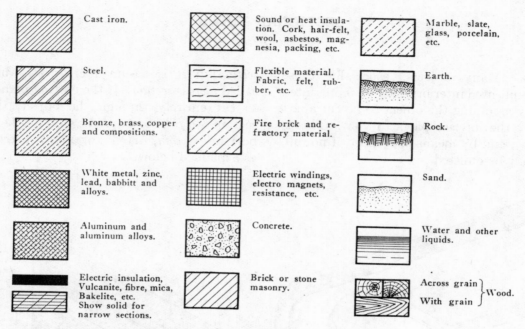

FIG. 46. AMERICAN STANDARD SYMBOLS FOR SECTION LINING

solid piece. To section these two portions in opposite directions would indicate two adjacent but separate pieces, as in the assembly drawing in Fig. 64.

The symbols used for various materials are shown in Fig. 46. Frequently, however, the symbol for cast iron is used for whatever kind of material may be used, since the exact material is usually specified by means of a note on the drawing in engineering work. An example of the use of various sectioning symbols in an assembly drawing is shown in Fig. 64.

Instead of crosshatch lines some draftsmen use solid shading with a drawing pencil or even a colored pencil, both producing grayish solid areas where sectioning occurs. Some companies even require that no section lines or shading be used, leaving sectioned areas perfectly blank.

ting plane and *in the direction of the arrows,* Fig. 48(c), and not against them.

The cutting plane is also indicated frequently by indicating the right-angled ends of the cutting-plane line and omitting the middle portion or filling in with a fine line to avoid the interference with the regular lines of the view, Fig. 47(b).

ARROWS INDICATE DIRECTION OF SIGHT FOR SECTIONAL VIEW

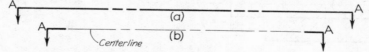

FIG. 47. TWO COMMON TYPES OF CUTTING PLANE LINES (FULL SIZE)

Frequently, in cases where the location of the cutting plane is evident from a mere inspection of the sectional views, the cutting-plane line is omitted.

43. Full Sections.

Example 1: Pump Bracket. In Fig. 48(a) a cutting plane is assumed cutting through the pump bracket. At (b) the right-hand half has been removed so that the observer, looking in the direction of the line of sight indicated, views the remaining half. Viewing the object in this manner the observer sees the cut surfaces "flat," that is, in true size and shape, with visible object lines bordering each sectioned area; and in addition he sees certain visible features of the

It should be observed that the view shown at Fig. 48(d) is *incomplete* because only the section-lined surfaces are shown. All visible lines are shown at (e), but hidden lines are omitted, since sections in

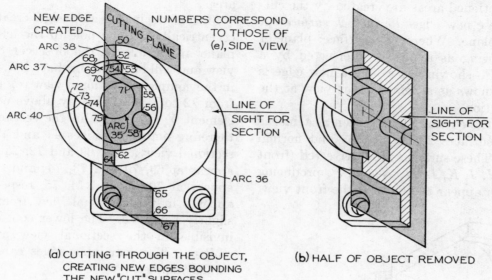

(a) CUTTING THROUGH THE OBJECT, CREATING NEW EDGES BOUNDING THE NEW "CUT" SURFACES.

(b) HALF OF OBJECT REMOVED

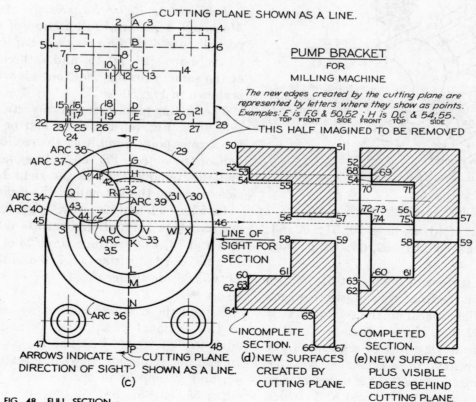

FIG. 48. FULL SECTION

object *behind* the cutting plane, but not hidden from view by some part of the object. The resulting sectional view, Fig. 48(e), is a *full section* because the cutting plane cuts completely through the object.

general are made to replace hidden-line representation.

It should be noted further, in the front view at Fig. 48(c), that the right half of the object was *not actually removed;* it was only *imagined* to be removed in order to show the side view "cutaway," or in section.

When an object is sectioned, new edges which are to bound the sectioned areas are created by the cutting plane. These new edges *lie in each surface* cut by the cutting plane. Wherever a surface (plane or cylindrical) showing as a line is intersected by a cutting plane also showing as a line, a new edge is created, which shows as a *point* in that view at the point of intersection.

In Fig. 48(c) the cutting plane is seen as a line, as are cylindrical surfaces 29, 30, 31, 33 and normal surface 47, 48. These surfaces are intersected (front view) at *F, G, H, J, K, L, M, N,* and *P*, producing new edges which appear as points in the front view,

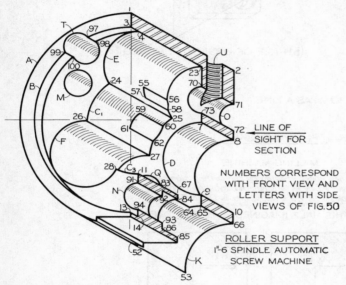

FIG. 49. PICTORIAL FULL SECTION OF ROLLER SUPPORT

and in the side view at (d) as lines 50, 51; 52, 53; 54, 55; 56, 57; 58, 59; 60, 61; 62, 63; 64, 65; and 66, 67.

The front normal surface of the object 22, 28 (top view) is intersected in the front view in two segments *F, G* and *M, N*, which appear in the sectional view (d) as 50, 52 and 62, 64. Normal surface 15, 21 is intersected in the front view in two segments *G, H* and *L, M*, which appear in the sectional view as 53, 54 and 60, 63. Normal surface 9, 14 is intersected in the front view in two segments *H, J* and *K, L*, which appear in the sectional view as 55, 56 and 58, 61. The back normal surface of the object 1, 4 is intersected in the front view in two segments *F, J* and *K, P*, which appear in the sectional view as 51, 57 and 59, 67. Normal surface 47, 48 is intersected in that

view at *P* and in the sectional view (d) at 66, 67. Normal surface 5, 6 is intersected in the front view at *N, P* which appears in the side view as 65, 66, thus completing the boundaries of the two sectioned areas.

Most of the intersection edges created by the large, eccentrically reamed hole to the left of the cutting plane are visible to the observer of the sectional view and will be shown in that view. Arc 37 appears in the completed sectional view (e) as a vertical line from 72 to a point slightly above 68. Top contour element *Y* is invisible in the sectional view and is therefore omitted. Edges 41 and 43 appear in the sectional view as 68, 69 and 72, 73; arcs 38 and 40 appear at 69, 70 and 73, 74; and edges 42 and 44 appear at 70, 71 and 74, 75, respectively. Arc 32 appears in the sectional view from 71 to a point slightly below 75. The lower contour element *Z* is invisible in the sectional view and is therefore omitted. The remaining edges can be analyzed in similar manner.

44. Full Sections.

Example 2: Roller Support for Automatic Screw Machine. A pictorial full section of the roller support discussed in the previous chapter, pages 62 to 65, is shown in Fig. 49, and a three-view drawing of the same, showing the front view in full section, is shown in Fig. 50.

The cutting plane is seen as a vertical line in either side view, Fig. 50, and it should be observed that the arrows point *away* from the sectional view. One half of the object, Fig. 50, is imagined as removed, and this removed half is the right half of the left side view and the left half of the right side view.

In Figs. 49 and 50, new edges created by the cutting plane are contour elements 1, 2 of surface *A*; 3, 4 and 13, 14 of surface *B*; 4, 23 of surface *E*; 70, 71 and 73, 72 of surface *O*; 7, 8 and 9, 10 of surface *D*; 65, 66 of surface *K*; 11, 67 of surface C_3, and so on.

Behind the cutting plane many edges are visible in the sectional view, Figs. 49 and 50, including edges 97, 98; 99, 100; 24, 25; 26, 27; 28, 29; 52, 53. In Fig. 50 (right side view) intersections 39, 41, 43, 45, and 47 appear in the sectional view as visible edges 55, 56; 57, 58; 59, 60; 61, 62; and 63, 64. If we read from Fig. 49 to Fig. 50, arc 4, 24 appears in the sectional view as straight line 4, 24; arc 24, 26 appears as straight line 24, 26, and so on.

Hole *U* is a threaded hole, and the threads are represented conventionally (see pages 121 and 122).

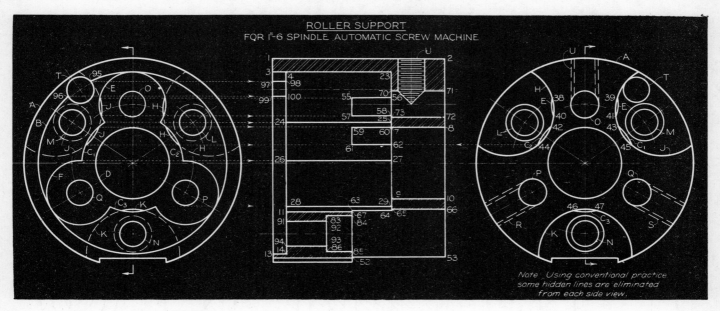

FIG. 50. FULL SECTION OF ROLLER SUPPORT

The roller support is shown in the complete assembly of the roller support rest in Fig. 64, showing exactly how the roller support fits and functions with its mating parts. In this figure the roller support is shown in the same full section as in Figs. 49 and 50, and the student is urged to study the assembly carefully and determine the reason for each cut made from the original piece of carburizing steel stock.

45. Half Sections. The top view of Fig. 51(b) is symmetrical about its vertical center line, and is symmetrical about its horizontal center line except for slight differences in the tapped holes. A front full section of this *disc driver* would eliminate the pipe tapped holes and the bosses altogether; therefore a *half section* is useful in such cases. In a half section the cutting plane cuts halfway through the

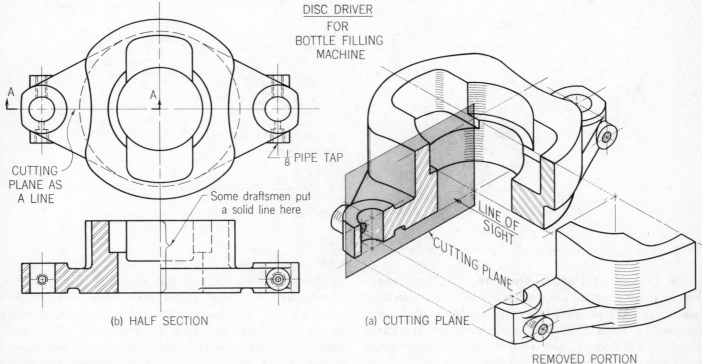

FIG. 51. HALF SECTION

object, and a quarter is imagined to be removed, Fig. 51(a).

The two halves of the sectional view (b) are separated usually by the vertical center line and not a solid line. However, practice varies and some blueprints may be seen in which an object line is used at

47. Revolved Sections. If the cutting plane is assumed perpendicular to the longitudinal center line of an object, a cross section showing the true geometric shape of the object is obtained. The cutting plane, carrying with it the cross section, is then assumed to be revolved 90° so that the true cross

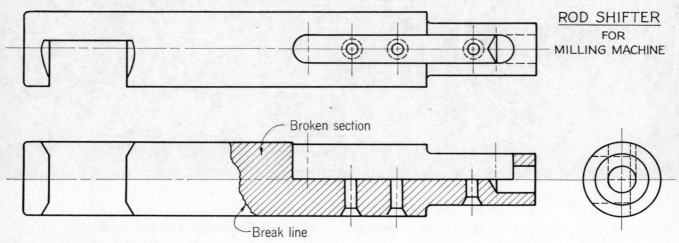

ROD SHIFTER
FOR
MILLING MACHINE

FIG. 52. BROKEN SECTION

this point. In any case, the half of the sectional view that is not sectioned is in every respect an ordinary view, and the half that is sectioned is the same as a full section. Hidden lines may be omitted entirely from the unsectioned half if not needed for dimensioning purposes, and are usually not included in the sectioned half.

section is seen in the same view in which the cutting plane had appeared as a line. Such a section is called a *revolved section*, Fig. 53. The cutting plane is not indicated in another view, as the center line of the section itself denotes where the section is taken. This center line is always at right angles to the major center line of the object sectioned. A number of

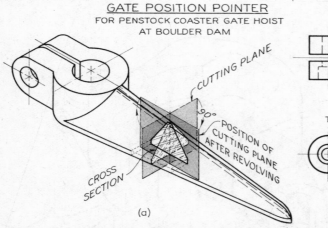

GATE POSITION POINTER
FOR PENSTOCK COASTER GATE HOIST
AT BOULDER DAM

(a)

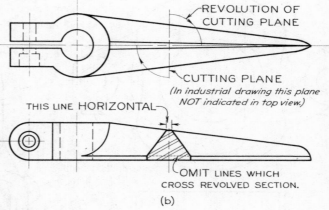

(b)

FIG. 53. USE OF THE CUTTING PLANE IN REVOLVED SECTIONS

46. Broken or Partial Sections. In some cases less or more than a half section is sufficient to expose interior parts; in such instances *broken sections* are frequently used, Fig. 52. An irregular freehand *break line* is used to separate the sectioned portion from the unsectioned portion of the view.

typical revolved sections are shown in Fig. 54. As shown in this figure, break lines may be used (h) to "set off" the section more clearly, and *partial revolved sections* (m) may be employed where desirable. As shown at (b), solid lines are not continued across the section.

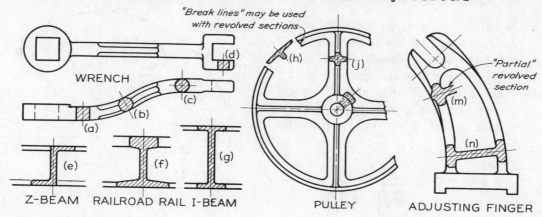

"Break lines" may be used with revolved sections

WRENCH (a) (b) (c) (d)

Z-BEAM (e)   RAILROAD RAIL (f)   I-BEAM (g)

PULLEY (h) (j)

ADJUSTING FINGER "Partial" revolved section (m) (n)

FIG. 54. REVOLVED SECTIONS

48. Detail Sections. A cross section that cannot be easily shown "revolved" in place may be removed and shown at any convenient location on the drawing. Such sections are popular with draftsmen, and any "removed" section is called a *detail section*. Twelve detail sections are shown in Fig. 55, and it should be noted that each detail section is clearly identified as to where and from what direction it was viewed in the regular view. The cutting-plane lines indicate the positions of the cutting planes; the arrows indicate the direction of sight for each section; and the notes Section *A–A*, Section *B–B*, and so on, identify each detail section with the cutting-plane lines in the regular view.

Section *N–N* is, in reality, a broken section projected directly from the right end view and is not a detail section.

49. Conventional Violations of Projections. In some cases *true projections* are awkward or confusing, and conventional methods of representing such parts are widely accepted.

In Fig. 56, the section at (b) seems to indicate that there are no holes in the outer flange of the Packing Gland Base, while at (a) the holes are shown as if they had been revolved in the front view to the vertical center line, and then projected horizontally to the sectional view. The form at (a) is generally preferred and will be frequently encountered.

Another common violation of projection relates to *webs* in section. In Fig. 57(a) the web on the left, shown in section, gives a false impression of *mass*. Furthermore, the rear web on the right is seen obliquely, resulting in a very awkward and misleading representation. The generally preferred section

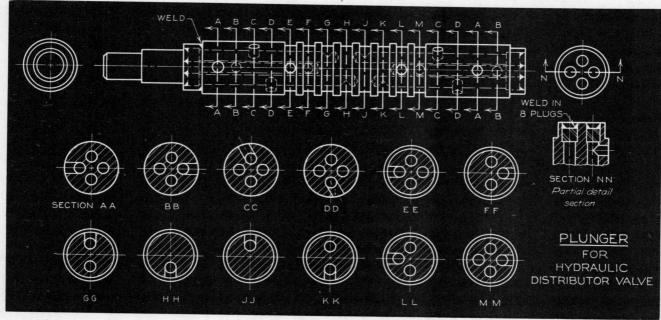

WELD   A B C D E F G H J K L M C D A B

WELD IN 8 PLUGS

SECTION NN
Partial detail section

SECTION A A   B B   C C   D D   E E   F F

G G   H H   J J   K K   L L   M M

PLUNGER FOR HYDRAULIC DISTRIBUTOR VALVE

FIG. 55. DETAIL SECTIONING

is shown at (b) in which the web on the right has been revolved, two holes on the left have been revolved, and neither of the webs is crosshatched.

Webs, or ribs, ordinarily serve to strengthen a part and are usually placed *longitudinally* along major center lines. If a cutting plane should pass "edgewise" through a web or rib (that is, be passed

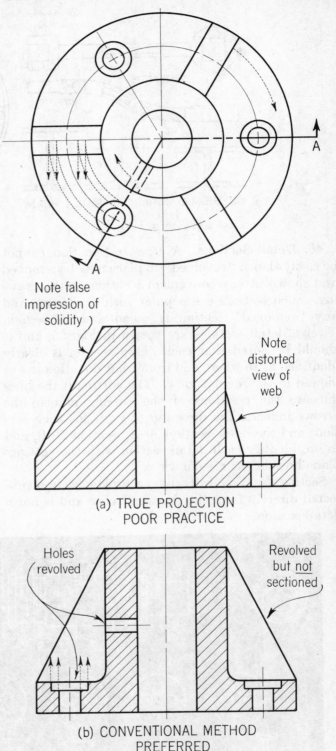

Note false impression of solidity

Note distorted view of web

(a) TRUE PROJECTION
POOR PRACTICE

Holes revolved

Revolved but not sectioned

(b) CONVENTIONAL METHOD
PREFERRED

FIG. 57. WEBS IN SECTION

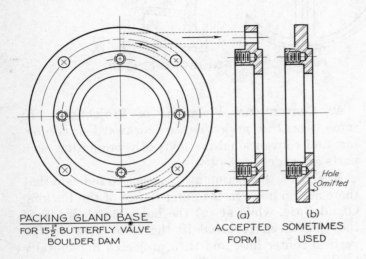

PACKING GLAND BASE
FOR 15½" BUTTERFLY VALVE
BOULDER DAM

(a)
ACCEPTED
FORM

(b)
SOMETIMES
USED

Hole
Omitted

FIG. 56. CONVENTIONAL VIOLATION OF PROJECTION

through it centrally and parallel to the two principal faces) as is the case in Fig. 58, the web or rib should ordinarily not be sectioned, (a). If it is sectioned a false impression of thickness or solidity is given, (b). The cutting plane for the detail section *B–B*, however, cuts perpendicularly through the two webs and the webs *are sectioned*. The horizontal web in Fig. 58(a) is also sectioned for the same reason.

However, there are cases in which the nonhatching of webs or ribs causes confusion as to whether or not there is a web or rib at all, as shown in Fig. 59(b). In this case the edge of the web coincides with the vertical object line outlining the view, and the presence of the web, if not crosshatched, is not evident. In Fig. 59(a) the web is shown with *alternate hatching* to distinguish it from the other sectioned areas, and the web is clearly defined. In alternate hatching every other line of the regular sectioned areas is allowed to continue into the alternate sectioned area.

The accepted method of showing gear teeth, spokes, and splines in section is shown in Fig. 60(a). The gear teeth are not sectioned although theoretically the cutting plane cuts through them, in order to give a clearer picture of the section through the rim. The splines are not sectioned in order to give

a clearer representation of the splined hole and the hub. The spokes are not sectioned as this would seem to indicate a solid web between the rim and hub. The lower spoke is shown in revolved position to avoid the "amputated" appearance at (b).

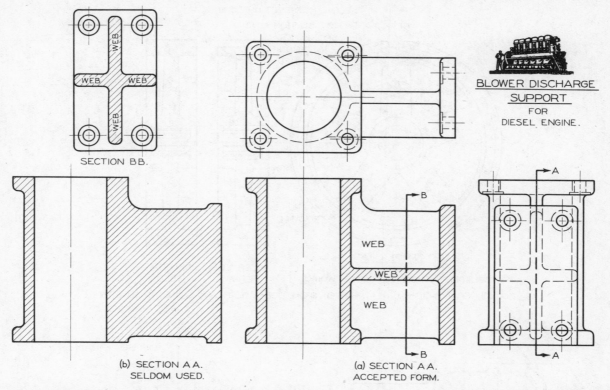

SECTION B.B.

BLOWER DISCHARGE
SUPPORT
FOR
DIESEL ENGINE.

WEB

WEB

WEB

(b) SECTION A.A.
SELDOM USED.

(a) SECTION A.A.
ACCEPTED FORM.

FIG. 58. TREATMENT OF WEBS IN SECTION. (CUTTING PLANE CUTS LONGITUDINALLY THROUGH ONE WEB AND PERPENDICULARLY TO ANOTHER)

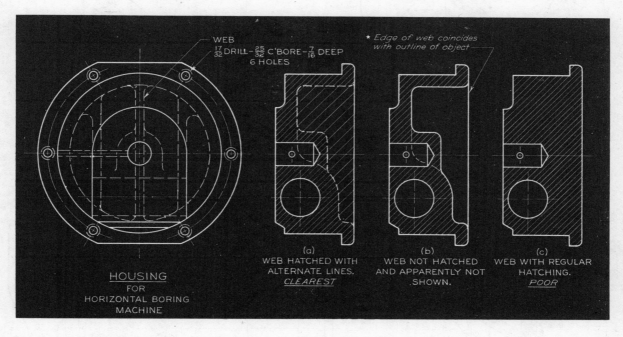

WEB
17/32 DRILL- 25/32 C'BORE- 7/16 DEEP
6 HOLES

* Edge of web coincides
with outline of object

HOUSING
FOR
HORIZONTAL BORING
MACHINE

(a)
WEB HATCHED WITH
ALTERNATE LINES.
CLEAREST

(b)
WEB NOT HATCHED
AND APPARENTLY NOT
SHOWN.

(c)
WEB WITH REGULAR
HATCHING.
POOR

FIG. 59. ALTERNATE HATCHING

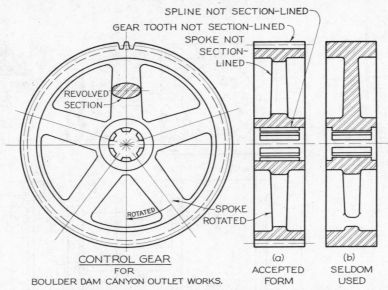

SPLINE NOT SECTION-LINED
GEAR TOOTH NOT SECTION-LINED
SPOKE NOT SECTION-LINED

REVOLVED SECTION

ROTATED

SPOKE ROTATED

CONTROL GEAR
FOR
BOULDER DAM CANYON OUTLET WORKS.

(a)
ACCEPTED FORM

(b)
SELDOM USED

FIG. 60. CONVENTIONAL TREATMENT OF SPOKES, GEAR TEETH AND SPLINES IN SECTION

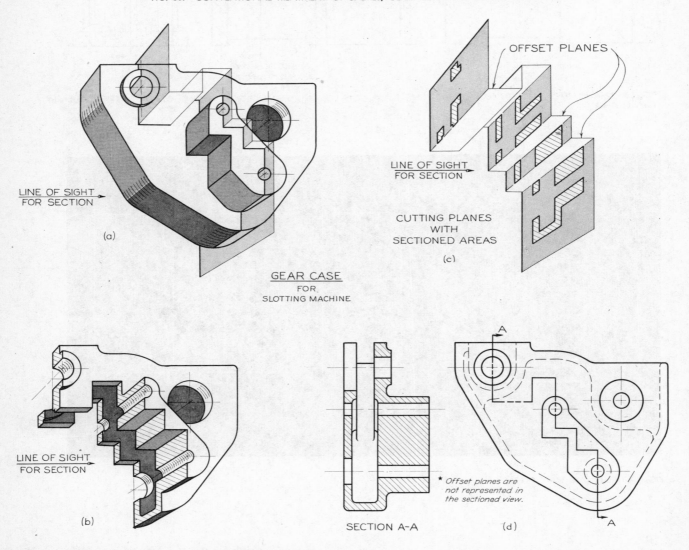

LINE OF SIGHT FOR SECTION

(a)

GEAR CASE
FOR
SLOTTING MACHINE

OFFSET PLANES

LINE OF SIGHT FOR SECTION

CUTTING PLANES
WITH
SECTIONED AREAS

(c)

LINE OF SIGHT FOR SECTION

(b)

SECTION A-A

* Offset planes are not represented in the sectioned view.

(d)

FIG. 61. OFFSET SECTION (Courtesy Ecole Nationale Professionelle, Nantes, France.)

Among the objects or parts of objects which usually are not hatched in section are the following: webs, ribs, spokes, shafts, gear teeth, splines, keys, cotters, cotter keys, dowel pins, bolts, nuts, rivets, nails, screws, ball or roller bearings, lugs, and objects of similar form which are solid — not hollow.

50. Offset Sections. It is not necessary that a cutting plane be a continuous plane surface; it may

Phantom sections are also used to indicate adjacent parts, Fig. 63.

With permission of the foreman, phantom hatching may be added to any blueprint by the blueprint reader.

52. Sectioning in Assembly. Any of the above types of sectioning may be employed in assembly drawings. A full section of the assembly of the roller

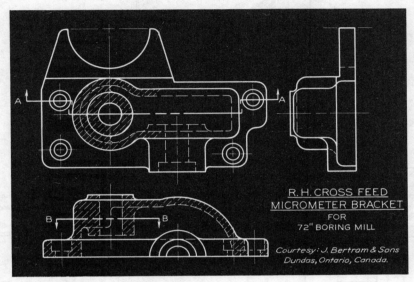

FIG. 62. PHANTOM SECTIONING

be "broken" or offset so as to form a set of surfaces so placed as to cut through the features of the object desired in the section. A series of such offsets is employed in the section of a gear case for a slotting machine in Fig. 61(a). The removed portion of the object is omitted at (b), and the offset cutting plane is shown alone at (c) together with the sectioned areas. The offset section itself is shown at (d), the position of the left side view. It should be noted that the offsets, or "breaks," are indicated by the irregular cutting-plane line in the front view at (d) but do not show in the sectional view; the section is shown as if the entire section were taken on a single plane. A note under the sectional view identifies it with the cutting plane, which is labeled *A–A*, or *B–B*, or other letters.

51. Phantom Sections. A *phantom section* is one in which the part in front of the cutting plane is *not removed* in order to retain those features in the sectional view, Fig. 62. As an alternative, detail sections could have been made of these two sectional views. The sectioning is indicated by dashed section lines, which cross both visible and hidden lines wherever necessary.

support rest is shown in Fig. 64. The roller support is the same as that previously discussed under Cylindrical Surfaces and Edges, Art. 37. It should be noted in the assembly that screws and shafts are not hatched though the cutting plane theoretically passes through them, and that section lines for adjacent but different parts run in *opposite* directions. If this rule were not followed, it would be very difficult to determine which sectioned areas in Fig. 64 belong together for each part in the assembly. The

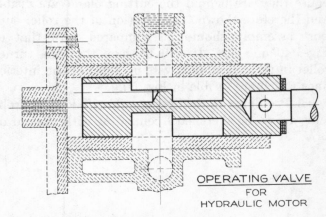

OPERATING VALVE
FOR
HYDRAULIC MOTOR

FIG. 63. PHANTOM SECTIONING

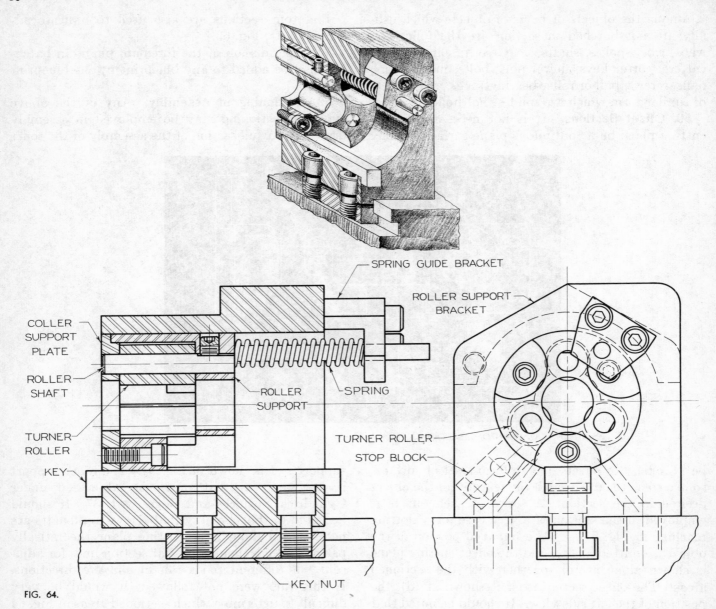

SPRING GUIDE BRACKET

ROLLER SUPPORT
BRACKET

COLLER
SUPPORT
PLATE

ROLLER
SHAFT

ROLLER
SUPPORT

SPRING

TURNER
ROLLER

TURNER ROLLER

STOP BLOCK

KEY

KEY NUT

FIG. 64.

spring and a number of other features, not cut because they are behind the cutting plane, are visible
and therefore shown. The section of the roller support assembly should be compared with that of
Figs. 49 and 50. It will be seen that the turner
roller in the assembly covers up some of the interior
lines which are visible in Fig. 50.

53. Problems — Sectioning. The following problems are to be sketched freehand or with the aid of
a small rule. Care should be taken to keep section
lines parallel and very fine in contrast to the object
lines. Unless otherwise specified, the material in
each problem is understood to be cast iron. For cast
iron the section lines should be sketched about $\frac{1}{16}''$
apart. The student should study the various notes
attached to these drawings, for by this means he
can gradually enlarge his vocabulary of information
concerning various shop operations.

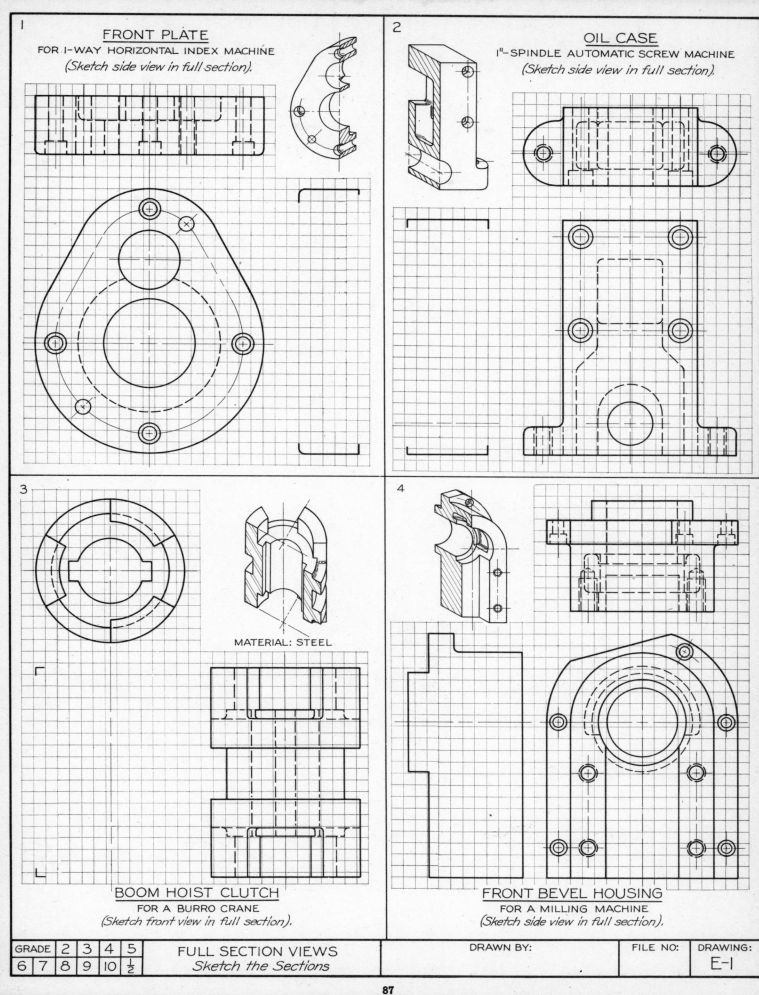

1

FRONT PLATE
FOR I-WAY HORIZONTAL INDEX MACHINE
(Sketch side view in full section).

2

OIL CASE
I"-SPINDLE AUTOMATIC SCREW MACHINE
(Sketch side view in full section).

3

BOOM HOIST CLUTCH
FOR A BURRO CRANE
(Sketch front view in full section).

MATERIAL: STEEL

4

FRONT BEVEL HOUSING
FOR A MILLING MACHINE
(Sketch side view in full section).

GRADE	2	3	4	5		FULL SECTION VIEWS	DRAWN BY:	FILE NO:	DRAWING:
	6	7	8	9	10	½	*Sketch the Sections*			E-I

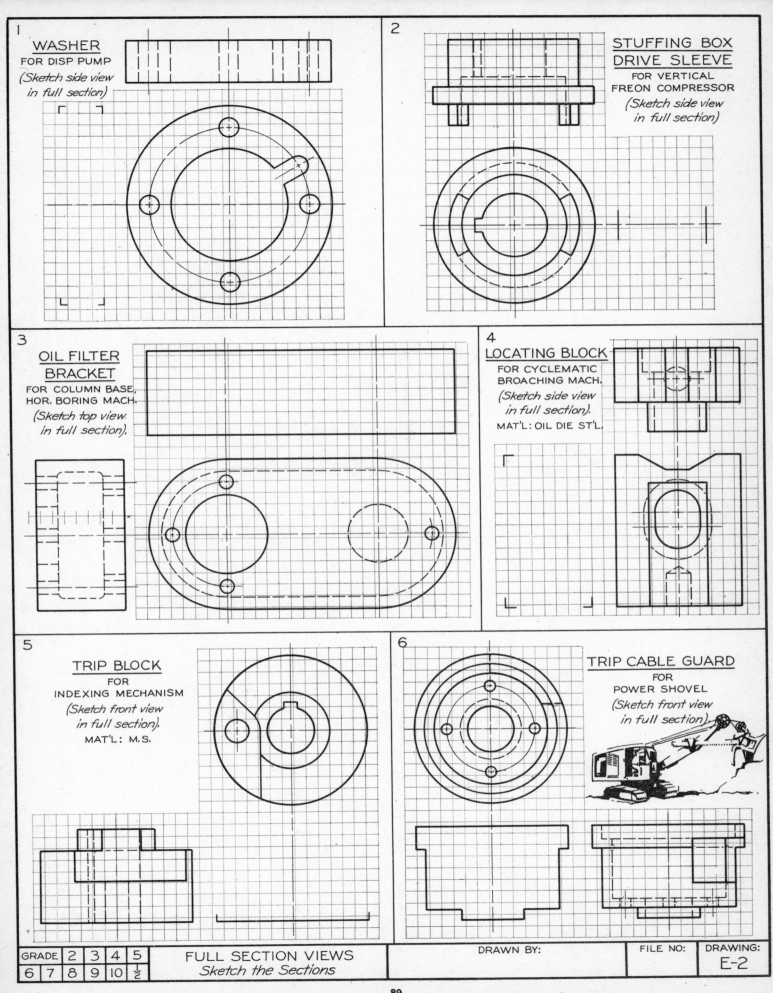

1 WASHER
FOR DISP PUMP
(Sketch side view in full section)

2 STUFFING BOX DRIVE SLEEVE
FOR VERTICAL FREON COMPRESSOR
(Sketch side view in full section)

3 OIL FILTER BRACKET
FOR COLUMN BASE, HOR. BORING MACH.
(Sketch top view in full section).

4 LOCATING BLOCK
FOR CYCLEMATIC BROACHING MACH.
(Sketch side view in full section).
MAT'L: OIL DIE ST'L.

5 TRIP BLOCK
FOR INDEXING MECHANISM
(Sketch front view in full section).
MAT'L: M.S.

6 TRIP CABLE GUARD
FOR POWER SHOVEL
(Sketch front view in full section).

GRADE	2	3	4	5
	6	7	8	9	10	½

FULL SECTION VIEWS
Sketch the Sections

DRAWN BY:

FILE NO:

DRAWING: E-2

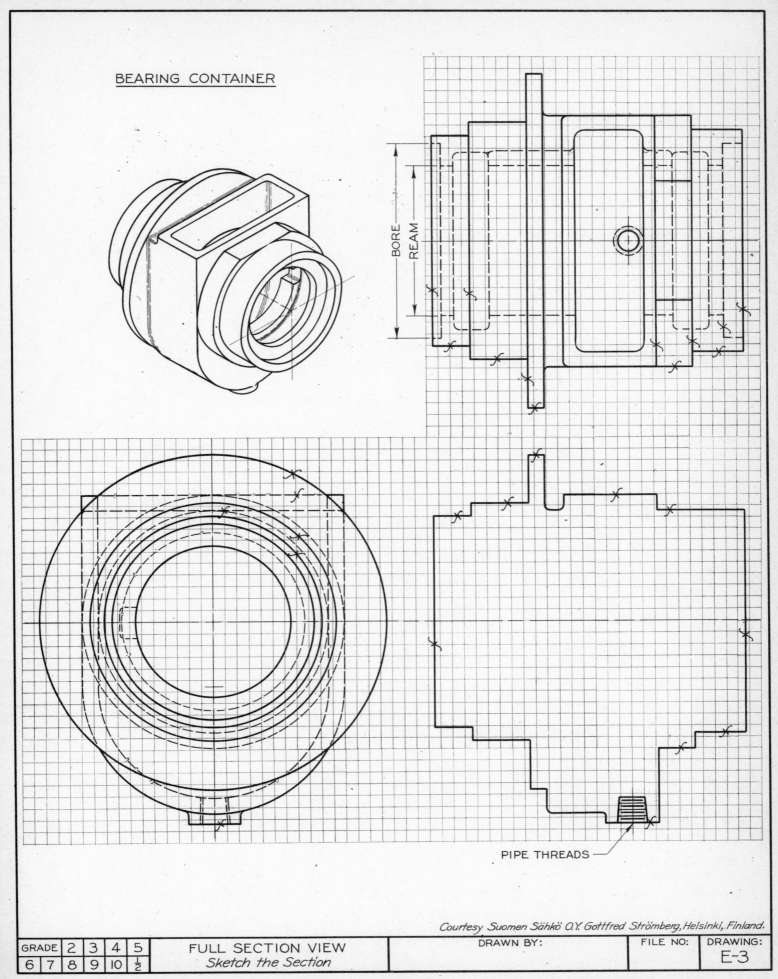

BEARING CONTAINER

BORE
REAM

PIPE THREADS

Courtesy Suomen Sähkö O.Y. Gottfred Strömberg, Helsinki, Finland.

GRADE	2	3	4	5	FULL SECTION VIEW	DRAWN BY:	FILE NO:	DRAWING:
	6	7	8	9	10	½	*Sketch the Section*			E-3

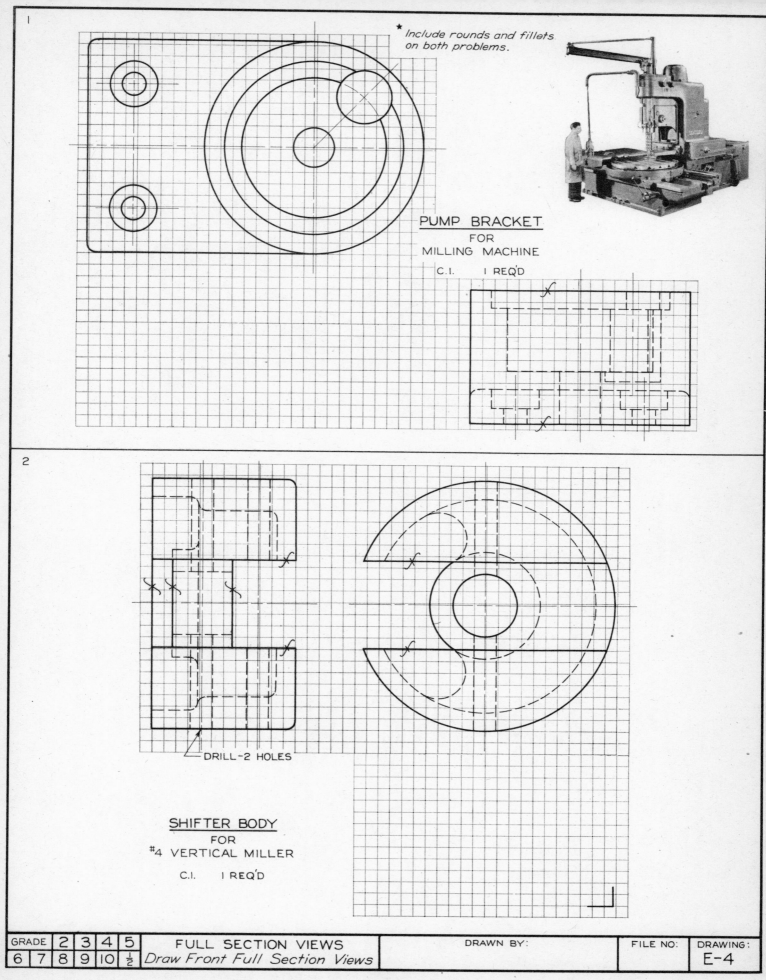

1

*Include rounds and fillets on both problems.

PUMP BRACKET
FOR
MILLING MACHINE

C.I.   1 REQ'D

2

DRILL-2 HOLES

SHIFTER BODY
FOR
#4 VERTICAL MILLER

C.I.   1 REQ'D

GRADE	2	3	4	5	FULL SECTION VIEWS	DRAWN BY:		FILE NO:	DRAWING:
	6	7	8	9	10	½	Draw Front Full Section Views			E-4

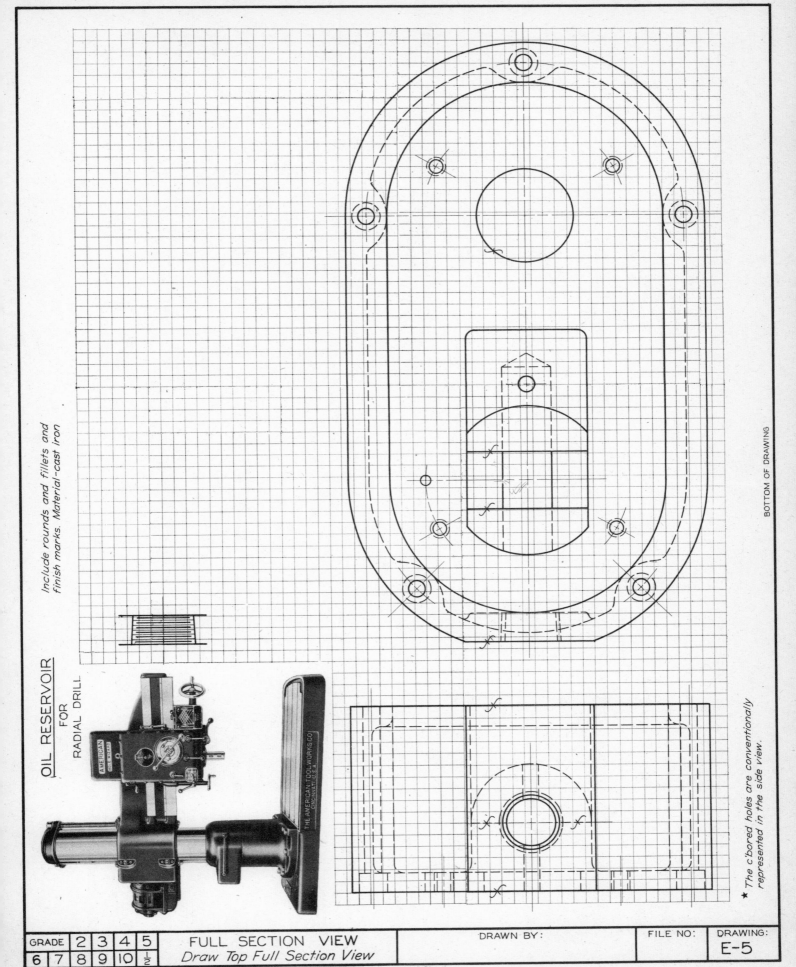

Include rounds and fillets and
finish marks. Material-cast iron

OIL RESERVOIR
FOR
RADIAL DRILL

BOTTOM OF DRAWING

* The c'bored holes are conventionally
represented in the side view.

GRADE	2	3	4	5	FULL SECTION VIEW	DRAWN BY:	FILE NO:	DRAWING:
	6	7	8	9	10	½	*Draw Top Full Section View*			E-5

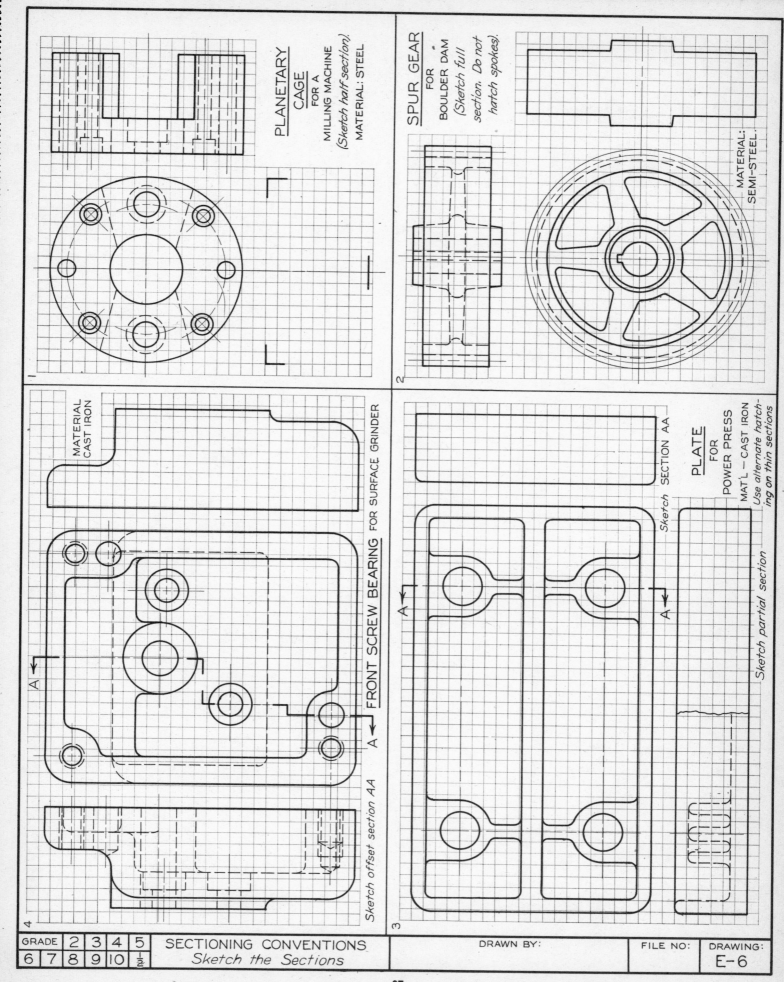

PLANETARY
CAGE
FOR A
MILLING MACHINE
(Sketch half section).
MATERIAL: STEEL

SPUR GEAR
FOR
BOULDER DAM
(Sketch full
section. Do not
hatch spokes).

MATERIAL:
SEMI-STEEL.

MATERIAL
CAST IRON

FRONT SCREW BEARING FOR SURFACE GRINDER

Sketch offset section AA

PLATE
FOR
POWER PRESS
MAT'L — CAST IRON
Use alternate hatch-
ing on thin sections

Sketch   SECTION AA

Sketch partial section

GRADE	2	3	4	5	SECTIONING CONVENTIONS	DRAWN BY:	FILE NO:	DRAWING:
6	7	8	9	10	$\frac{1}{2}$	*Sketch the Sections*			E-6

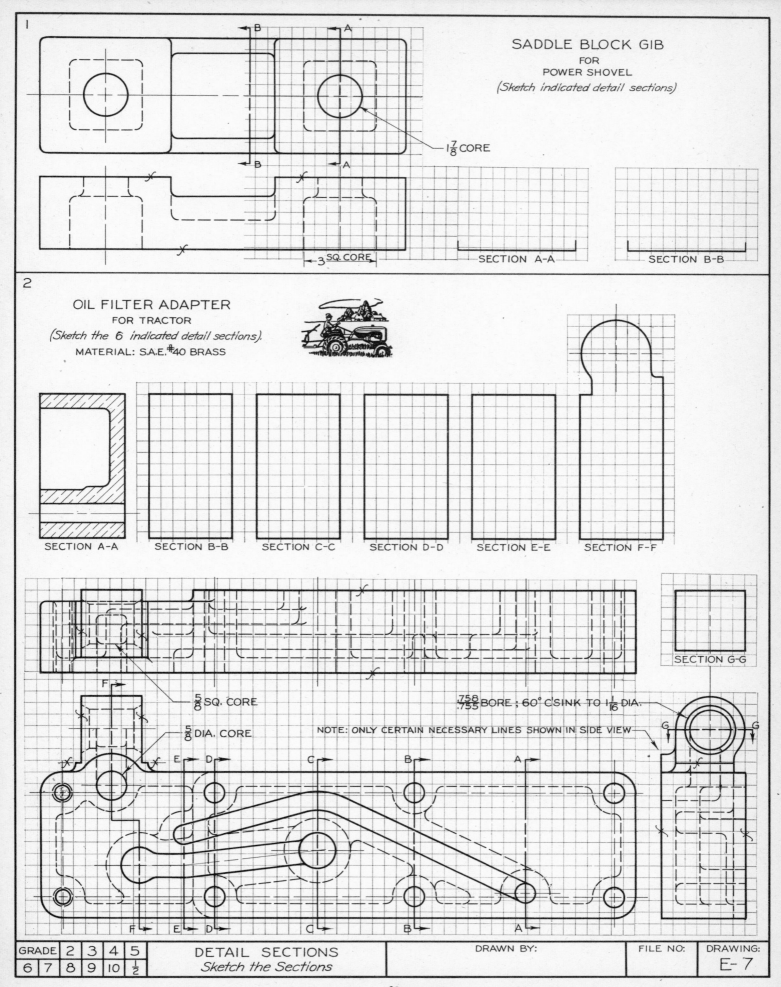

1

SADDLE BLOCK GIB
FOR
POWER SHOVEL
(Sketch indicated detail sections)

$1\frac{7}{8}$ CORE

3 SQ. CORE

SECTION A-A

SECTION B-B

2

OIL FILTER ADAPTER
FOR TRACTOR
(Sketch the 6 indicated detail sections).
MATERIAL: S.A.E. #40 BRASS

SECTION A-A   SECTION B-B   SECTION C-C   SECTION D-D   SECTION E-E   SECTION F-F

SECTION G-G

$\frac{5}{8}$ SQ. CORE

$\frac{5}{8}$ DIA. CORE

$\frac{.758}{.755}$ BORE; 60° C'SINK TO $1\frac{1}{6}$ DIA.

NOTE: ONLY CERTAIN NECESSARY LINES SHOWN IN SIDE VIEW

GRADE	2	3	4	5
6	7	8	9	10	$\frac{1}{2}$

DETAIL SECTIONS
Sketch the Sections

DRAWN BY:

FILE NO:

DRAWING:
E-7

CHAPTER VII

AUXILIARY VIEWS

54. Need for Auxiliary Views. Most machine parts are rectangular in general shape or composed of surfaces which can be fully described by the regular views. The line of sight for any one of the three regular views is at right angles to the lines of sight for the other two views; that is, the lines of sight are *mutually perpendicular* to each other.

means of a top view and a special *auxiliary view*. It should be noted that the semicircular surface *AB* is shown as a line in the top view and as a surface, true size, in the auxiliary view.

It is especially important to observe that the *direction of sight for the auxiliary view is at right angles to the direction of sight for the top view*. The auxiliary

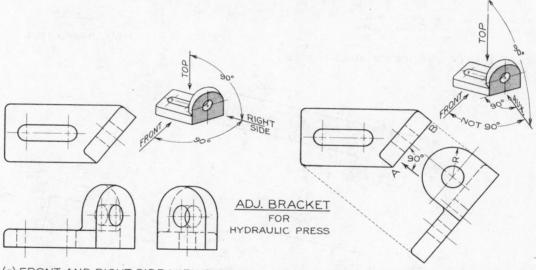

(a) FRONT AND RIGHT SIDE VIEWS SHOW THE CIRCULAR HOLE AND SEMICIRCULAR FACE AS ELLIPSES.

(b) A TOP AUXILIARY VIEW SHOWS THE CIRCULAR HOLE AND SEMICIRCULAR FACE AS TRUE CIRCLES.

ADJ. BRACKET
FOR
HYDRAULIC PRESS

FIG. 65. NEED FOR AN AUXILIARY VIEW

Some objects, however, have inclined surfaces or oblique surfaces whose *true views must be shown* on the blueprint, particularly so that the true dimensions for those parts may be shown. This is to say that such objects must be viewed in a direction other than any of those for the regular views. More specifically a *new line of sight*, perpendicular to the surface whose true view is required, must be assumed.

In Fig. 65(a) a three-view drawing of the adjusting bracket is evidently not complete because the true shape of the semicircular surface is not shown in any view. At (b) the same object is fully described by

view will always be projected from a view with which the lines of sight are mutually perpendicular.

55. Top Auxiliary Views. If an auxiliary view is projected from the top view — which is to say that the line of sight for the auxiliary view is perpendicular to the line of sight for the top view — it is called a *top auxiliary view*, Fig. 65(b).

Evidently an observer may assume an infinite number of positions around an object, all of which have lines of sight perpendicular to the line of sight for the top view, Fig. 66. All of the views thus obtained are therefore top auxiliary views, and the

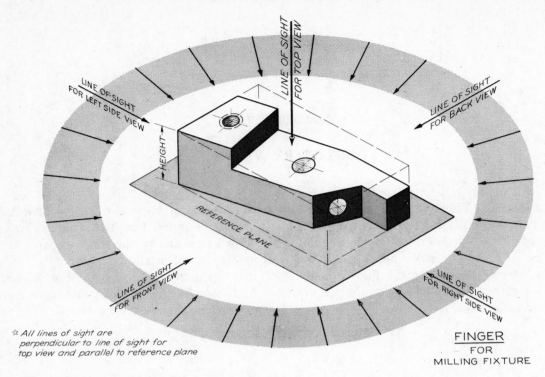

☆ All lines of sight are
perpendicular to line of sight for
top view and parallel to reference plane

FIG. 66. LINES OF SIGHT FOR TOP AUXILIARY VIEWS

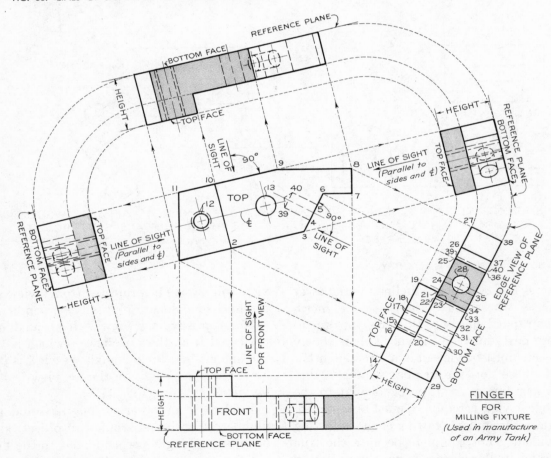

FIG. 67. TOP AUXILIARY VIEWS

true height of the object will be shown in each. Five possible views taken in this manner are shown in Fig. 67, each showing one significant dimension of the object, *height*. It should be observed that in a sense the front view of an object may be regarded as a top auxiliary view.

A reference plane is always assumed (but not actually drawn) through the center line of a symmetrical object or coinciding with a principal face of an unsymmetrical object. This imaginary plane is

is shown edgewise as circle 28, the true shape of the hole. Circle 13 is the edge view of another cylindrical surface, shown at 22, 24, 35, 33. The dotted and solid circles 12 represent the end of a threaded hole shown conventionally at 15, 17, 31, 30 by pairs of dotted lines. Inclined surface 10, 2 is not shown true size in the auxiliary view at 16, 19, 21, 20 although the true height dimension of this surface is shown. The remaining surfaces and edges should be analyzed by the student in this manner.

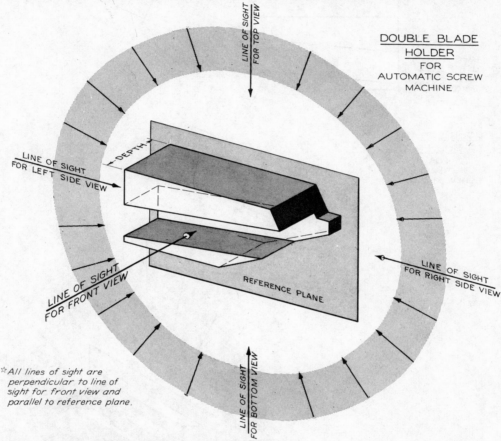

FIG. 68. FRONT AUXILIARY VIEW LINES OF SIGHT

always assumed at right angles to the line of sight for the view from which the auxiliary view is projected; this is to say that the reference plane is always assumed parallel to the line of sight for the auxiliary view and will always show as a line in that view. This line will always be perpendicular to the projection lines between the views, Figs. 66 and 67. All *height* measurements in Fig. 67 are taken perpendicular to the reference line or edge view of the reference plane.

In Fig. 67, inclined surface 3, 6 (central, or top view) is shown true size in the lower right auxiliary view at 23, 25, 36, 34. Cylindrical surface 4, 39, 40, 5

56. Front Auxiliary Views. If an auxiliary view is projected from the front view, it is called a *front auxiliary view*. Here again the observer may assume an infinite number of positions in all of which the lines of sight are perpendicular to the front-view line of sight, Fig. 68. Five possible views taken in this manner are shown in Fig. 69, one of which is the top view. The significant dimension of the object in all of these views projected from the front view is *depth* and is measured parallel with the lines of projection to each auxiliary view.

The reference plane was assumed perpendicular to the front-view line of sight, Fig. 68, and is shown

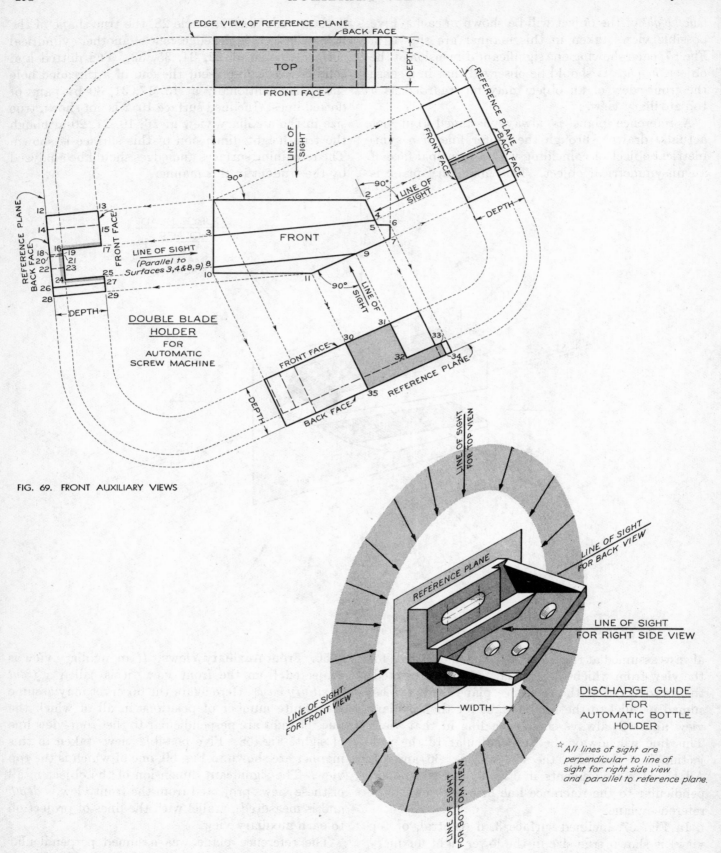

FIG. 69. FRONT AUXILIARY VIEWS

FIG. 70. SIDE AUXILIARY VIEW LINES OF SIGHT

edgewise in each view projected from the front view. The depth dimensions are measured perpendicular to the edge views of the reference planes.

In practice, the front view and left-hand auxiliary view alone would probably be used.

size, at 30, 31, 32, 33, 34, 35. All other surfaces and edges should be analyzed by the student in this manner.

57. Side Auxiliary Views. If an auxiliary view is projected from the side view, it is called a *side*

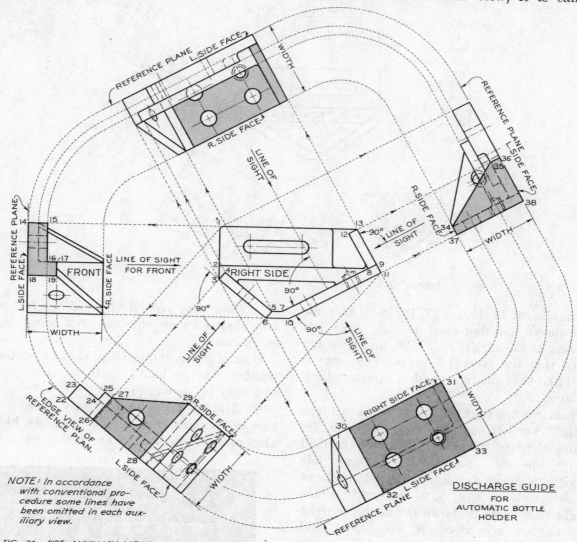

NOTE: In accordance with conventional procedure some lines have been omitted in each auxiliary view.

FIG. 71. SIDE AUXILIARY VIEWS

In Fig. 69, inclined surfaces 3, 4 and 8, 9 (front view) are shown in the left-hand auxiliary view at 16, 17 and 24, 25, respectively. Normal surface 3, 4, 5, 6, 7, 9, 8 is shown true size in the front view and as line 16, 24 in the auxiliary view. Thus the longitudinal slot is shown in its true cross section or true shape at 25, 24, 16, 17, which is to say that the true 90° angles between surfaces 24, 25; 24, 16; and 16, 17 are shown in the auxiliary view. The groove may be dimensioned in this view.

Inclined surface 11, 7 (front view) is shown in the lower auxiliary view as an L-shaped surface, true

auxiliary view. Here also the observer may assume an infinite number of positions in all of which the lines of sight are perpendicular to the side-view line of sight, Fig. 70. Five possible views taken in this manner are shown in Fig. 71, one of which is the front view. The significant dimension of the object in all of these views projected from the side view is *width*.

The reference plane was assumed perpendicular to the side-view line of sight, Fig. 70, and is shown edgewise, Fig. 71, in each view projected from the right side view. The width dimensions are all measured perpendicular to the edge views of the reference plane.

In Fig. 71 normal surface 1, 3 (central, or right side view) is shown in the front view as an L-shaped

front view and several partial auxiliary views are necessary for a complete description of the object, Fig. 72. This figure is more easily read than Fig. 71. Thus, for the more complicated objects the blueprint

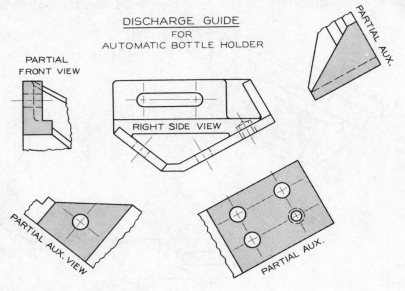

FIG. 72. PARTIAL VIEWS

surface, true size, at 14, 15, 16, 17, 19, 18. This same surface is shown foreshortened in the lower left auxiliary view at 22, 23, 24, 25, 27, 26, and it should be observed that the general L-shaped character is maintained and that the true *width* is shown in both of these views.

Inclined surface 3, 6 (right side view) is shown true shape in the lower left auxiliary view at 27, 29, 28, 26, including the true cylindrical shape of the drill hole through the wall. Surface 27, 29 (lower left auxiliary view) is shown as a foreshortened surface in the right side view at 3, 4, 5, 6. Inclined surface 13, 11 (right side view) is shown in the upper right auxiliary view true size at 35, 36, 38, 37, 34, and inclined surface 10, 11 is shown in the lower right auxiliary view, true size, at 30, 31, 33, 32, including the true shapes and relative locations of the four holes.

Other important features of the object should be similarly analyzed by the student.

58. Minimum Shape Description. In Fig. 65 the two views complete at (b) are required to show the shape of the object. In Fig. 67 only the top and lower right auxiliary view complete are needed for a clear description of the object. In Fig. 69 the front view and left-hand auxiliary view complete are sufficient without additional views. In Fig. 71 the complete right side (central view) and partial

may show only partial views of the features whose true shapes are required and not complete views in every case.

If an object is symmetrical about a center line in a regular view or in an auxiliary view, only a *half view* may be shown, Fig. 73.

59. Hidden Lines in Auxiliary Views. As is the case in regular views, Fig. 43, page 64, hidden lines are omitted where they are not needed for clear-

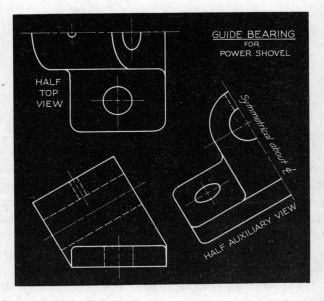

FIG. 73. HALF AUXILIARY VIEW

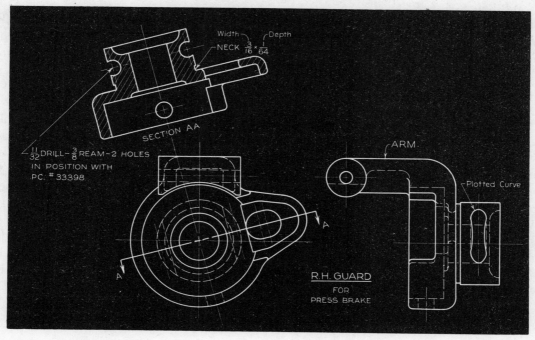

FIG. 74. AUXILIARY SECTION

ness. In general the various shapes will be adequately described in views showing these parts with visible object lines, and it is not necessary to repeat these features in all other views with hidden lines. An inspection of Fig. 72 will show that a number of hidden lines have been omitted and yet each feature is completely shown by representation in at least two views.

60. Auxiliary Sections. Occasionally it is necessary on a blueprint to describe some feature of an object by means of an auxiliary view in section, Fig. 74. Here an auxiliary exterior view would

include the arm, and interior shapes would be shown by hidden lines — no clearer than in the right side view. The auxiliary section clearly shows interior shapes as seen in the direction which is best for showing them.

61. Revolving the Blueprint. It was shown above that among the infinite number of positions which the observer can assume around an object, some of these in each case will actually produce the regular views. Conversely, we can take a blueprint already made and revolve it so that the projection lines to any auxiliary view projected from the regular

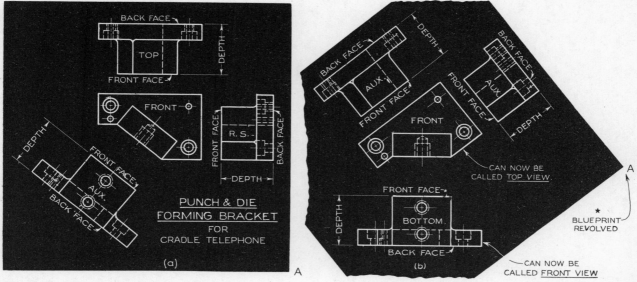

FIG. 75. TURNING AN AUXILIARY VIEW DRAWING

central view are in a vertical line above or below it or in a horizontal line to the left or right of it. In each such case the former auxiliary view becomes a regular view. For example, in Fig. 75 the blueprint at (a) can be revolved counterclockwise until the lower auxiliary view is directly under the front view as shown at (b), in which case it then becomes a *bottom view* and the top and right side views become auxiliary views. It is evident that these views may now be renamed, as indicated.

The position that an object occupies on the blueprint is often dictated by the necessity to show it in the same position it occupies on the machine, so that either (a) or (b) might be shown. However, the blueprint reader might simplify the reading of any auxiliary view simply by turning the sheet so that the auxiliary view becomes one of the regular views.

62. Problems — Auxiliary Views. Sufficient locating points are given so that the student will have no undue difficulty projecting the auxiliary views to the correct position on the sheets. A typical top auxiliary section is required on sheet F–3, and the student should make object lines heavy and section lines extremely fine, using a sharp pencil. It will be found helpful to use a straightedge at least for drawing the section lines, which should be drawn at 45° to the main rectangular lines of the view. Care should be taken not to draw the section lines too close together. Hidden lines should be omitted in the sectional views.

Complete auxiliary views are to be drawn on all sheets, including all necessary hidden lines, unless otherwise assigned by the instructor. Indicate reference plane lines in all problems.

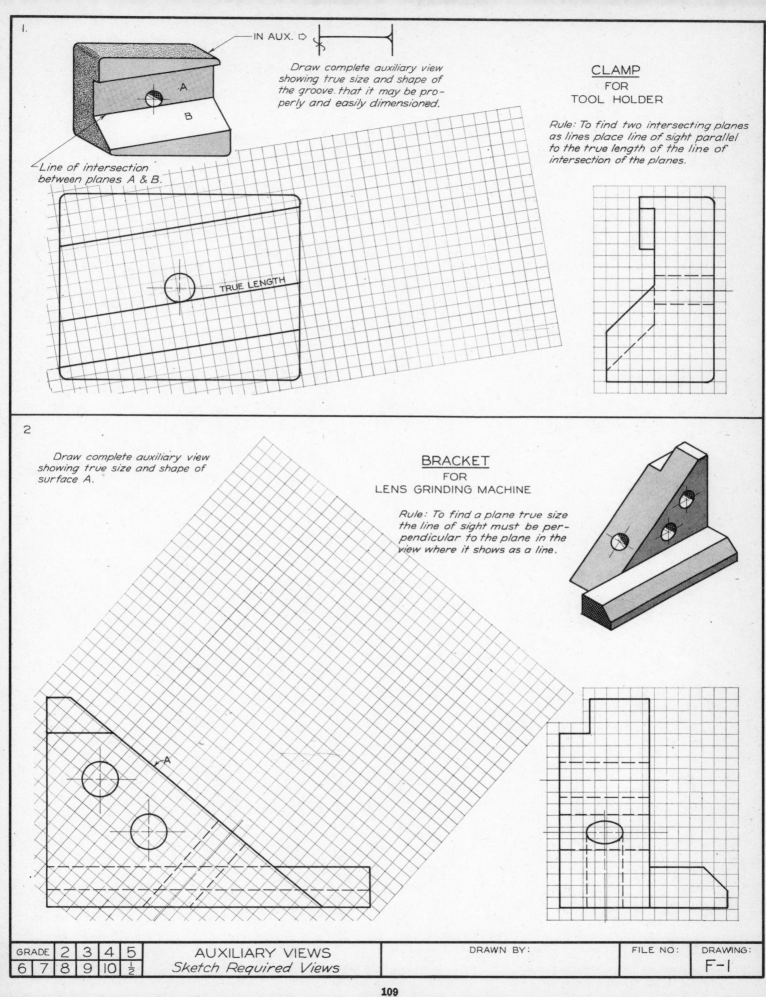

1.

─ IN AUX. ▷

Draw complete auxiliary view
showing true size and shape of
the groove, that it may be properly and easily dimensioned.

Line of intersection
between planes A & B.

TRUE LENGTH

CLAMP
FOR
TOOL HOLDER

*Rule: To find two intersecting planes
as lines place line of sight parallel
to the true length of the line of
intersection of the planes.*

2

Draw complete auxiliary view
showing true size and shape of
surface A.

─A

BRACKET
FOR
LENS GRINDING MACHINE

*Rule: To find a plane true size
the line of sight must be perpendicular to the plane in the
view where it shows as a line.*

GRADE	2	3	4	5	AUXILIARY VIEWS	DRAWN BY:	FILE NO:	DRAWING:
6	7	8	9	10	½	*Sketch Required Views*			F-1

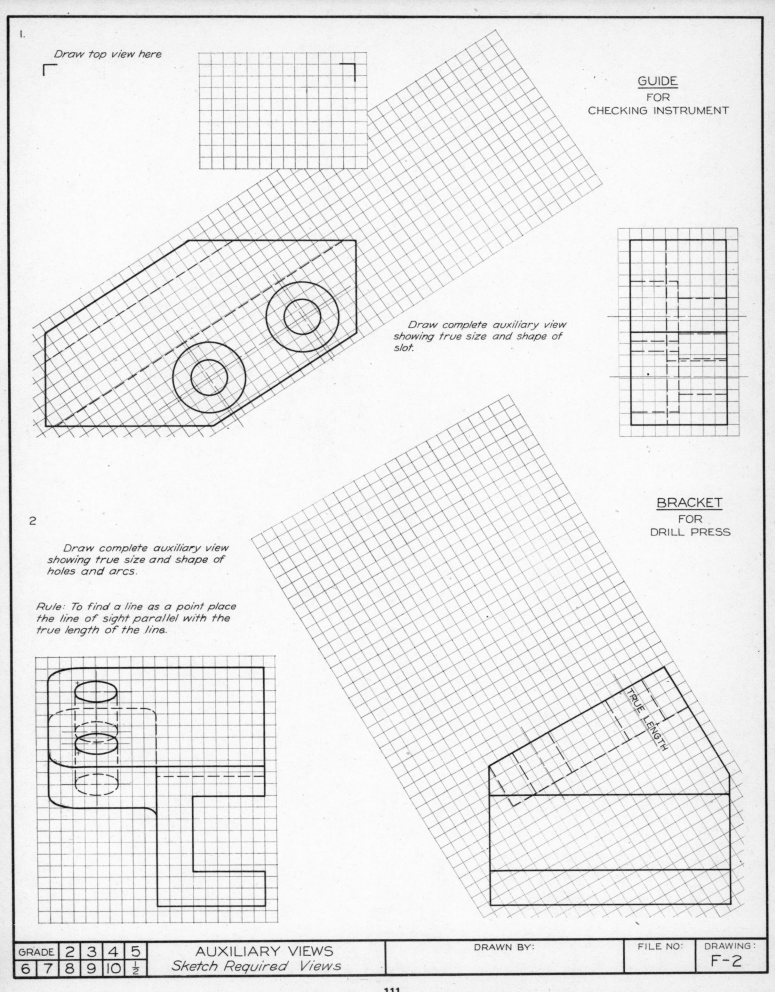

1.

Draw top view here

GUIDE
FOR
CHECKING INSTRUMENT

Draw complete auxiliary view
showing true size and shape of
slot.

BRACKET
FOR
DRILL PRESS

2

Draw complete auxiliary view
showing true size and shape of
holes and arcs.

Rule: To find a line as a point place
the line of sight parallel with the
true length of the line.

TRUE LENGTH

GRADE	2	3	4	5	AUXILIARY VIEWS	DRAWN BY:	FILE NO:	DRAWING:
6	7	8	9	10	½	Sketch Required Views			F-2

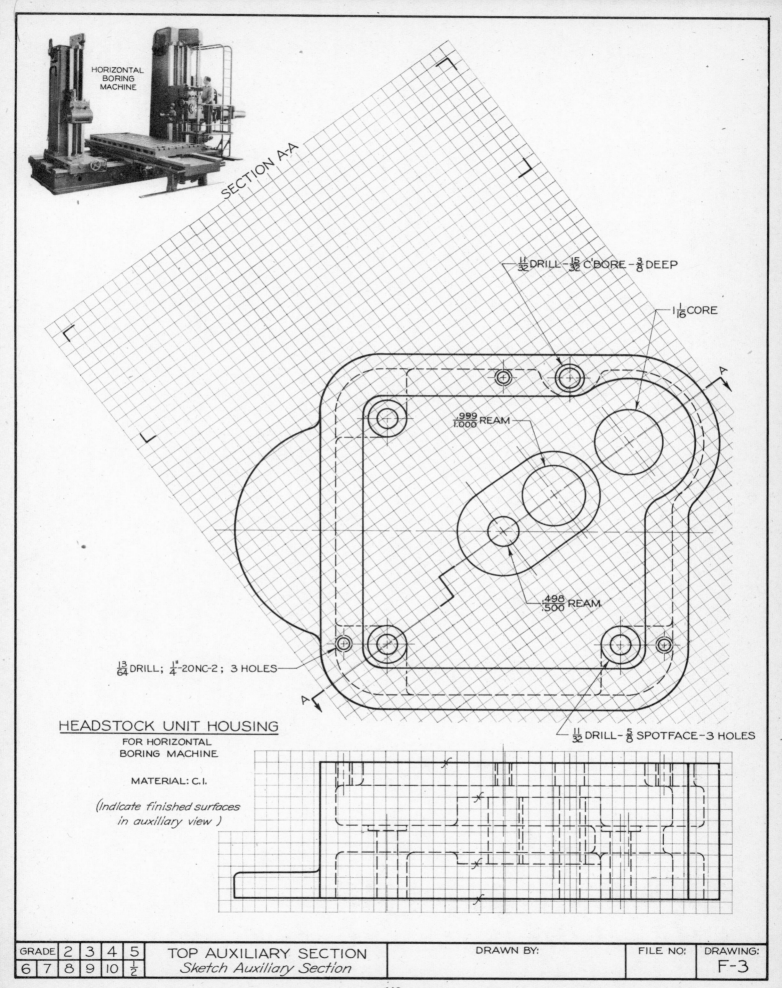

HORIZONTAL BORING MACHINE

SECTION A-A

$\frac{11}{32}$ DRILL - $\frac{15}{32}$ C'BORE - $\frac{3}{8}$ DEEP

$1\frac{1}{16}$ CORE

$\frac{.999}{1.000}$ REAM

$\frac{.498}{.500}$ REAM

$\frac{13}{64}$ DRILL; $\frac{1}{4}"$-20NC-2; 3 HOLES

$\frac{11}{32}$ DRILL - $\frac{5}{8}$ SPOTFACE - 3 HOLES

A
A

HEADSTOCK UNIT HOUSING
FOR HORIZONTAL BORING MACHINE

MATERIAL: C.I.

(Indicate finished surfaces in auxiliary view)

GRADE	2	3	4	5	TOP AUXILIARY SECTION	DRAWN BY:	FILE NO:	DRAWING:
	6	7	8	9	10	$\frac{1}{2}$	*Sketch Auxiliary Section*			F-3

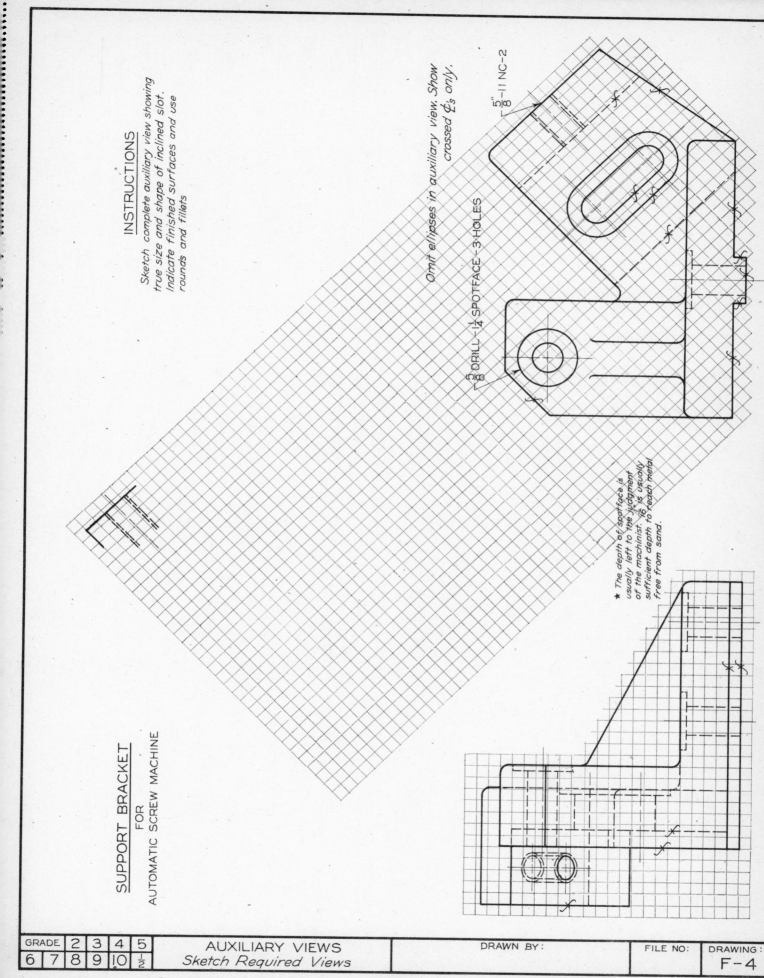

INSTRUCTIONS

Sketch complete auxiliary view showing
true size and shape of inclined slot.
Indicate finished surfaces and use
rounds and fillets

Omit ellipses in auxiliary view. Show
crossed ℄s only.

5"/8 -II NC-2

5/8 DRILL-1¼ SPOTFACE-3 HOLES

★ The depth of spotface is
usually left to the judgment
of the machinist. It is usually
sufficient depth to reach metal
free from sand.

BOTTOM OF DRAWING

GRADE	2	3	4	5
6	7	8	9	10	½

AUXILIARY VIEWS
Sketch Required Views

DRAWN BY:

FILE NO:

DRAWING:
F-4

CHAPTER VIII

SCREW THREADS AND FASTENERS

63. Screw-Thread Terminology. The various common devices used to fasten machine parts together occur so frequently on blueprints that the blueprint the threads shown in the nut are those in the *back half* of the internal thread as a result of the section, they must incline in a direction *opposite* to those on

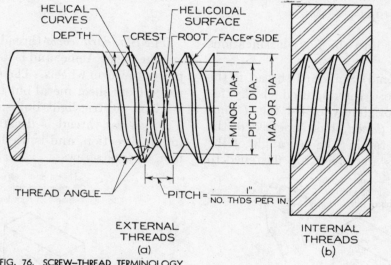

FIG. 76. SCREW—THREAD TERMINOLOGY

reader must be familiar with the methods of representation of such parts on drawings. These fasteners are *permanent*, such as rivets, or *movable*, such as bolts, screws, keys, and cotter pins.

Screw threads form such an essential part of most fasteners that their representation should be understood thoroughly.

The various terms used with respect to threads are illustrated in Fig. 76. It should be observed that the *crest lines* and *root lines* on the back side of the screw, shown hidden in Fig. 76, are inclined in an opposite direction to those on the front side. Since

the front side of the screw, or parallel to the dotted lines representing the threads on the back side of the screw, Fig. 76.

The *pitch* of a thread is the distance from a point on a thread to a corresponding point on the adjacent thread and equals one inch divided by the number of threads (or ridges) per inch, Fig. 76.

64. Screw-Thread Forms. The *form* of a thread is the true shape of the section of the ridge obtained by a cutting plane through the center line of the screw, Fig. 76(b). Various forms of threads are in use to perform three principal functions: (1) to hold

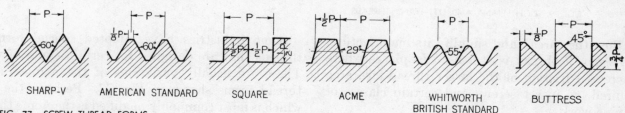

FIG. 77. SCREW—THREAD FORMS

parts together; (2) to adjust parts with respect to each other; and (3) to transmit power.

Any designer may create a special form of thread to suit a special purpose, but this greatly increases the costs of manufacture and is never done if the standard forms can be used. Hence, practically all

The *Whitworth* thread is used mostly in Great Britain and roughly corresponds to our American Standard thread.

The *square* and *Acme* threads are most commonly used for power transmission, the Acme being a modification of the square and largely replacing it.

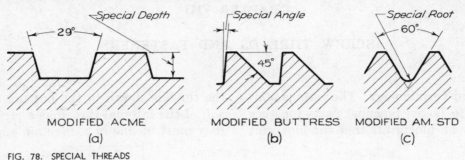

FIG. 78. SPECIAL THREADS

thread forms in use fall into the few classifications shown in Fig. 77.

The American (National) Standard thread is the most common all-purpose thread, used chiefly for *holding*. This thread, originally called the *United States Standard (USS) thread*, has superseded the old sharp-V thread but retains the 60° angle of the thread faces. The roots and crests are flattened to

The *Standard worm* thread is deeper but otherwise similar to the Acme, and is used on shafts to transmit power to worm wheels. The *knuckle* thread is usually rolled from sheet metal but is sometimes cast, and is used on electric-light bulbs, bottle tops, and so on. The *buttress* thread is designed to withstand shock in one direction, and is used in breech locks on cannon, or jack screws.

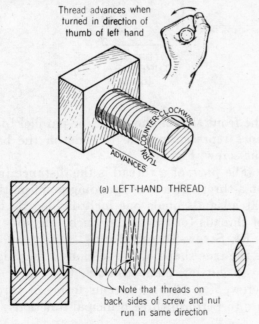

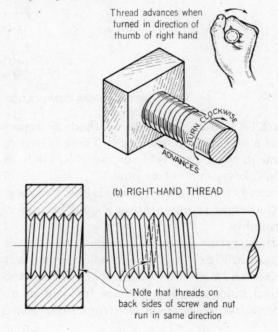

FIG. 79. RIGHT-HAND AND LEFT-HAND THREADS

strengthen the thread and simplify its manufacture.

The *sharp-V* thread is still used in places where the increased friction of the larger thread-face area is required, as in set screws and certain classes of brass pipe work.

Some industries have adopted special forms of threads that are designed for certain types of work. These are usually variations of the regular screw-thread forms shown in Fig. 77. Perhaps the form which is most commonly modified is the Acme thread;

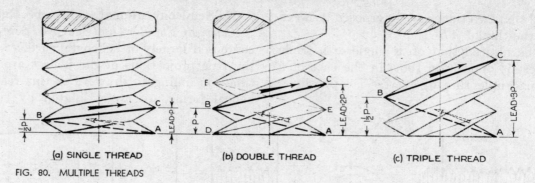

(a) SINGLE THREAD   (b) DOUBLE THREAD   (c) TRIPLE THREAD

FIG. 80. MULTIPLE THREADS

and the change usually consists in a different depth while maintaining the usual 29° angle so that standard cutters may be used, Fig. 78(a). The buttress thread (coming into wider use) is frequently varied by changing the vertical face a small amount, usually from 3° to 7°, Fig. 78(b). A modification of the American Standard form is shown in Fig. 78(c), in which the flat root is replaced by a fillet.

Besides these variations, various special patented forms of threads designed for self-locking are on the market, such as the Dardalet thread.

A thread may be "special" also by virtue of a change (from standard tables) in the number of threads per inch, without any change in the form of the thread. For example, a thread cut on a thin-walled, large-diameter tube might have to be very small, the number of threads per inch thus being increased.

65. Right- and Left-Hand Threads. A *right-hand* (R.H.) thread engages and advances into a nut when turned *clockwise;* a *left-hand* (L.H.) thread engages and advances into a nut only when turned *counter-*

clockwise, **Fig. 79.** *Any thread not designated L.H. on a drawing is understood to be R.H.*

66. Multiple Threads. The *lead* of a screw thread is the distance, measured parallel to the axis, that a screw advances in one turn; or lead may be defined as the distance, measured parallel to the axis, from a point on one thread to a corresponding point on the *next turn of the same ridge.*

A *single* thread is composed of one ridge, each turn adjacent to the previous turn. In Fig. 80(a), if the crest is followed around the back side of the screw from A to B, then around the front side from B to C, it will be seen that the distance from A to C is the lead, and in the case of a single thread it is equal to the pitch.

In Fig. 80(b), if the crest is followed around from A to B to C it will be evident that AC is the lead, and in the case of a double thread it must be twice the pitch. It should be noticed that another thread DEF is interposed between the turns of the thread ABC.

In Fig. 80(c), it is seen that the lead is three times

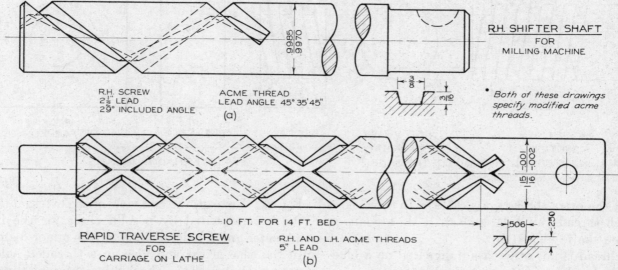

R.H. SHIFTER SHAFT
FOR
MILLING MACHINE

R.H. SCREW
2½" LEAD
29° INCLUDED ANGLE

ACME THREAD
LEAD ANGLE 45° 35′ 45″
(a)

• *Both of these drawings specify modified acme threads.*

RAPID TRAVERSE SCREW
FOR
CARRIAGE ON LATHE

R.H. AND L.H. ACME THREADS
5″ LEAD
(b)

FIG. 81. SINGLE THREADS WITH MULTIPLE LEADS

the pitch and that two ridges are interposed between the turns of the thread *ABC*.

It should be noticed that on a single or a triple thread, a crest is opposite a root; in the case of a double or quadruple thread, a crest is opposite a crest.

67. Semiconventional Thread Representation.

American Standard and Sharp-V: Screw threads are composed largely of helicoidal surfaces, Fig. 76, and the true projections of the helices are difficult and time-consuming to draw. For this reason the true helical forms are approximated by straight lines,

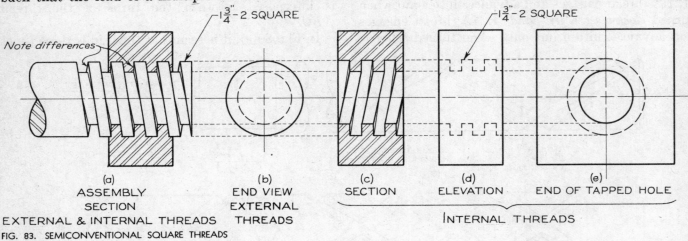

(a) ASSEMBLY SECTION   (b) END VIEW EXTERNAL
EXTERNAL & INTERNAL THREADS   THREADS

(c) SECTION   (d) ELEVATION   (e) END OF TAPPED HOLE
INTERNAL THREADS

FIG. 82. SEMICONVENTIONAL AMERICAN STANDARD THREADS

A double thread in one turn advances two pitches, a triple thread advances three pitches, and so on; in each case the distance advanced is the lead. Multiple threads are used where quick action, but not great power, is desired, as on fountain pens, toothpaste caps, valve stems, lead screws.

A multiple thread consists of two or more threads cut side by side like the colored stripes on a barber pole. Occasionally, the design of a single thread is such that the lead of a multiple thread is used but

Fig. 82. The flats are not shown as in Fig. 76, because of the closeness of the lines and the small sizes of threads on blueprints; but instead, the double lines of the crest and root are each combined into one line as shown. The true 60° *form* of thread is maintained, except that the flats are eliminated.

The true projection of the intersection of the helicoidal surfaces of the threads with the plane of the end of the screw or threaded hole is not shown,

(a) ASSEMBLY SECTION   (b) END VIEW EXTERNAL
EXTERNAL & INTERNAL THREADS   THREADS

(c) SECTION   (d) ELEVATION   (e) END OF TAPPED HOLE
INTERNAL THREADS

Note differences

FIG. 83. SEMICONVENTIONAL SQUARE THREADS

without the extra threads, Fig. 81(a). In some cases two such threads, an L.H. and an R.H., are cut on the same shaft, Fig. 81(b).

If a thread is not otherwise designated on a blueprint, it is understood to be a single thread.

Fig. 82. Instead, the end view of the external thread (b) is represented by a solid circle for the major diameter and a hidden circle for the minor diameter. In the case of the end view of a threaded hole the reverse is the case. The hidden internal thread is

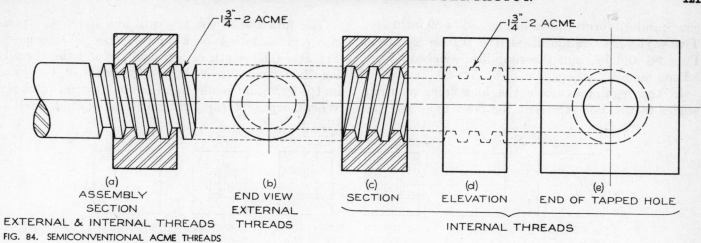

$1\frac{3}{4}"-2$ ACME　　　　　　　　　　$1\frac{3}{4}"-2$ ACME

(a)　　　　　　　　(b)　　　　　　(c)　　　　　(d)　　　　　(e)
ASSEMBLY　　　END VIEW　　SECTION　　ELEVATION　　END OF TAPPED HOLE
SECTION　　　EXTERNAL
EXTERNAL & INTERNAL THREADS　THREADS

INTERNAL THREADS

FIG. 84. SEMICONVENTIONAL ACME THREADS

represented with hidden V's, and the crest lines and root lines are omitted for simplicity.

No distinction is made in the American Standard and sharp-V thread representation.

The semiconventional thread representation is usually limited to the larger diameters to save drafting time, and even then the simpler conventional representation (§ 68) is often used.

Square Threads: The semiconventional representation of square threads is comparable to that for the American Standard in that the helical curves are represented by means of straight lines. A careful study of the thread shapes, Fig. 83(a), will show a slight difference in construction of the external thread *alone* and the external thread *when mated* with the sectioned internal thread. In the latter case small parts of the ridges of each are covered by the mating thread. The true profile, unaffected by any mating thread, appears at (c) and (d).

It should be noted that the thread in Fig. 83 is a single thread; and, like the American Standard, a crest is opposite a root. If the thread were a double thread, a crest would be opposite a crest; if a triple thread, a crest would again be opposite a root.

Acme Threads: Semiconventional representation of Acme threads is shown in Fig. 84. It should be

observed that this is a single thread and that when the external thread is mated with the internal thread in section, there is no overlapping of thread parts as in square-thread drawings. Overlapping occurs only when the thread is a triple thread or greater multiple.

68. Conventional Thread Representation.

All Thread Forms: For thread sizes of approximately 1″ dia. or less on the blueprint, and where

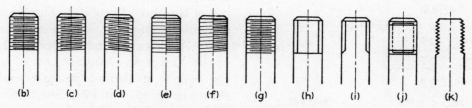

(b)　　(c)　　(d)　　(e)　　(f)　　(g)　　(h)　　(i)　　(j)　　(k)

FIG. 85. CONVENTIONAL METHODS OF THREAD REPRESENTATION

drawings are made hastily, the *conventional* methods of representation are used.

In spite of the great strides made in recent years toward standardization of conventional thread representation, there are still a great many forms in use today, the most common of which are shown in Fig. 85. Most widely accepted, however, are the Ameri-

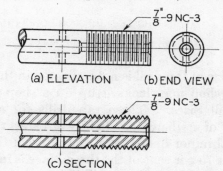

$\frac{7}{8}"-9$ NC-3

(a) ELEVATION　　(b) END VIEW

$\frac{7}{8}"-9$ NC-3

(c) SECTION

FIG. 86. EXTERNAL THREAD SYMBOLS — REGULAR

can Standard forms shown in Figs. 86 to 89 inclusive. Two styles are standardized, the regular symbols, Figs. 86 and 87, and the simplified symbols, Figs. 88 and 89.

In the regular symbols the long lines at right angles to the axis represent the crest lines and the

The function of the tap drill and its effect upon the representation of a tapped hole is shown in Fig. 90. The depth of tap drill beyond the thread length depends upon the requirements of the job, and is generally made equal to four thread pitches. Where depth of tap drill must be limited, and a

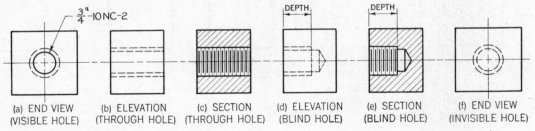

(a) END VIEW (VISIBLE HOLE)   (b) ELEVATION (THROUGH HOLE)   (c) SECTION (THROUGH HOLE)   (d) ELEVATION (BLIND HOLE)   (e) SECTION (BLIND HOLE)   (f) END VIEW (INVISIBLE HOLE)

FIG. 87. INTERNAL THREAD SYMBOLS — REGULAR

short lines, the root lines. Although spaced by eye these lines are supposed to approximate roughly the actual pitch of the thread except in very fine threads.

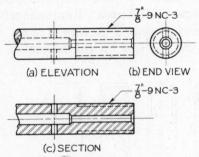

(a) ELEVATION   (b) END VIEW

(c) SECTION

FIG. 88. EXTERNAL THREAD SYMBOLS — SIMPLIFIED

It should be noted that the V form (or square or Acme form) is shown when the external conventional thread is sectioned, Fig. 86(c).

bottoming tap is used, the threads will be shown down to the drill-point portion of the hole.

69. Threads in Assembly Drawings. Both conventional and semiconventional thread representations are used on assembly drawings of threads, depending upon the diameters represented. It should be noted that the conventional external thread is mated with the internal thread without the showing of the thread profiles. Threaded shafts and nuts are customarily not sectioned in assembly, Fig. 91.

70. American Standard Screw Threads. The *form* of the American Standard thread is the same as the old Sellers or United States Standard (U.S.S.), as shown in Figs. 76 and 77. See Table IV in Appendix. Five series of threads are embraced in the Standard, all having the same form, but having different numbers of threads per inch and consequently *different pitches*, depending upon diameters.

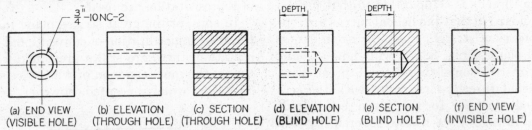

(a) END VIEW (VISIBLE HOLE)   (b) ELEVATION (THROUGH HOLE)   (c) SECTION (THROUGH HOLE)   (d) ELEVATION (BLIND HOLE)   (e) SECTION (BLIND HOLE)   (f) END VIEW (INVISIBLE HOLE)

FIG. 89. INTERNAL THREAD SYMBOLS — SIMPLIFIED

If the size of tap drill is not indicated in the thread note, the shop man looks it up on a shop chart of "Tap Drill Sizes." These tap drills for standard work are of a diameter slightly greater than the theoretical minor diameter of the internal thread so that about 75 per cent of the thread face is in contact with the mating thread.

(1) The *coarse thread* (NC) is a general-purpose thread. This was originally the old U.S.S. thread and is so labeled on older drawings. See Table IV, in Appendix.

(2) The *fine thread* (NF) has a greater number of threads per inch, and is used extensively in the automobile and aircraft industries where extreme vibra-

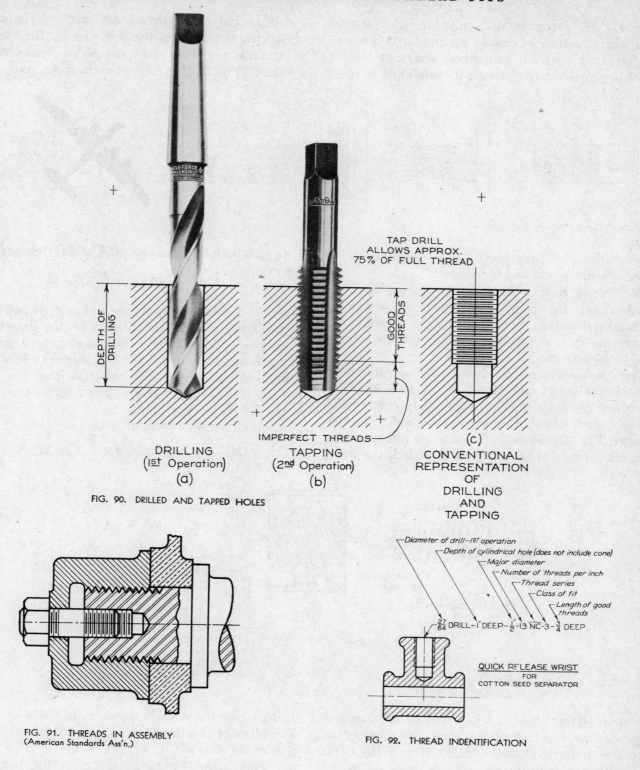

DRILLING
(1st Operation)
(a)

TAPPING
(2nd Operation)
(b)

TAP DRILL
ALLOWS APPROX.
75% OF FULL THREAD

IMPERFECT THREADS

CONVENTIONAL
REPRESENTATION
OF
DRILLING
AND
TAPPING
(c)

FIG. 90. DRILLED AND TAPPED HOLES

FIG. 91. THREADS IN ASSEMBLY
(American Standards Ass'n.)

Diameter of drill—1st operation
Depth of cylindrical hole (does not include cone)
Major diameter
Number of threads per inch
Thread series
Class of fit
Length of good threads

$\frac{27}{64}$ DRILL—1" DEEP—$\frac{1}{2}$"—13 NC—3—$\frac{3}{4}$ DEEP

QUICK RELEASE WRIST
FOR
COTTON SEED SEPARATOR

FIG. 92. THREAD INDENTIFICATION

tion is a factor in design. This was originally the S.A.E. thread and is so labeled on older drawings. See Table IV, in Appendix.

(3) The *8-pitch* (N8), *12-pitch* (N12), and *16-pitch* (N16) series specify a certain number of threads per inch (as 8, 12, or 16) for all diameters in each series, for special requirements in pressure vessels, and other construction.

71. American Standard Screw-Thread Fits. Four classes of *fits* are also standardized, ranging from

Class 1 Fit, "recommended only for screw thread work where clearance between mating parts is essential for rapid assembly and where shake or play is not objectionable," to *Class 4 Fit*, "intended to meet

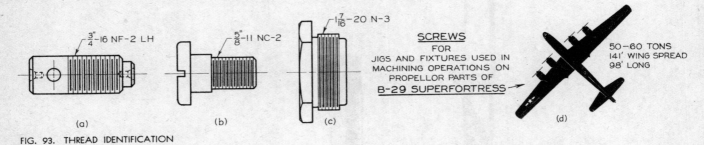

FIG. 93. THREAD IDENTIFICATION

very unusual requirements . . . a selective fit if initial assembly by hand is required."

72. Thread Notes. A group of symbols has been standardized for specifying American Standard threads on drawings, in correspondence, on shop and storeroom cards, and in specifications for parts, taps, dies, tools, and gages.

The most common symbols are illustrated and defined in Figs. 92 and 93. It should be noted that the major diameter is always specified, whether the thread is an internal or an external thread. The last number, **Fig. 93**, indicates fit and does not specify a multiple thread. If the latter is intended, the word

Square and Acme threads are specified simply by giving the major diameter, followed by the number of threads per inch and the word "square" or "Acme," Fig. 94. The practice in some companies is to give both the *lead* and *pitch* of multiple threads; for example:

$$4\,P - 1\tfrac{1}{2}\ \text{Lead, L.H. Acme}$$

Here, as is often the case, the diameter is not given in the note, but instead directly on the drawing of the thread. The 4 P, or 4 Pitch, means four pitches, or threads, per inch; the pitch is therefore ¼". The degree of multiple is also omitted from the note, but the lead (1½") is given. The degree of multiple is 1½" ÷ ¼ = (Sextuple).

Another common form of note is as follows:

$$1\tfrac{1}{16}'' - 3\,P - \text{QUADRUPLE} - \text{R.H. ACME}.$$

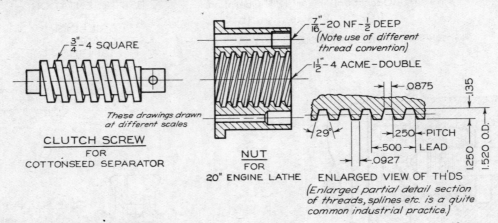

FIG. 94. THREAD IDENTIFICATION

(or abbreviation) *double*, *triple*, and so on, must be appended to the end of the note. Otherwise the thread is understood to be single. If only the letter N is used to indicate the thread series, a special pitch is understood, Fig. 93(c).

If the letters L.H. are used, the thread is a left-hand thread; and if these letters do not appear in the thread note, the thread is understood to be R.H.

In this case the outside diameter is given as 1⅟₁₆". The pitch of the thread is ⅓", and the lead for the quadruple thread is 4 × ⅓ = 1⅓". The R.H., for "right hand," is commonly given for Acme and Square threads, though usually omitted in notes for American Standard Threads.

73. S.A.E.* Extra-Fine Threads. For use on thin metal where the length of thread engagement is

* Society of Automotive Engineers.

small, and in cases where close adjustment is required or vibration is great, the *S.A.E. Extra-Fine* thread may be used. This standard specifies a greater number of threads per inch than any series of the American Standard.

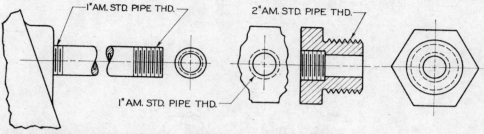

FIG. 95. REPRESENTATION OF AMERICAN STANDARD PIPE THREADS — REGULAR

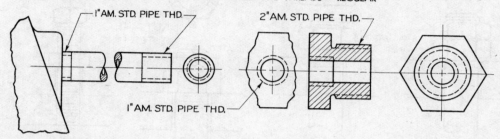

FIG. 96. REPRESENTATION OF AMERICAN STANDARD PIPE THREADS — SIMPLIFIED

74. Pipe Threads. Tables are also available for *American Standard Pipe Threads*, including *taper* threads and *straight* threads. Methods of representation and specification are illustrated in Figs. 95 and 96. The actual taper may or may not be drawn to scale or shown at all on the blueprint. Pipe threads are always considered to be tapered unless specified straight.

75. Bolts. A *bolt* is usually understood to mean a "through bolt," Fig. 97(a) and (b), which is used with a nut to hold two parts together.

A *cap screw*, Fig. 97(c), is the same as a through bolt except that it usually has a greater thread length, since it is used without a nut.

A *stud*, Fig. 97(d), is a steel rod threaded on both ends. As a rule, it is passed through a clearance hole in one member and screwed into another member, a nut being used on the free end.

American Standard regular hexagon head bolts are classified as *unfinished*, *semifinished*, and *finished*, Fig. 97(a), and square head bolts as *unfinished* and *semifinished* (b). The finished hexagon head bolt and nuts have a $\frac{1}{64}$"-thick "washer-face," Fig. 97(a), or bearing, on the inside of the head or nut; the others are without this feature.

American Standard *heavy bolts* have thicker heads than do the regular bolts. In general, bolts do not

appear on detail drawings except where a *special bolt* has been designed, or where certain alterations are to be made upon a standard bolt. They are of course included on all assemblies of which they are a part. See Fig. 91.

76. Identification and Dimensioning of Bolts. The length of a bolt is always understood to extend from the *under side* of the head, or bearing surface, to the extreme end. The thread length is measured from the end. See Fig. 98.

An example of a complete bolt specification is:

$$\tfrac{3}{4}'' \times 1\tfrac{3}{4}''\text{-}10 \text{ NC-2 FIN. HEX. HD. BOLT}$$

in which the first figure is the diameter, the second is the length, followed by the thread specification, finish, and type of head.

77. Nut Locks. Many types of locking devices to prevent nuts from unscrewing are available, a few of the most common of which are shown in Fig. 99.

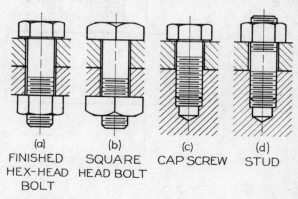

(a)	(b)	(c)	(d)
FINISHED HEX-HEAD BOLT	SQUARE HEAD BOLT	CAP SCREW	STUD

FIG. 97. BOLTS

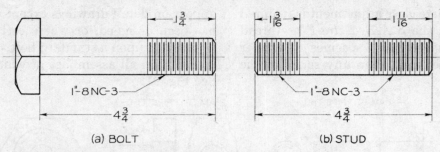

FIG. 98. IDENTIFICATION AND DIMENSIONING OF BOLTS

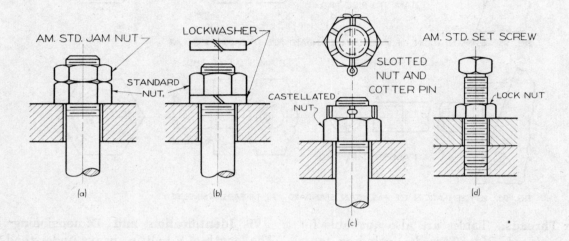

FIG. 99. NUT LOCKS

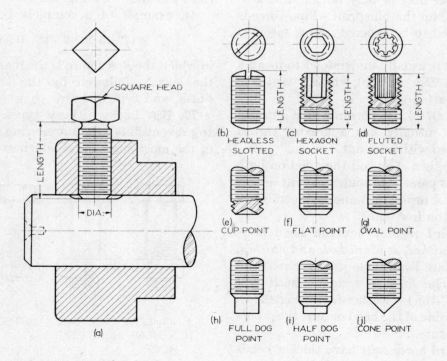

FIG. 100. SET SCREWS

The American Standard *jam nut* may be chamfered on one or both sides (a) and (d).

78. American Standard Set Screws. *Set screws* are used to prevent relative motion (usually *rotary*) between two mating parts, as, for example, a hub of a pulley on a shaft. The point of the set screw is

A typical cap-screw specification is:

$$\tfrac{3}{8}'' \times 2\tfrac{1}{2}''\text{--}16 \text{ NC--3 HX. HD. CAP SCR.}$$

80. American Standard Machine Screws. There are four standard machine screws, Fig. 102, corresponding roughly to some of the cap screws, but they

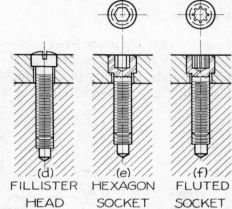
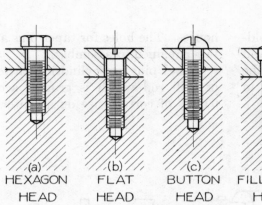

FIG. 101. AMERICAN STANDARD CAP SCREWS

(a) HEXAGON HEAD (b) FLAT HEAD (c) BUTTON HEAD (d) FILLISTER HEAD (e) HEXAGON SOCKET (f) FLUTED SOCKET

forced against one of the parts, the type of point depending upon the requirements of the design.

The American Standard *square-head set screw* is shown in Fig. 100(a); two American Standard *sockets* for headless set screws are shown at (c) and (d); and American Standard *set-screw points* are shown from (e) to (j). The headless set screws are coming into greater use because the projecting head of headed set screws has caused many industrial accidents.

Since set screws are largely used on the rougher grades of work, the coarse thread series is generally used. It is evident that set screws are not efficient where the load is heavy or suddenly applied.

A typical set-screw specification is:

$$\tfrac{3}{8}'' \times \tfrac{3}{4}''\text{--}16 \text{ NC--1, SQ. HD. SET SCR.}$$

79. American Standard Cap Screws. Six heads are standard for cap screws, Fig. 101. The length is specified from the under side of the head for all except the flat head screw at (b).

Cap screws are regularly produced in finished form only, and hence are used instead of bolts where appearance is important.

Cap screws ordinarily pass through a clearance hole in one member and screw into another member, and are usually made with National Coarse threads. They are extensively used in machine tool and other high grades of machine manufacturing.

are relatively smaller. They are regularly produced in finished form, may have National Coarse or National Fine threads, and all have screw-driver slots.

Machine screws are particularly adapted to use with materials of thin sections, and all the smaller screws are threaded to the head. They are extensively used in firearms, jigs, fixtures, and dies.

A typical machine-screw specification is:

$$\#10 \times \tfrac{5}{8}''\text{--}24 \text{ NC--3 FILL. HD. MACH. SCR.}$$

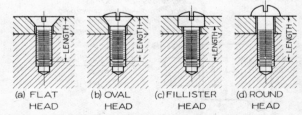

(a) FLAT HEAD (b) OVAL HEAD (c) FILLISTER HEAD (d) ROUND HEAD

FIG. 102. AMERICAN STANDARD MACHINE SCREWS

81. Keys. *Keys* are used chiefly to prevent relative rotary movement between shafts and wheels, couplings, cranks, and similar parts attached to or supported by shafts, Figs. 103 and 104.

For light duty a *round* or *pin key* may be used, while for heavy duty only *rectangular* keys are suitable, and sometimes two rectangular keys are necessary in one connection. The width of a rectangular key is generally about one-fourth the diameter of the shaft.

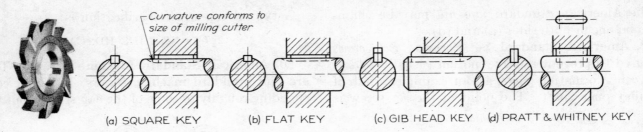

FIG. 103. SQUARE AND FLAT KEYS

Ordinary flat and square keys are made from cold-finished stock and are not machined. The Pratt and Whitney key has rounded ends, Fig. 103(d), and the Woodruff, or "half-moon," key is semicircular in shape, Fig. 104.

houses. The holes for taper pins are drilled and then taper reamed in assembly.

Dowel pins are cylindrical in form and are made of drill rod which is ground accurately to within 0.001″ of correct size on a centerless grinder. Drill

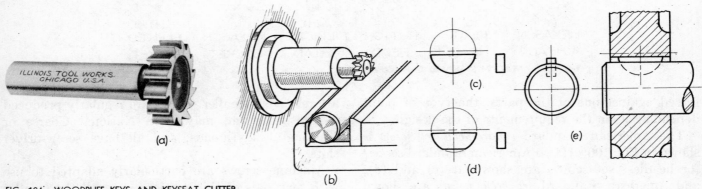

FIG. 104. WOODRUFF KEYS AND KEYSEAT CUTTER

82. Taper Pins and Dowel Pins. For comparatively light work the taper pin is effective in fastening hubs or collars to shafts, Fig. 105.

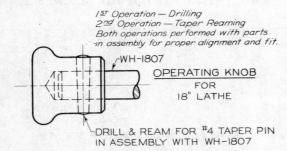

FIG. 105. TAPER PIN APPLICATION

Taper pins have a standard taper of ¼″ per foot and are purchased as a standard item from supply

rod is a standard purchaseable item. Dowels are used to prevent relative misalignment or sliding of two contacting surfaces, or as a stop.

A common use of the dowel is for the alignment of a cover plate with its mating housing. The dowel may be fitted tightly in the housing, while the hole for the dowel in the cover plate is made two or three thousandths larger than the dowel; this will allow the cover plate to be assembled or removed easily. If the two parts are not intended to be separated occasionally the dowel will be given a force fit with both parts.

83. Problems — Screw Threads and Fasteners. On sheet G–1 sketches are to be made of the indicated threads. Great accuracy is not expected, but the student should estimate spaces carefully by eye, as for example, the equal spaces between threads.

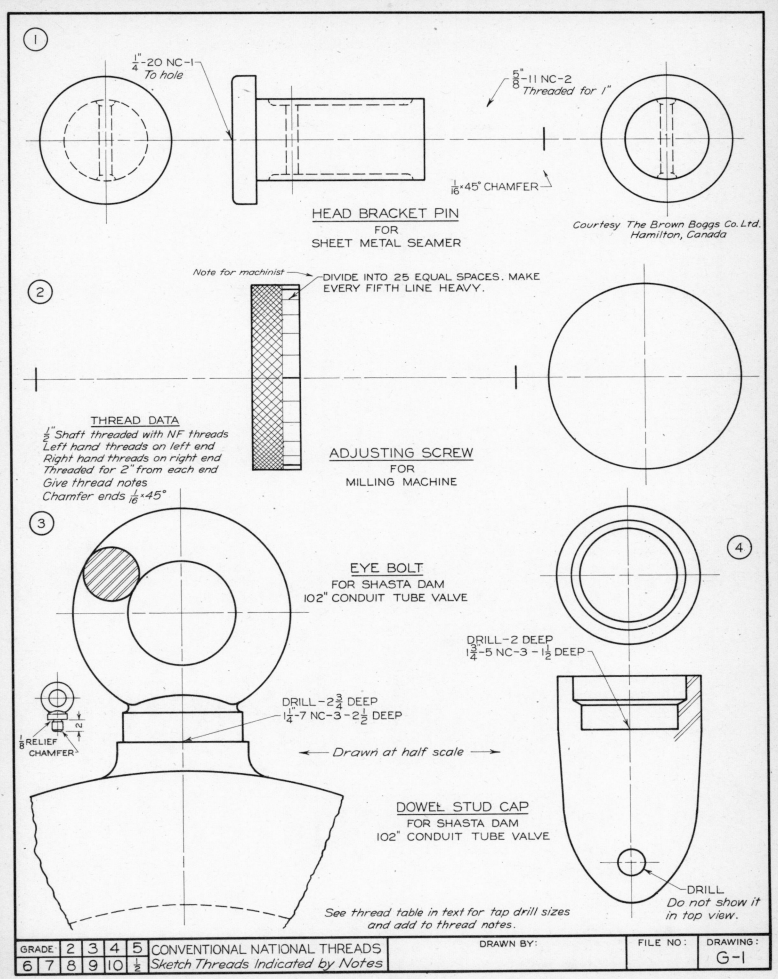

1

$\frac{1}{4}$"-20 NC-1
To hole

$\frac{5}{8}$"-11 NC-2
Threaded for 1"

$\frac{1}{16}$"×45° CHAMFER

HEAD BRACKET PIN
FOR
SHEET METAL SEAMER

*Courtesy The Brown Boggs Co. Ltd.
Hamilton, Canada*

2

Note for machinist
DIVIDE INTO 25 EQUAL SPACES. MAKE
EVERY FIFTH LINE HEAVY.

THREAD DATA
$\frac{1}{2}$" Shaft threaded with NF threads
Left hand threads on left end
Right hand threads on right end
Threaded for 2" from each end
Give thread notes
Chamfer ends $\frac{1}{16}$"×45°

ADJUSTING SCREW
FOR
MILLING MACHINE

3

EYE BOLT
FOR SHASTA DAM
102" CONDUIT TUBE VALVE

$\frac{1}{8}$" RELIEF
CHAMFER

2

DRILL—2$\frac{3}{4}$ DEEP
1$\frac{1}{4}$"-7 NC-3-2$\frac{1}{2}$ DEEP

← *Drawn at half scale* →

4

DRILL-2 DEEP
1$\frac{3}{4}$"-5 NC-3 - 1$\frac{1}{2}$ DEEP

DOWEL STUD CAP
FOR SHASTA DAM
102" CONDUIT TUBE VALVE

DRILL
*Do not show it
in top view.*

*See thread table in text for tap drill sizes
and add to thread notes.*

GRADE	2	3	4	5	CONVENTIONAL NATIONAL THREADS	DRAWN BY:		FILE NO:	DRAWING:
	6	7	8	9	10	$\frac{1}{2}$	*Sketch Threads Indicated by Notes*		G-1

CHAPTER IX

DIMENSIONING

84. Introduction. Designing and production functions were closely allied in the early years of machine manufacturing, and in many cases these operations were carried out by one person. Design drawings, usually assembly drawings, were scaled by the workman to get the basic dimensions, and the correct all such information, which is given in the form of dimensions on the working drawings.

The shop man, therefore, has the responsibility of producing the parts according to the specifications as shown on the blueprints. Often this in itself is a rigorous task. He must, of course, use his judgment

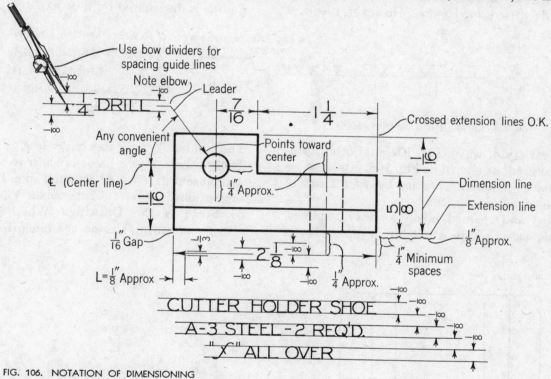

FIG. 106. NOTATION OF DIMENSIONING

functioning of the machine depended primarily upon the skill and judgment of the workman. Therefore it was not necessary for working drawings to present complete detailed size information.

Today, when it is usually necessary for workmen in widely separated localities, or even in different sections of the same plant, to work on the individual mating parts of a single machine, the workman cannot exercise judgment as to *sizes*. Instead, the engineering department is the responsible source for

in interpreting dimensions correctly; for, unfortunately, the draftsman is often not sufficiently aware of the shop problems involved, and dimensions sometimes are not given in a satisfactory manner. The shop man must use his judgment to carry out the *intent* of the dimensions, and should call actual errors on the blueprint to the attention of the foreman, who may in turn have to consult the engineering department.

At no time should the workman scale a blueprint

to obtain a dimension. The drawing might not be made with enough accuracy to justify this practice, and besides, blueprints are subject to considerable shrinkage. Again, in such cases, the workman should consult his foreman.

specifically called for in a shop note on the blueprint, a finish mark will usually not be shown.

If an object is to be finished all over, a note such as "Finish all over," "*f* all over," or "F.A.O." will be used.

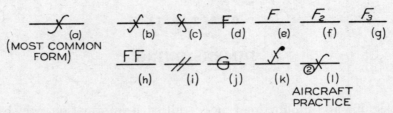

FIG. 107. FINISH MARKS

85. Notation. A definite set of lines and symbols has come into general use in dimensioning practice.

In Fig. 106 are shown the various lines and symbols which are used in dimensioning. The italic *f* is still the most widely used *finish mark*. However, it is exe-

The symbol for *inches* (″) is usually omitted, and the dimensions are understood to be in inches.

Diameter is designated by the abbreviation DIA., DIAM., or D.

Radius is designated by R or RAD.

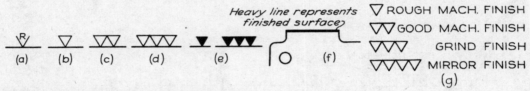

FIG. 108. OTHER TYPES OF FINISH MARKS

cuted in a variety of ways, Fig. 107, and other symbols are also used, as shown in Fig. 108. In all cases *the finish mark is shown only on the edge views of surfaces to be finished*, Fig. 109.

For drilled and reamed holes, keyways, splines, and in other cases where a machining operation is

The symbol ℄ indicates *center line*.

The symbol "c to c" means *center-to-center*.

A representative list of common shop terms and of abbreviations is given in Appendixes V and VI.

86. Scale of the Drawing. Where practicable, parts are shown full size on the blueprint, but often

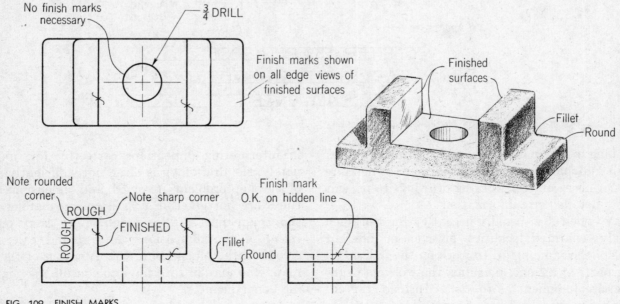

FIG. 109. FINISH MARKS

they must be drawn to a reduced scale, as *half size*, *quarter size*, or even *eighth size*. The scale is indicated in the title strip by the italicized words above or by ratios, such as 12″ = 1′-0″ (full size), 6″ = 1′-0″ (half size), 3″ = 1′-0″ (quarter size), 1½″ = 1′-0″ (eighth size). Frequently the ratio is expressed entirely in inches, as 1″ = 1″ (full size), ½″ = 1″ (half size)

forms are shown in Fig. 110. There are, of course, all sorts of variations of these shapes, but the general scheme of dimensioning conforms to those shown. A common exception is the *shop note*, Fig. 114, which specifies the machine operation to be performed and frequently also gives certain dimensions.

88. Location Dimensions. The *locations* of the geometric shapes with respect to each other in a

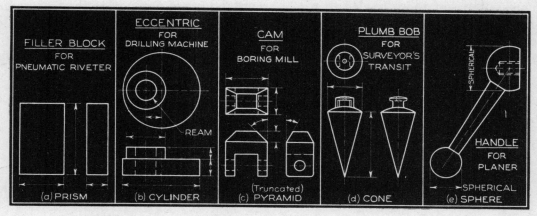

FIG. 110. SIZE DIMENSIONS

However, the workman reads the drawing according to the dimensions shown, and the scale is of use to him only in visualizing the sizes of parts, and occasionally in detecting errors in dimensions.

87. Size Dimensions. Any part may be broken down into its component geometric shapes. These are mostly *prisms* and *cylinders*; but *cones*, *pyramids*, and *spheres* are also frequently found.

The usual dimensions given for these elemental

given part are shown by means of *location dimensions*. The dimensions of a keyway are *size dimensions*, while the dimensions which place the keyway where it may be useful on the part are *location dimensions*. A practical application of size and location dimensions is shown in Fig. 111(a).

89. Patternmaker's Dimensions. As described in § 103, the patternmaker is concerned only with the dimensions he needs to construct the pattern from

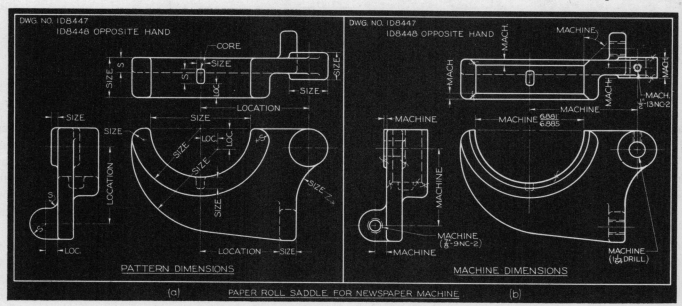

FIG. 111. PATTERN AND MACHINE DIMENSIONS COMPARED

which the rough casting is to be made. He builds the pattern by the nominal dimensions given, and his work may vary slightly above or below the actual dimensions given. He pays particular attention to finish marks, because he must always make allowances of extra material where machining is called for. He is not concerned with many of the dimensions needed primarily by the machinist and accordingly ignores all except those needed to produce the pattern.

90. Machine Dimensions. It is not unusual on large complicated castings, to have two separate

to-center distance between two bosses, with corresponding drill holes. The size dimensions are certain to be changed in the transition from the rough to the finished casting because metal must be removed in machining.

In Fig. 111 it should be noticed that several of the size and location dimensions are not affected by the machining operations. These are "rough" dimensions and are of use only to the patternmaker.

A typical example of pattern (rough) dimensions and machine dimensions combined is shown in Fig. 112. Where a size or a location dimension is

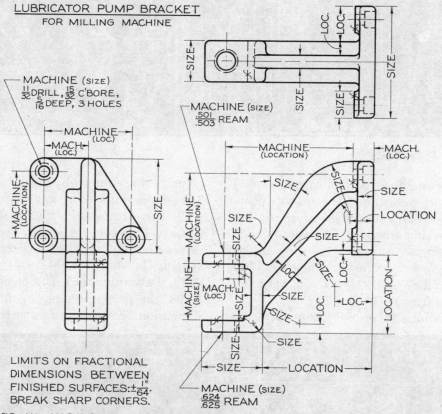

LUBRICATOR PUMP BRACKET FOR MILLING MACHINE

FIG. 112. MACHINE AND PATTERN DIMENSIONS

and distinct drawings, one exclusively for the use of the patternmaker, and the other for the machinist, Fig. 111. As shown in Art. 91 separate drawings are also frequently made for the forge shop or the die-casting shop. Separate forging drawings are more common than separate pattern drawings.

In Fig. 111(a) all dimensions are size dimensions and location dimensions, while at (b) some of these have been "promoted" to *machine dimensions*. The location dimensions seldom change in numerical value, the patternmaker and the machinist working from the same dimensions; as, for example, the center-

also a *machine dimension* it is designated by the latter more important term. The dimensions are so given that the machinist, without understanding the use of the part in assembly, can without any addition or subtraction obtain all necessary information to build the part so it will fit accurately with mating parts.

In general a machinist should not have to make any calculations, however simple, to obtain necessary dimensions from a properly dimensioned blueprint. This is so because the drawing is dimensioned as the part *will finally be after machining* and in such a way as to bring about the required accuracy in that machining. If this same drawing is used by the patternmaker, as is usually the case, the latter will frequently find it necessary to do a bit of figuring to obtain necessary dimensions. In locating the rough elements of a wood pattern, the patternmaker often

It is interesting to note that in general the size dimensions give the *strength*, and the location dimensions give the *positions* of the various geometric elements, while the machine dimensions make the part *useful* and satisfactory in the assembly with mating parts.

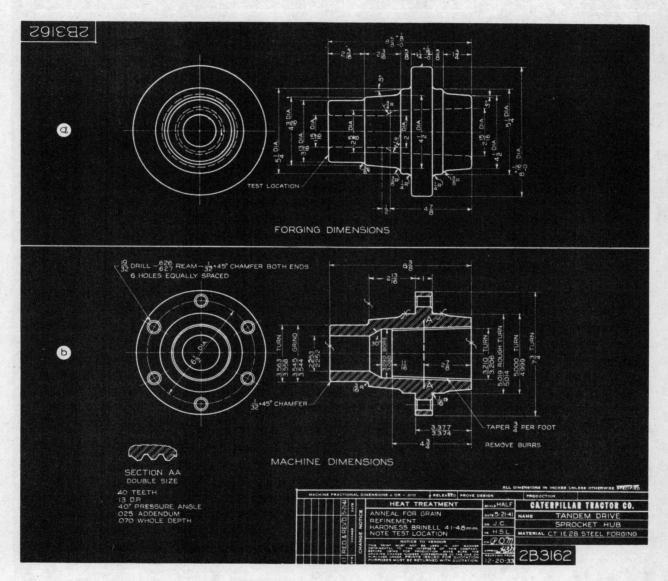

FIG. 113. FORGING DIMENSIONS AND MACHINE DIMENSIONS

finds machine dimensions inconvenient and troublesome because of the accuracy "built into" them for the benefit of the machinist. It simply is impossible to give the dimensions to suit both the machinist and the patternmaker, and since the latter uses the drawing only once, while the machinist uses it over and over, the drawing is dimensioned primarily for the convenience of the machinist.

91. Forging Dimensions. In the forge shop the diemaker is concerned only with the dimensions needed to build the die to hammer out the rough forging. Diemaking is a very expensive operation, and frequently special forging drawings are made, giving only the dimensions needed in the forge shop Fig. 113(a). The corresponding machine drawing is shown in the lower part of the same figure at (b).

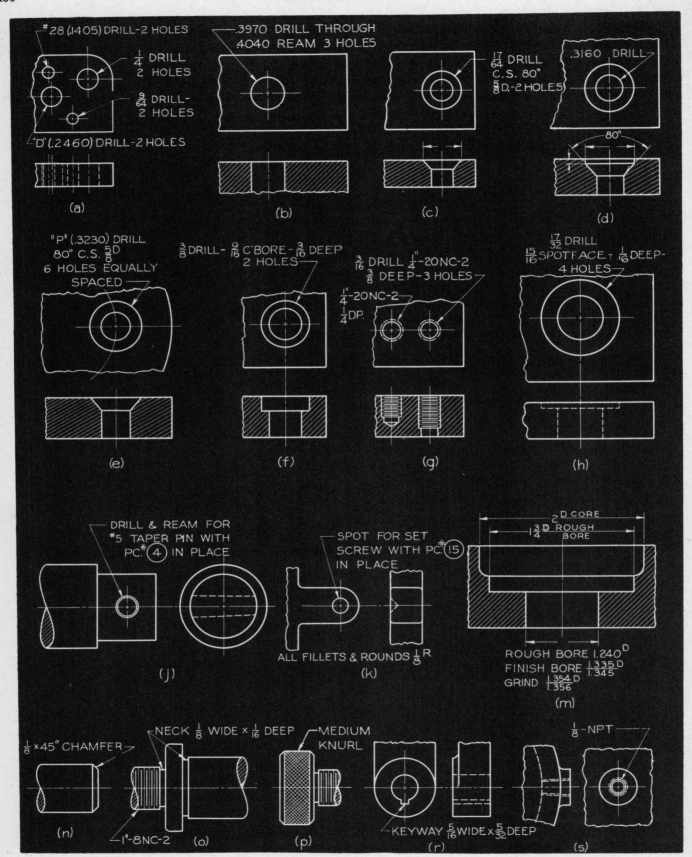

FIG. 114. SHOP NOTES

A comparison of the dimensions of the two drawings shows clearly how the rough dimensions of the forging drawing become exact dimensions, frequently in decimals, on the machine drawing. For example, on the forging drawing, the diameter at the left end, $3\,{}^{13}\!/_{16}$, is shown on the machine drawing by means of two dimensions:

$$\frac{3.563}{3.558}\ \text{TURN, and}\ \frac{3.545}{3.544}\ \text{GRIND.}$$

92. Accuracy. While the machinist does not use the pattern rough dimensions or forging rough dimensions, many of his problems grow out of the inevitable inaccuracies of the casting or forging.

As shown in §§ 101 and 105, a casting is certain to be inaccurate because of the *crust*, or scale, formed by the combination of sand and molten metal; shrinkage and warping resulting from the uneven cooling of the metal; "shake" necessary in removing the pattern from the sand; and draft built into the pattern to facilitate withdrawing from the mold. In the case of the wood pattern, moisture from the "green" sand may even cause expansion or warping of the pattern itself.

It is evident, therefore, that the machinist has a problem of producing an accurately machined part from a *relatively inaccurate bulk of material.* In general *he must take care not to make important measurements from rough surfaces.* Only the *first* or *starting dimension,* to locate the principal center line or main key point from which the other dimensions must stem, should be given to a rough surface. The shop man should also remember that the correct procedure, to obtain the accuracy required, may involve considerable difficulty; whereas, if the workman resorts to some easy scheme instead of following the dimensions as given and not taking into account the inherent inaccuracies of the rough casting or forging, the work, though fully machined, is likely to become *scrap,* because it would not fit in the assembly. *It should be remembered that drawings are not dimensioned for the convenience of the workman, but with the purpose of producing accurate parts.*

From this point on, the machinist will be concerned with avoiding inaccuracies in the machine operations. These inaccuracies are due largely to taking dimensions from rough surfaces, allowing an accumulation of small inaccuracies to add up to a considerable error, and to the inaccuracies inherent in the machine tools themselves.

The inaccuracies of surfaces not to be machined are usually not sufficient to affect the operation or strength of the part, because such surfaces do not usually come in contact with other surfaces of mating parts.

93. Accuracy Implied by Machine Dimensions. If a dimension is given in simple whole numbers and fractions, as 6″, 1¼″, or ½″, the machinist is usually allowed a tolerance (range of variation in size) of ¹⁄₆₄″, and this allowable error is frequently stated in a note on the blueprint as a standard part of the title strip. The machinist uses the common steel scale having ¹⁄₆₄″ divisions, and hence he is not expected to measure closer than ¹⁄₆₄″ with this scale. If the dimensions are properly given by the draftsman, no accumulation of tolerances can be sufficient to affect the use of the part adversely. When dimensions are not so given, the shop man must be alert to the possibility of *errors due to accumulated tolerances.*

Dimensions which must be held to closer limits than a tolerance of ¹⁄₆₄″ are given in decimal form. An example of this is the center-to-center distance between mating gears. A decimal dimension, given to three places, such as 3.500″, is intended to be held within a tolerance of one-thousandth inch (0.001″) or plus-or-minus one-half thousandth inch (± 0.0005″). If given to two places, it must be held to a tolerance of one-hundredth inch (0.01″), or plus-or-minus five-thousandths inch (± 0.005″).

In interchangeable manufacturing *limit dimensions* are necessary in which the upper and lower limits within which dimensions must be held are given. See Art. 96.

94. Dimensions of Holes. Holes which are drilled, reamed, punched, swaged, cored, and so on, are designated by diameter, given usually on a leader, followed by the word or phrase indicating the operation and the number of holes to be made, Fig. 114.

Holes which are to be machined after coring or casting have finish marks and finished dimensions specified.

For counterbored holes, the diameters and depths are given in a note, and for countersunk holes the "included angles" and diameters at the surface are given.

Some of the more common types of holes, together with the tools used to form them, are shown in Fig. 115.

Threaded holes are also specified by notes, Fig. 114(g). For a general treatment of threads and specifications on drawings, see §§ 63–73.

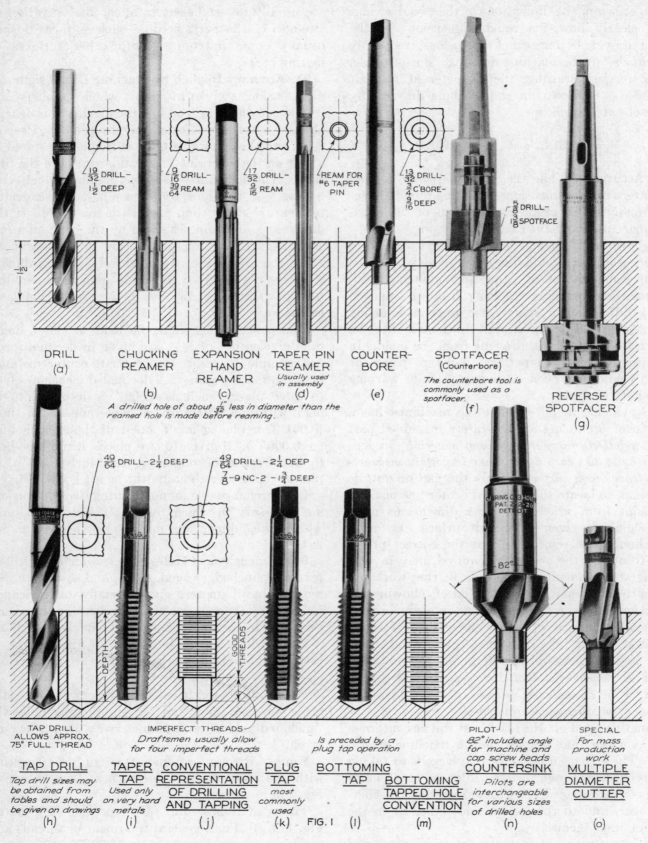

DRILL
(a)

CHUCKING
REAMER
(b)

EXPANSION
HAND
REAMER
(c)

TAPER PIN
REAMER
*Usually used
in assembly*
(d)

COUNTER-
BORE
(e)

SPOTFACER
(Counterbore)
*The counterbore tool is
commonly used as a
spotfacer.*
(f)

REVERSE
SPOTFACER
(g)

*A drilled hole of about $\frac{1}{32}''$ less in diameter than the
reamed hole is made before reaming.*

TAP DRILL
ALLOWS APPROX.
75° FULL THREAD

TAP DRILL
*Tap drill sizes may
be obtained from
tables and should
be given on drawings*
(h)

IMPERFECT THREADS
*Draftsmen usually allow
for four imperfect threads*

TAPER
TAP
*Used only
on very hard
metals*
(i)

CONVENTIONAL
REPRESENTATION
OF DRILLING
AND TAPPING
(j)

PLUG
TAP
*most
commonly
used*
(k)

*Is preceded by a
plug tap operation*

BOTTOMING
TAP
(l)

BOTTOMING
TAPPED HOLE
CONVENTION
(m)

PILOT
*82° included angle
for machine and
cap screw heads*
COUNTERSINK
*Pilots are
interchangeable
for various sizes
of drilled holes*
(n)

SPECIAL
*For mass
production
work*
MULTIPLE
DIAMETER
CUTTER
(o)

FIG. I

FIG. 115 A

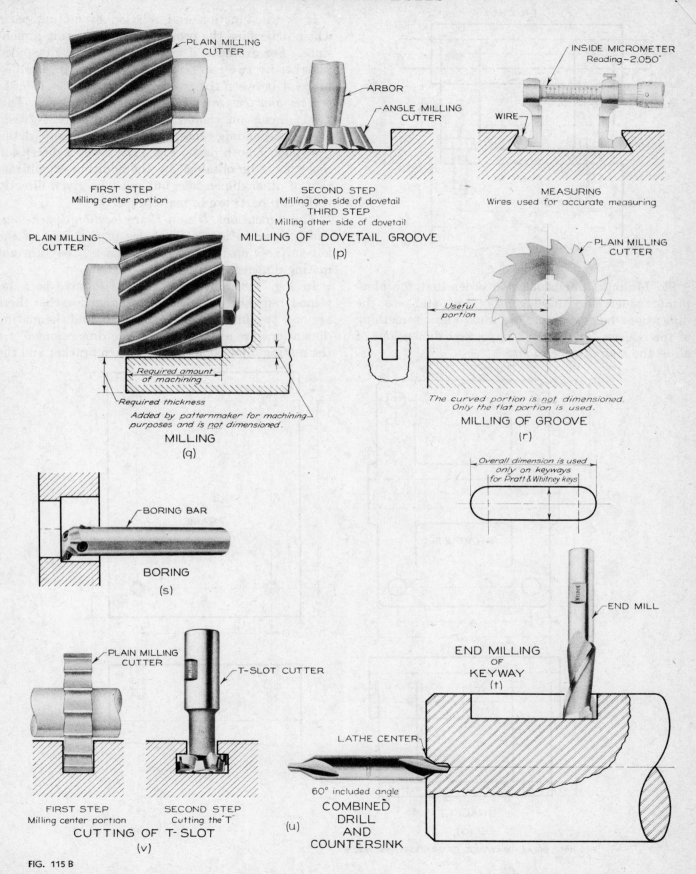

PLAIN MILLING CUTTER

ARBOR

ANGLE MILLING CUTTER

INSIDE MICROMETER
Reading – 2.050"

WIRE

FIRST STEP
Milling center portion

SECOND STEP
Milling one side of dovetail
THIRD STEP
Milling other side of dovetail

MEASURING
Wires used for accurate measuring

MILLING OF DOVETAIL GROOVE
(p)

PLAIN MILLING CUTTER

PLAIN MILLING CUTTER

Useful portion

Required amount of machining

Required thickness

Added by patternmaker for machining purposes and is not dimensioned.

MILLING
(q)

The curved portion is not dimensioned.
Only the flat portion is used.

MILLING OF GROOVE
(r)

BORING BAR

BORING
(s)

Overall dimension is used only on keyways for Pratt & Whitney keys

END MILL

END MILLING
OF
KEYWAY
(t)

PLAIN MILLING CUTTER

T-SLOT CUTTER

LATHE CENTER

FIRST STEP
Milling center portion

SECOND STEP
Cutting the "T"

60° included angle

COMBINED
DRILL
AND
COUNTERSINK

CUTTING OF T-SLOT
(v)

(u)

FIG. 115 B

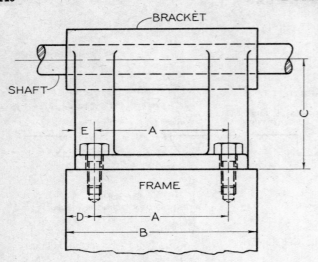

FIG. 116. BRACKET ASSEMBLY

95. Mating Dimensions. In order that the blueprint reader may intelligently read and use the dimensions he encounters, he must know something of the reasons for the most important dimensions of all — the *mating dimensions*.

It is the function and relation of mating parts which determine the proper choice of mating dimensions. For example, if two parts are to be fastened together by two cap screws, as in Fig. 116, the distance *A* between the two cap-screw holes *on both the bracket and the frame* is a mating dimension. This same dimension should be given directly between the corresponding center lines on the separate detail drawings of both parts, Fig. 117. Such a dimension must never be obtained by the addition or subtraction of other dimensions but must be given directly if the two parts are to mate properly.

The dimensions *D* and *E* are *location dimensions*, which serve to locate the holes to the right of the left surfaces on their respective parts; they are not mating dimensions.

In Fig. 118, dimensions *B* and *C* have been retained, but the design has been changed so that there are now two brackets instead of one; and the mating dimensions are also changed. The dimensions *F* are the mating dimensions between each bracket and the

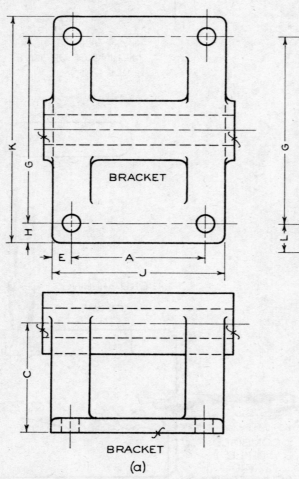

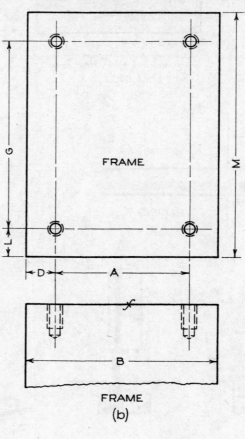

(b)

(a)

FIG. 117. DETAIL DRAWINGS OF BRACKET AND FRAME

frame, and should be given directly on the detail drawings of both parts, as shown in Fig. 119.

96. Limit Dimensions. Where accurate fits are required, the old practice was to give the basic or nominal sizes of both mating parts in common whole numbers and fractions and to specify in a note the types of fits desired, such as "running fit," "drive fit," and so on. The workman in the shop made the parts so that they would fit properly.

The tremendous development of technical knowledge and experience has widened the gap between design and execution, and today in most shops the workman is no longer expected to decide upon fits of mating parts. Moreover, mass production has introduced *interchangeable manufacturing* by which mating parts may be made in different factories and possibly assembled in a third factory, and by which replacement parts, purchased later, may be used with the assurance that they will fit properly. Thus it is necessary, on drawings of closely fitting parts, to specify sizes in such a manner that machine operators in widely separated shops can produce parts which are interchangeable.

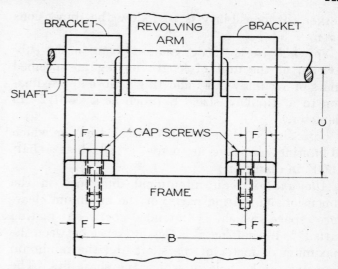

FIG. 118. BRACKET ASSEMBLY

This would be a simple task if it were possible to manufacture parts exactly to the dimensions intended in the design, but the fact is that more or less error is inevitable. Therefore, the best practice is to specify the error which can be *tolerated* and still permit the satisfactory functioning of the part. The

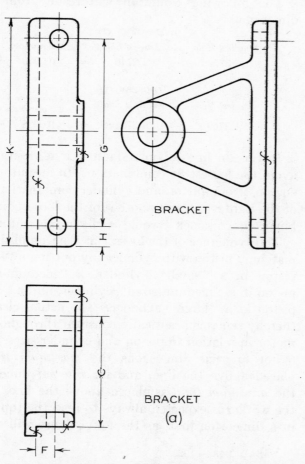

BRACKET

(a)

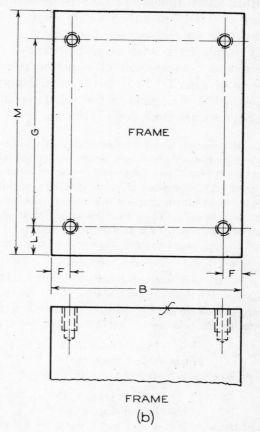

FRAME

(b)

FIG. 119. DETAIL DRAWING OF ONE BRACKET AND THE FRAME

worker's responsibility is to follow the dimensions given.

Nominal size is "a designation given to the subdivision of the unit of length having no specified limits of accuracy but indicating a close approximation to a standard size." * (Such as a shaft 2″ in diameter.)

Basic size is "the exact theoretical size from which all limiting variations are made." * (Such as a shaft 2.000″ in diameter.)

Allowance is "an intentional difference in the dimensions of mating parts; or the minimum clearance space which is intended between mating parts." * In shafting, it is the difference between the maximum diameter of the shaft and the minimum diameter of the hole in which the shaft fits. The allowance is *positive* for *loose fits* in which it represents a small clearance between the parts, and it is *negative* for *tight fits* in which it represents a small interference.

Example: A shaft dimensioned 0.874″ and a hole dimensioned 0.875″ represents an allowance of 0.001″ which is a clearance between the parts. The same hole with a shaft dimensioned 0.876″ represents an allowance of 0.001″ also; but as the shaft is larger than the hole this allowance becomes a negative quantity or interference between the parts.

Tolerance is "the amount of variation permitted in the size of a part." * It is the total amount of error *tolerated* in the machining of a part or the difference between the limits of a given part.

Note: In the example under *allowance*, the ideal condition and the tightest fit permissible have been given, but in manufacturing large numbers of pieces these sizes could not be produced exactly without great expense; hence variations must be made that will not prevent proper functioning but will make it possible to produce them economically. These variations must, therefore, tend toward *greater looseness*. If a manufacturing tolerance of 0.001″ is required on each member, the parts would be dimensioned as follows:

The largest the shaft can be: 0.874″ + 0.000″ = 0.874″.
The smallest the shaft can be: 0.874″ − 0.001″ = 0.873″.
The largest the hole can be: 0.875″ + 0.001″ = 0.876″.
The smallest the hole can be: 0.875″ − 0.000″ = 0.875″.

Largest hole: 0.876″
Minus smallest shaft: 0.873″
Greatest looseness in mating of parts: 0.003″

Smallest hole: 0.875″
Minus largest shaft: 0.874″
Greatest tightness in mating of parts: 0.001″ = Allowance

* American Standards Association Bulletin B4A — 1925.

This defines a condition in which the greatest looseness is 0.003″ and the greatest tightness gives an allowance of 0.001″.

Limits are "the extreme permissible dimensions of a part." *

An example is shown in Fig. 120, in which the maximum limit on the shaft is 1.3740, the minimum limit is 1.3731, the tolerance being the difference

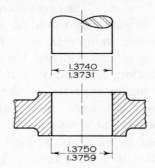

FIG. 120. LIMIT DIMENSIONS

between these limits, or 0.0009″. On the hole the maximum limit is 1.3759″, the minimum limit is 1.3750″, and the tolerance is 0.0009″, as was the case with the shaft.

The following condition will result from these dimensions:

	TIGHTEST FIT	
Smallest Hole	*Largest Shaft*	*Allowance*
1.3750	− 1.3740 =	0.0010

	LOOSEST FIT	
Largest Hole	*Smallest Shaft*	*Allowance + 2 Tolerances*
1.3759	− 1.3731 =	0.0028

In certain lines of manufacture it is desirable to avoid the loosest fit combination. In an automobile engine, if one piston and cylinder combination were of the tightest fit and another of the loosest fit combination, a "knock" would result in the motor.

The avoidance of the loosest fit is accomplished by matching piston with cylinder: by putting a "small" piston in a "small" cylinder, a "medium-sized" piston in a "medium-sized" cylinder, and a "large" piston in a "large" cylinder. The actual clearance thereby remains practically constant throughout the motor in relation to piston and cylinder sizes.

For *external* dimensions the *maximum limit* is placed above the line, and for *internal* dimensions the *minimum limit* is placed above the line. Thus the worker is expected always to read the top figure in a dimension first, as the lower figure will always

* ASAB B4A — 1925.

indicate the removal of additional metal. In other words, a shaft is cut from "large to small"; therefore the larger figure is given above the line and the smaller figure below the line. A hole, on the other hand, is cut from "small to large"; hence the smaller figure is given above the line and the larger figure below the line.

97. Use of Limit Tables. From the limit tables, Appendix II, the nominal hole size (the intended diameter as scaled) on the drawing, is found under "Nominal Size." Then on a horizontal line across the table in the column representing the class of fit required, the amounts to be added or subtracted from the basic size are found. The basic size is the decimal equivalent of the nominal size. To figure the limits for Fig. 120, using a class 3 fit, find the nominal size 1⅜″ in the table (basic size = 1.3750″). Then calculate the limits as follows:

Hole: $\dfrac{1.3750'' + 0.0000''}{1.3750'' + 0.0009''} = \dfrac{1.3750''}{1.3759''}$ $\left(\begin{array}{l}\text{Allowance is } 0.0010\\ \text{Tolerance is } 0.0009\end{array}\right)$

Shaft: $\dfrac{1.3750'' - 0.0010''}{1.3750'' - 0.0019''} = \dfrac{1.3740''}{1.3731''}$ $\left(\begin{array}{l}\text{Allowance is } 0.0010\\ \text{Tolerance is } 0.0009\end{array}\right)$

The allowance is 0.0010″, representing the tightest fit between the parts. The tolerance on each member is 0.0009″ representing the permissible variation for each part.

98. Problems — Dimensioning. The problem sheets on dimensioning include either a pictorial of the assembled parts or an assembly drawing. The pictorial and the assembly drawings are to be studied as to the function of each detail part and its mating features with adjacent parts. Care must be taken that mating dimensions, except for occasional tolerances and allowances, be identical on the mating parts. Thread notes are also to be considered mating dimensions.

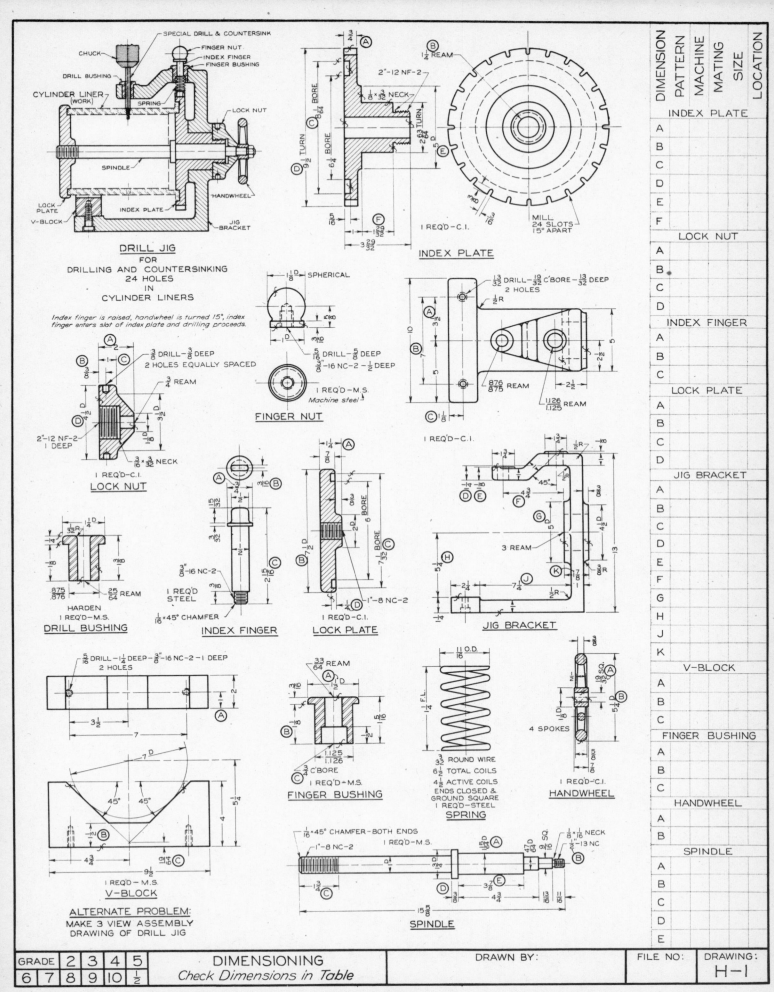

DRILL JIG
FOR
DRILLING AND COUNTERSINKING
24 HOLES
IN
CYLINDER LINERS

Index finger is raised, handwheel is turned 15°, index finger enters slot of index plate and drilling proceeds.

LOCK NUT

FINGER NUT

DRILL BUSHING

INDEX FINGER

LOCK PLATE

INDEX PLATE

JIG BRACKET

V-BLOCK

ALTERNATE PROBLEM:
MAKE 3 VIEW ASSEMBLY
DRAWING OF DRILL JIG

FINGER BUSHING

SPRING

HANDWHEEL

SPINDLE

DIMENSION	PATTERN	MACHINE	MATING	SIZE	LOCATION
INDEX PLATE					
A					
B					
C					
D					
E					
F					
LOCK NUT					
A					
B					
C					
D					
INDEX FINGER					
A					
B					
C					
LOCK PLATE					
A					
B					
C					
D					
JIG BRACKET					
A					
B					
C					
D					
E					
F					
G					
H					
J					
K					
V-BLOCK					
A					
B					
C					
FINGER BUSHING					
A					
B					
C					
HANDWHEEL					
A					
B					
SPINDLE					
A					
B					
C					
D					
E					

GRADE	2	3	4	5	DIMENSIONING	DRAWN BY:	FILE NO:	DRAWING:
	6	7	8	9	10	½	*Check Dimensions in Table*			H-1

145

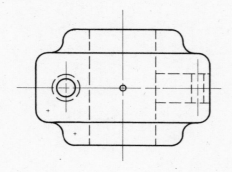

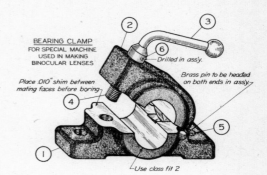

BEARING CLAMP
FOR SPECIAL MACHINE
USED IN MAKING
BINOCULAR LENSES

Place .010" shim between
mating faces before boring

Drilled in ass'y.

Brass pin to be headed
on both ends in ass'y

Use class fit 2

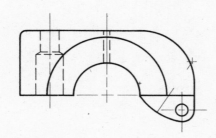

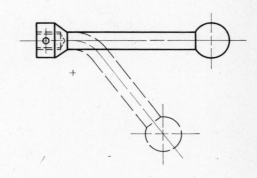

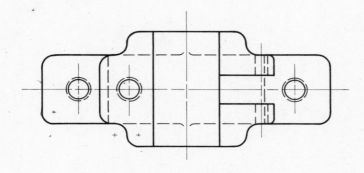

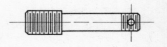

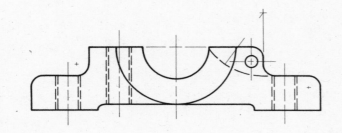

SCALE—HALF SIZE

GRADE	2	3	4	5	DIMENSIONING	DRAWN BY:	FILE NO:	DRAWING:
6	7	8	9	10	½	*Add Complete Dimensions*			H-2

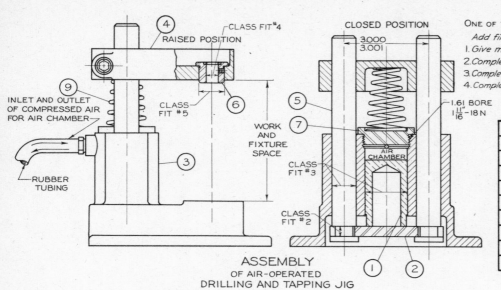

④ RAISED POSITION
CLASS FIT #4

⑨ INLET AND OUTLET OF COMPRESSED AIR FOR AIR CHAMBER

RUBBER TUBING

CLASS FIT #5

⑥

③

CLOSED POSITION

3.000
3.001

⑤

⑦

1.61 BORE
1 11/16"-18 N

AIR CHAMBER

WORK AND FIXTURE SPACE

CLASS FIT #3

CLASS FIT #2

① ②

ASSEMBLY
OF AIR-OPERATED
DRILLING AND TAPPING JIG

One of the Following Procedures Will Be Assigned

Add finish marks where necessary.
1. Give machine dimensions only.
2. Completely dimension and encircle machine dimensions.
3. Completely dimension and label mating dimensions with M.D.
4. Completely dimension similar to fig. 112.

PART NO.	DESCRIPTION	MATERIAL	NO. REQ'D
1	PLUNGER	BRONZE	1
2	LOWER PLATE	C.R.S.	1
3	BASE	C.I.	1
4	TOP PLATE	C.I.	1
5	GUIDE RODS	1315-X	2
6	MASTER BUSHING	1315-X	1
7	CYLINDER CAP	C.R.S.	1
8	3/8-16 NC x 1 3/8 CAP SCR.	STEEL	2
9	SPRING (ST'D.)	STEEL	1

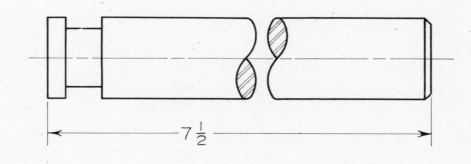

$7\frac{1}{2}$

SCALE—FULL SIZE

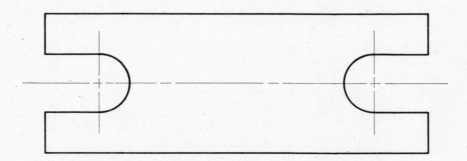

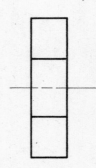

SCALE—FULL SIZE

See assembly above for class fits and special dimensions

GRADE	2	3	4	5	DIMENSIONING	DRAWN BY:	FILE NO:	DRAWING:
6	7	8	9	10 ½	Add Complete Dimensions			H-3a

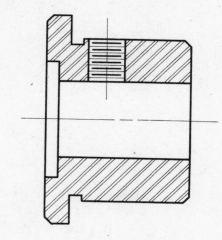

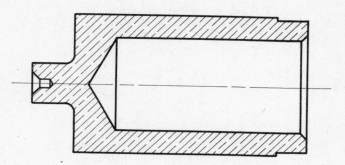

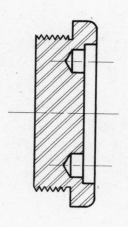

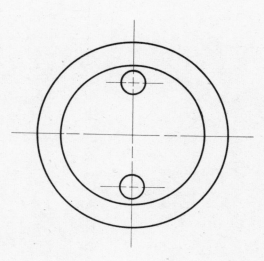

GRADE	2	3	4	5	DIMENSIONING	DRAWN BY:	FILE NO:	DRAWING:
	6	7	8	9	10	½	*Add Complete Dimensions*			H-3b

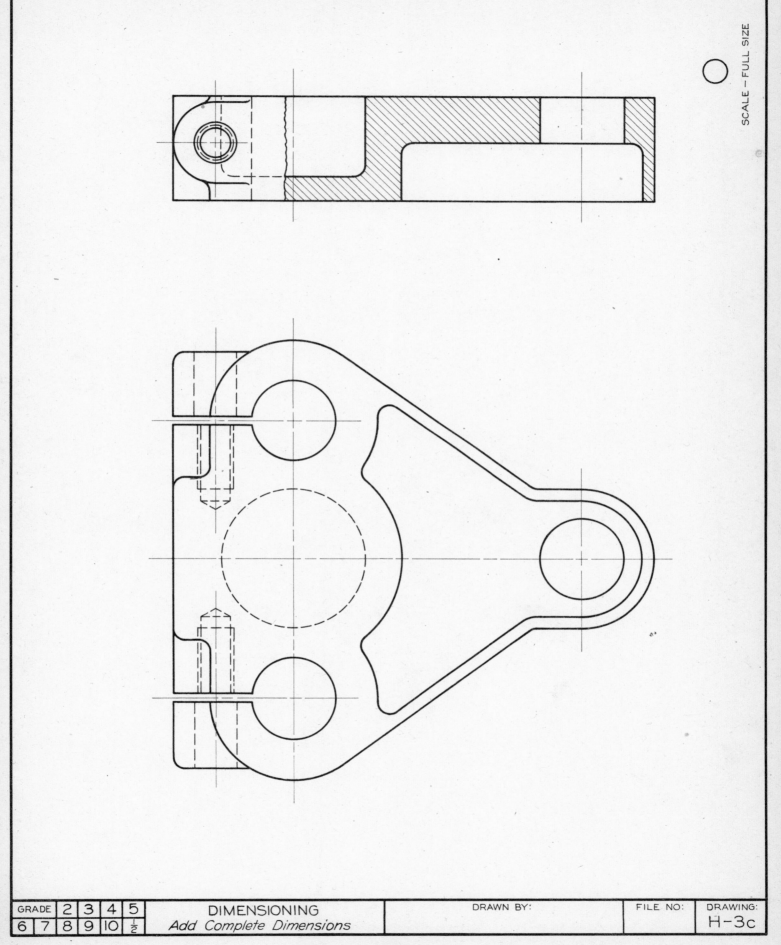

GRADE	2	3	4	5	DIMENSIONING	DRAWN BY:	FILE NO:	DRAWING:
6	7	8	9	10	½	*Add Complete Dimensions*			H-3c

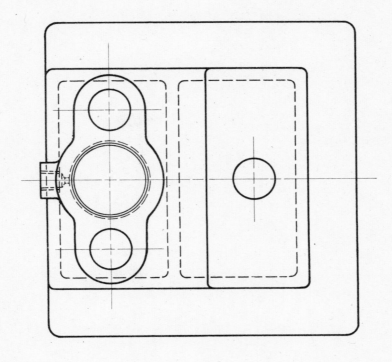

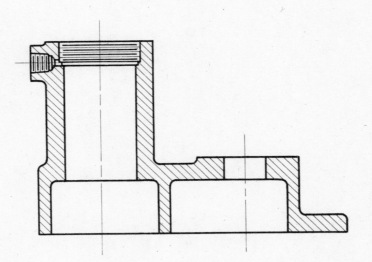

SCALE—HALF SIZE

GRADE	2	3	4	5	DIMENSIONING	DRAWN BY:	FILE NO:	DRAWING:
	6	7	8	9	10	½	Add Complete Dimensions			H-3d

155

CHAPTER X

SHOP PROCESSES

99. Forming of Metals. Many who study this book will be already more or less familiar with the common shop processes, but for those whose experience may be limited a brief survey of the fundamental processes is included here.

Metals are formed by three general processes: (1) Melting the metals and pouring them into molds of various kinds. This process is the basis of *foundry work*. (2) Pressing metals into various shapes, either while the metal is cold or hot, and under steady pressure or by means of hammer blows. These processes include *forging*, *rolling*, and *drawing* in which the metals are poured while hot, and *press work*, *drawing*, and *stamping* while the metals are cold. If the metals are soft, they may be *extruded* when hot, or *spun* when cold. (3) Cutting the metal (machining) with tools that have been hardened and having one or more cutting edges. This process usually supplements the other two above, as in machining castings or forgings to closer dimensions than possible under those processes. *Grinding* must be classified as a cutting process.

The language of the shop, with all of its special terms, will be found to be a part of every working drawing. The blueprint reader, therefore, must understand the meanings of the various shop terms in order to understand clearly the instructions on the blueprint. Many of these terms may be learned from the shop notes on the problem sheets in this book. A glossary of shop terms is included in Appendix VI.

100. Castings. A *casting* is produced by pouring molten metal into a mold or cavity, the shape of which the metal retains after it has cooled. Sand molds are the most common, and are made by *ramming* sand around a *pattern* in the shape of the piece to be cast, and then carefully removing the pattern, leaving a cavity to receive the molten metal. Molding sand has some damp clay mixed with it which makes it hold the molded shape.

At least two boxes for the sand are used, the upper being called the *cope*, and the lower the *drag*, Fig. 121. Together they are called the *flask*, (b). For more complicated work, one or more intermediate boxes, called *cheeks*, may be inserted between the cope and drag.

The pattern must be of such shape that it will "pull away" from the packed sand in both the cope and drag. The line of separation of the two halves of the pattern marks the *parting line* on the pattern and mold, Fig. 121(a). On each side of the parting line, the pattern must be tapered inward slightly (called *draft*) to permit easy withdrawal of the pattern from the sand without damaging the delicate sand walls. Two or three degrees is sufficient draft for small patterns. A very shallow pattern may require little or no draft. The draft is always formed by *adding* to the thickness rather than subtracting from it so as to take no chance of making the casting weaker than intended.

A *sprue stick*, or round tapered dowel, is placed in the sand along with the pattern, and then removed, to leave a hole through which the metal is poured. The part of the hole adjacent to the casting is called the *gate*, and the vertical part the *sprue*, Fig. 121. Another vertical hole, called a *riser*, is provided to allow the molten metal, during pouring, to rise so that it may "feed" into the casting during the cooling process, and to allow gases to escape, Fig. 121(b). Small openings to the cavity are provided by inserting wires to form *vents*. These are necessary to permit the escape of gases.

When it is necessary to form the sand into shapes that will not permit the necessary adhesion and strength of the sand shapes, or when it is necessary to form interior shapes the forms for which cannot be removed along with the main parts of the pattern, *dry-sand cores* are used. The most common use of a core is to extend it through a casting to form a *cored hole*.

157

Cores are formed by molding dry sand mixed with linseed oil or some other binder, in *core boxes,* Fig. 121(a). Most cores are made in halves and then pasted together, as shown, while some are molded

Since considerable shrinkage occurs when metals cool, patterns must be made slightly oversize; therefore the patternmaker uses a shrink rule, whose units are oversize according to the shrinkage charac-

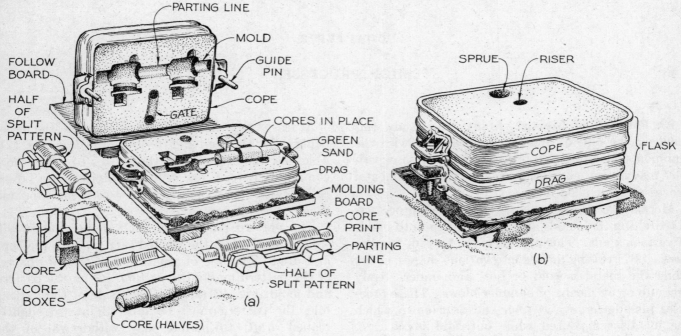

FIG. 121. SAND MOLDING

complete at once. These cores thus formed are then baked in an oven to harden them for use. After the main portions of the pattern have been molded and withdrawn from the cope and drag, the cores are inserted in place in the cavity. *Core prints,* built into the main pattern, leave small projecting cavities from the main cavity, which provide anchors for the cores.

When a core cannot be properly supported by the use of core prints, metal pieces of various shapes, called *chaplets,* are used to help hold the cores in place. These chaplets fuse together with the molten metal and thereby become an actual part of the casting.

Usually some metal finds its way between the two contacting surfaces between the cope and drag or between the sand and the core. These rough projections on the cooled casting are called *fins;* they are removed by striking them with a hammer and by grinding.

101. Patterns. Patterns are usually made of white pine, mahogany, or other light, strong woods. If the same pattern is to be used repeatedly in production, a metal pattern of aluminum, brass, or other metals may be made from the wooden pattern.

teristics of the metal to be used. Approximate shrinkage rates of the common metals are as follows:

Cast iron: $\frac{1}{10}''$ to $\frac{1}{8}''$ per foot
Steel: $\frac{1}{8}''$ to $\frac{1}{4}''$ per foot
Aluminum: $\frac{3}{16}''$ to $\frac{1}{4}''$ per foot
Brass: $\frac{3}{16}''$ to $\frac{7}{32}''$ per foot

Allowance for shrinkage is never made on a working drawing, for it always shows the finished product. Draft is frequently not shown and must be added at the discretion of the patternmaker.

Finish marks are fully as important to the patternmaker as to the machinist, as he must make an allowance of $\frac{1}{16}''$ to $\frac{3}{4}''$ of extra material for each finished surface, the exact amount depending upon the size of the casting.

102. Fillets and Rounds. Sharp corners are difficult to produce on a casting and are always unsatisfactory, for several reasons. The metal structure is such that the crystals, in cooling, tend to align themselves at right angles to the surfaces. If two surfaces intersect at a sharp corner, a weak area is produced at the corner, which later may result in failure, Fig. 122.

Also, sharp corners are apt to be destroyed by the movement of the molten metal, and the sand mixes with the metal and reduces its quality.

In the absence of a specific radius dimension for a corner on a drawing, or of other instructions, the patternmaker will round the corner according to his shop judgment. A rounded exterior corner is called a *round* and is produced merely by rounding the wood at the corner. A rounded interior corner is called a *fillet* and is produced by adding beeswax pressed in place with a special round-end tool, or by applying ready-made wood or leather fillets, with glue. See Fig. 122(a).

103. Pattern for a "Choke Release Cylinder." A typical working drawing as received by the pattern-maker is shown in Fig. 123. Such a drawing is always an all-purpose drawing for use by all shops; but, as shown in Art. 90, it must of necessity be made principally for the machine shop. The pattern-maker must make a number of changes and additions to provide a suitable guide for his work. Often he marks his changes directly upon the blueprint with a colored pencil. It may be necessary to make a freehand sketch of the pattern, or even to prepare a complete *pattern drawing,* showing all details.

A pattern drawing for the cope portion of the Choke Release Cylinder is shown in Fig. 124. This part is made of wood exactly as shown and will be

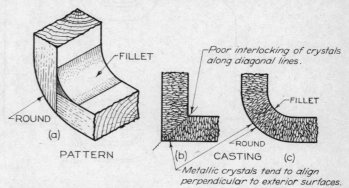

FIG. 122. FILLETS AND ROUNDS

used in the cope, Fig. 121, with the flat surface level with the flat surface of the sand in the cope. Then it will be removed to leave a corresponding part of the total cavity for the casting.

It will be seen that this half of the pattern corresponds to the upper portion of the piece in Fig. 123, but that several changes have been made. All holes are eliminated, and some extensions called *core prints* are added. These will form small auxiliary cavities

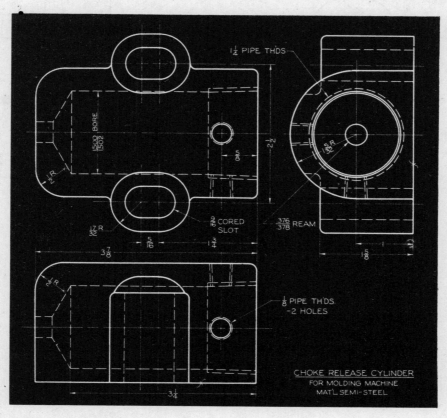

FIG. 123. THE WORKING DRAWING

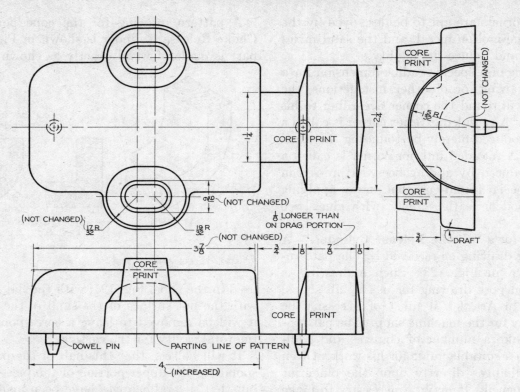

FIG. 124. PATTERN DRAWING OF COPE PORTION OF PATTERN

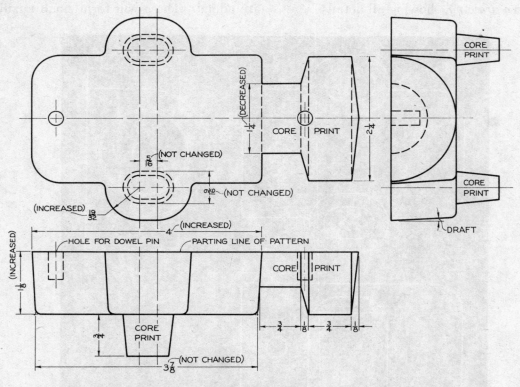

FIG. 125. PATTERN DRAWING OF DRAG PORTION OF PATTERN

in the sand to be used only to anchor the cores in place, as will be shown later. In addition two small dowels are added to keep the two halves of the pattern aligned. All vertical surfaces are tapered, or given "draft," and the entire pattern is slightly

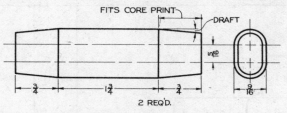

FIG. 126. CORES OF OVAL-SHAPED HOLES

oversize to compensate for the shrinkage of metal in cooling.

A pattern drawing for the drag portion of the pattern is shown in Fig. 125, and corresponding changes are made in this half of the pattern, as shown. This half will fit into the drag with its flat surface

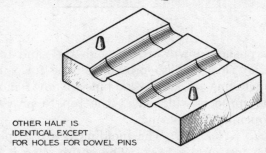

OTHER HALF IS IDENTICAL EXCEPT FOR HOLES FOR DOWEL PINS

FIG. 127. HALF OF CORE BOX FOR THE TWO OVAL-SHAPED HOLES

coinciding with the flat surface of sand in the drag. When the pattern is molded and removed, the cavities in the cope and drag will, of course, correspond exactly.

The cores and the corresponding core boxes for the Choke Release Cylinder are shown in Figs. 126 to 129. If the core has a flat surface upon which it may rest, it may be made in one piece. Figure 127 shows half of the core box for the two oblong cores for the two slots (which have flat surfaces). The round core

has no flat surface upon which it may rest and therefore it must be made in halves and pasted together after baking. Figure 129 shows the core box used for forming each of these halves of the round core for the bored hole.

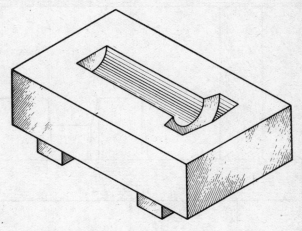

FIG. 129. CORE BOX FOR CORE OF BORED HOLE

104. Steps in Making Casting of Choke Release Cylinder.

Step I, Fig. 130: The drag portion of the pattern is placed upside down with the parting-line surface on the molding board, and the drag portion of the flask is also placed upside down around the pattern. The molding board and pattern are then dusted with parting powder to prevent cohesion of the sand with the molding board and pattern. The sand is then rammed about the pattern until a good mold has been formed (but not tightly enough to prevent the escape of gases formed by the chemical reaction of the molten metal with the sand), leveled off, and covered with the *bottoming board*.

Step II, Fig. 131: Starting with the position shown in Fig. 130, the drag, with the pattern, molding board, and bottoming board, are turned right side up as a unit until it rests upon the cleats of the bottoming board. The molding board is removed and the cope half of the pattern is placed over the drag

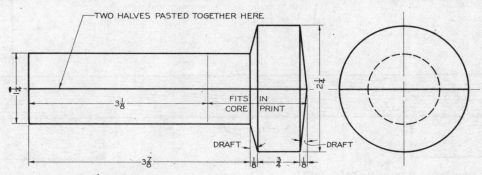

FIG. 128. CORE OF BORED HOLE

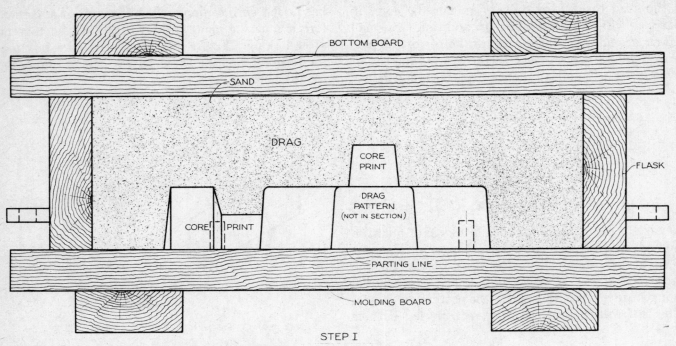

FIG. 130. MOLDING THE DRAG PORTION OF THE PATTERN

half, the dowel pins assuring the alignment, Fig. 131. Parting powder is dusted over the pattern and the sand on top of the drag.

Step III, Fig. 132: The cope half of the flask is put in place. Two conical pins for sprue and riser are held in place while sand is rammed about them and the pattern. The flask is filled to the top with sand and leveled off. A straight piece of wire is usually pushed downward through the sand to the pattern at this time to provide escape for various gases, including air. The wood pins are now removed, and the sprue is widened at the top to provide a larger opening for pouring.

Step IV, Fig. 133: The molding board is placed over the top of the flask. The entire cope is then removed and placed upside down, resting upon the

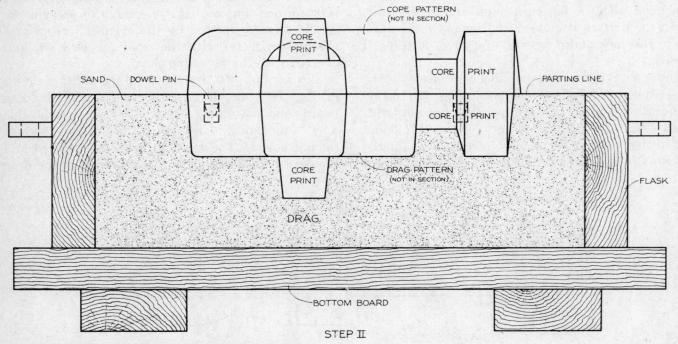

FIG. 131. ALIGNMENT OF COPE PATTERN WITH DRAG PATTERN

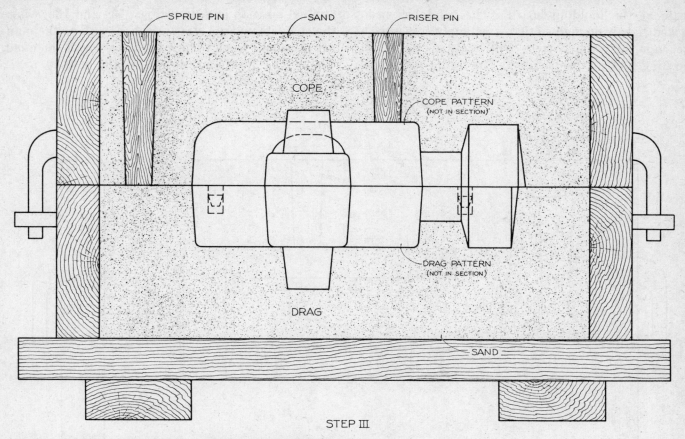

STEP III

FIG. 132. MOLDING COPE PORTION OF PATTERN; USE OF SPRUE AND RISER

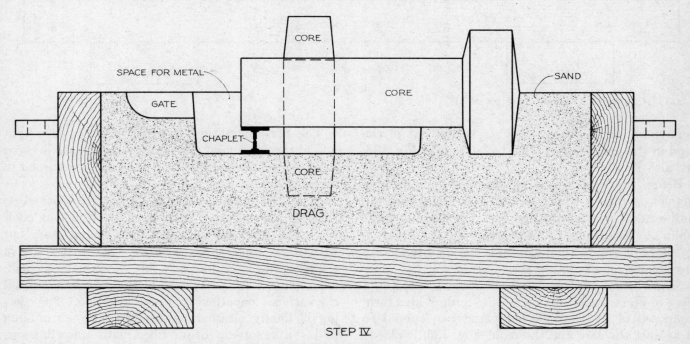

STEP IV

FIG. 133. REMOVING OF PATTERN AND LOCATING OF CORES AND CHAPLET

cleats of the molding board. The sand has been packed tightly enough so that it willingly comes with the cope, and the pattern will likely remain with the drag half of the pattern. The entire pattern is

original position as seen in Figs. 134 and 135, where the chaplets may be clearly seen, as well as the manner in which the cores fit into the cavity of the mold. The mold is now ready to receive the metal.

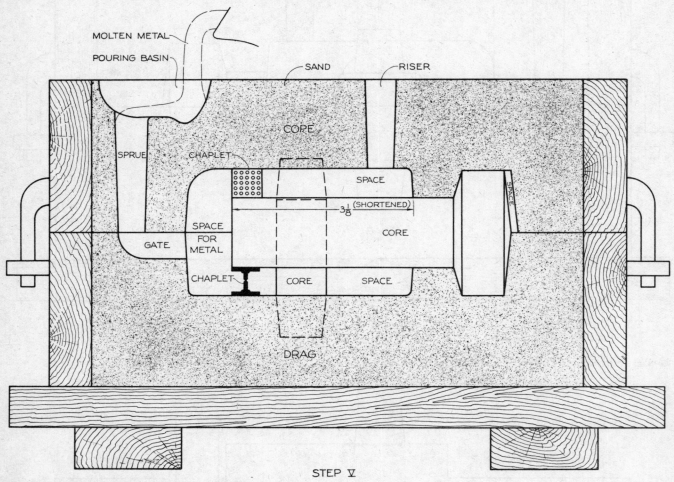

FIG. 134. POURING OF METAL INTO THE MOLD

removed from the flask. A gate is dug out of the sand in the drag as shown at the left side of **Fig. 133**. See also Fig. 121(a).

Before the horizontal core can be put in place, a chaplet is placed near the left end (otherwise the core would be without support) at the bottom of the mold. All three cores are now set in place. The knob at the right end of the horizontal core is intended to prevent movement of the core endwise.

Step V, Fig. 134: A chaplet, formed by folding a piece of perforated sheet metal into a four-sided form composed of two parallel sides and two curved to fit against the core and the mold, Fig. 135, is placed on top of the core approximately over the other chaplet. This prevents the core from "floating."

The cope half of the flask is then returned to its

The portion marked "space" between the right end of the horizontal core and the sand is to prevent sand being knocked off when the cope is returned to its original position.

After the metal solidifies, the flask is opened so that the casting may be removed to finish its cooling. The cores are removed by washing them out with water under high pressure. The metal left in the gate and riser, and any fins which have formed, are removed by a hammer blow or by sawing and the surfaces smoothed by rough grinding. The casting is finally cleaned by tumbling in a rumbling mill — a revolving drum filled with miscellaneous scrap — or by sandblasting.

105. Forging. Many machine parts, particularly those which are built for heavy duty and which

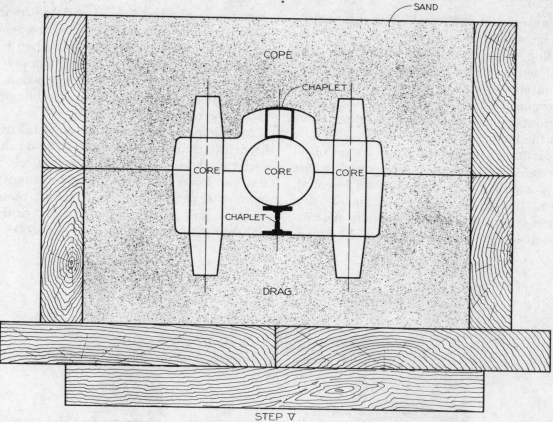

SAND

COPE

CHAPLET

CORE   CORE   CORE

CHAPLET

DRAG

STEP Ⅴ

FIG. 135. END VIEW IN SECTION — READY FOR POURING METAL

require high-grade material, are *forged* into shape while hot by hammering the metal and forcing it to conform in shape to specially made *dies*. The machine used is called the *drop hammer*, and is usually hydraulically operated to exert tremendous pressure.

In Fig. 136(a) is shown a forging as it comes from the drop hammer, in which extensive fins have been formed between the dies from excess metal. The

fins are then removed by trimming, as shown at (b), and the final pieces are touched up, if necessary, on the grinder (c). These rough pieces are now ready for machining.

It should be noted that "draft" is necessary on forgings as well as on castings, as the forging must not adhere to either of the dies.

The student should remember that both forgings

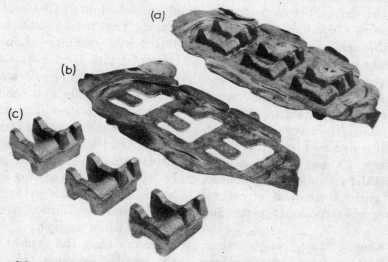

(a)

(b)

(c)

FIG. 136. FORGING OPERATIONS (Courtesy Chevrolet Motor Co.)

and castings are subject to several types of inaccuracies. These include draft, uneven shrinkage of the metal in cooling, fins, and warpage of the casting or forging, all of which tend to make pieces *not uniform*. The workman should realize when he works on a casting or forging that he is working with a piece which only roughly corresponds to the dimensions indicated on the blueprint.

106. Die-casting. Die-casting is the fastest of all casting processes, and is most often used where economy and rapidity in production are essential. Die-casting is limited to nonferrous metals and therefore is not generally used for types of work suitable for sand molding. The basic difference between

shop for machining critical surfaces to more accurate dimensions. As stated above, the general working drawing used by the previous shop is also used in the machine shop for which it is primarily drawn. When the machine shop has finished a piece, the part should match up with the blueprint which shows the completed article.

Machining is the removing of metal by means of hardened, sharp, cutting tools. The machines which perform these fundamental operations are called *machine tools*, the most common being the *engine lathe, drill press, boring mill, planer, shaper, milling machine*, and *grinder*. The lathe and drill press were the only machines invented before 1800.

FIG. 137. ENGINE LATHE (Courtesy Lodge & Shipley Co.)

die-casting and sand-casting is that the former is made in a "permanent" metal die, capable of producing many thousands of duplicate castings to very accurate dimensions, while the latter requires a new sand mold for each new casting, and the finished casting is not relatively accurate.

In die-casting, the molten metal — usually zinc alloys — is forced into the cavity between the dies under considerable pressure. Many parts that do not require great strength, such as carburetors, radio chassis, and adding-machine parts, are suitable for die-casting; and the process seems to be increasing in use.

107. Stock Forms. Many shapes of metal, wood, and other materials are so often used in the shop that their composition and sizes have been standardized and may be readily obtained from the manufacturer in the stock sizes. These include a large number of shapes of metal bars or rods, as square, hexagonal, round; the various common structural shapes used in building constructions; plate and sheet metal.

108. The Machine Shop. Most rough stock, castings, and forgings must come to the machine

For each fundamental machining operation, there must be some type of toolholder and a mechanism to move the toolholder or the work, or both.

The two main kinds of machine shops are the *job shop* and the *mass-production shop*. The job shop handles a wide variety of jobs, and is equipped with several or all of the fundamental machines listed above, which are capable of great flexibility in work done. The mass-production shop, of which the automobile machine shops are an example, are equipped with special semi-automatic and automatic production machines designed to do specific operations very rapidly and economically in great quantities. An outstanding example of an automatic machine is the so-called indexing machine (Greenlee Bros.), which produces one completely machined airplane-engine cylinder head every 45 seconds. From the time the casting enters the machine until it leaves the machine it is not touched by human hands, and the finished piece is accurate to the ten-thousandth of an inch.

In any case, the typical operations performed by the regular machine tools or by special tools are

the work revolves, and the tool is fed into the work manually or automatically in a manner required by the job. The tool is a simple rectangular bar with a special point, held in a tool post. The tool post is attached to the cross slide, which furnishes movement across the lathe bed.

Lathes may be operated at different speeds to accommodate the various jobs performed. The speed chosen for a particular job depends upon the diameter of the cut and the material used, expressed in feet per second traveled past the tool.

FIG. 138. FACING CUT ON SMALL FACE PLATE (Courtesy Lodge & Shipley Co.)

turning, facing, drilling, boring, counterboring, reaming, milling, shaping, planing, threading, broaching, grinding, punching, and *pressing.*

109. The Engine Lathe. The lathe, Fig. 137, is such a valuable all-purpose tool that every other machine tool could be made with it. It is extremely flexible, and is capable of many different rotary operations, such as facing, Fig. 138; boring, Fig. 139; drilling, reaming; and threading, Fig. 140.

The rough stock is held between two *centers,* a *live center* and a *dead center,* Fig. 137, or in a *chuck* on the *face plate,* Figs. 138–140. If held between centers, it is driven by the lathe dog on the face plate, which is clamped securely to the work. In any case

FIG. 140. THREAD CHASING ON SMALL FACE PLATE (Courtesy Lodge & Shipley Co.)

110. The Drill Press. The drill press is one of the most used machine tools in the shop. A chuck is attached to the spindle, and the drill is held securely in the chuck. The drill is made to revolve at a cutting speed appropriate to the diameter of the drill and the metal worked upon. The work is clamped to the table or is allowed to "float" while being prevented from turning. It may be held in a *drill vise* or in a *drill jig.*

The *sensitive drill press* is used for light work, and is fed by hand. The *heavy-duty drill press* is used for extremely heavy work. The *radial drill press,* Fig. 141, is designed so that the spindle may be moved to the desired position on the work, instead of adjusting the work to suit the position of the spindle; therefore this machine is very flexible and especially suitable for bulky work.

A *multiple spindle drill press,* Fig. 142, supports a number of spindles driven from the same shaft and is used to obtain faster production. The use of a

FIG. 139. BORING TAPER HOLE IN SMALL FACE PLATE (Courtesy Lodge & Shipley Co.)

FIG. 141. RADIAL DRILL PRESS (Courtesy The American Tool Works Co.)

FIG. 143. THE SHAPER (Courtesy The American Tool Works Co.)

typical drill jig is also shown in the illustration. The jig is a device for holding the work securely and guiding the drills to exact locations so that duplicates of the work will be very exact.

Other operations on the drill press may be performed merely by changing the cutting tool and using the appropriate chuck to perform reaming, counterboring, spot facing, tapping, and so on. See Fig. 115.

111. The Shaper. The shaper, Fig. 143, is used for the production of plane surfaces on relatively small work. The work is held upon an adjustable table with T-slots and clamps, and a reciprocating *ram* carries the clapper box, which carries the tool post, which in turn holds the tool. The tool is made to cut only on the forward stroke, and to save time, the shaper may be built so that the back stroke is more rapid than the forward stroke. The starting and ending of strokes are adjustable as is the position of the table. The shaper is especially useful where a surface must be shaped close to a shoulder, or other projection.

A typical operation on the shaper is shown in Fig. 144 in which a series of steel blocks is finished together.

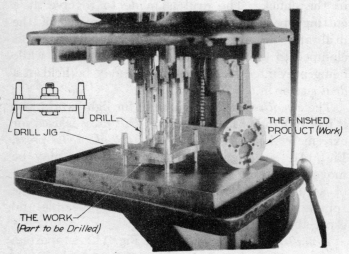

FIG. 142. MULTIPLE DRILLING.

FIG. 144. A TYPICAL SHAPER OPERATION — SHAPING SEVERAL STEEL BLOCKS SIMULTANEOUSLY, FOR USE AS WINDLASS LINERS ON SUBMARINES (Courtesy of Machinery)

112. The Planer. The planer is perhaps the best tool for producing highly accurate broad plane surfaces. The most common type is built with two lengthwise under the tool at various speeds. The tool has a single point, taking a single cut on each backward stroke of the table. The planer is suitable

FIG. 145. THE PLANER (Courtesy Cincinnati Planer Co.)

uprights, supporting a cross rail which can be moved vertically at will. The toolholder is mounted on the rail and can be moved along the rail or fed vertically or at an angle with the work. The table is characterized by considerable length, and is made to move especially for large or long work, or for a series of duplicate pieces to be planed simultaneously, as shown in Fig. 145.

113. The Boring Mill. *Boring machines* or *boring mills*, Fig. 146, are classified as "vertical" or "horizontal." The vertical boring machine has a

FIG. 146. THE BORING MILL (Photo by Railway Mechanical Engineer)

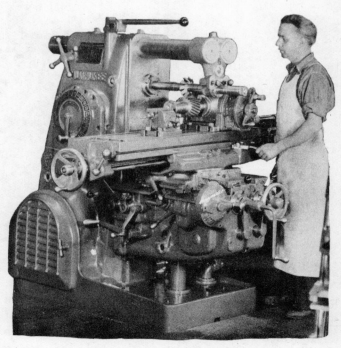

FIG. 147. THE MILLING MACHINE (Courtesy Kearney & Trecker Co.)

horizontal revolving table upon which the work is fastened by means of radial T-slots, and the tool or tools are held in heads which feed toward the work in a variety of ways.

Fundamentally, the boring mill is a specialized

duty from a single cutting point to twelve, sixteen, or more, so that these cutters have a much longer life than a single-pointed tool. These cutting edges may be straight or curved in a variety of forms, some of which are shown in Fig. 148.

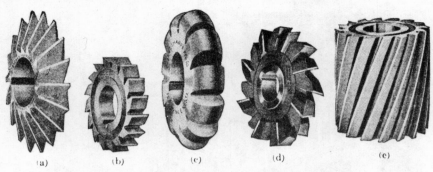

(a)   (b)   (c)   (d)   (e)

FIG. 148. MILLING CUTTERS (Courtesy Brown & Sharpe Mfg. Co.)

lathe, accommodating chucking jobs too large for the face plate of the lathe. It is especially suitable for large bulky work which cannot be easily held between centers as in a lathe but can rest solidly upon the revolving table.

The milling machine is built in a wide variety of forms, with the general purpose of bringing the work into contact with *revolving cutters*. In all cases the table is adjustable and in some cases the cutter may be fed into the work. In Fig. 147, a milling cutter is

FIG. 149. THE GRINDER

114. The Milling Machine. The *milling machine*, Fig. 147, is characterized by the use of one or more revolving cutters, Fig. 148, having a number of teeth which successively remove the metal as the cutter rotates. The effect is to distribute the cutting

being machined. A *dividing head* is used to regulate the exact division of the complete perimeter into the desired number of teeth. The work is made to rotate at a constant speed while the teeth are being cut, to provide the necessary helical form.

Milling machines are relatively very fast in production because of the larger number of cutting edges used simultaneously and the special forms of the cutters. It is, therefore, one of the most important machine tools in modern mass production.

115. The Grinder. A *grinding machine*, or grinder, is used to remove a relatively small amount of material to bring the work to a very accurate and smooth finish. The grinding wheel is made of emery or

116. The Broaching Machine. The *broaching machine* is used principally to produce square, hexagonal, or other irregularly shaped holes, and for slots of various shapes which could not be produced on the milling machine. The broach, Fig. 150, is composed of a straight stem along which are teeth, each of which protrudes slightly more than the previous one until the last tooth is exactly the shape desired. This tool is forced with great pressure through a hole

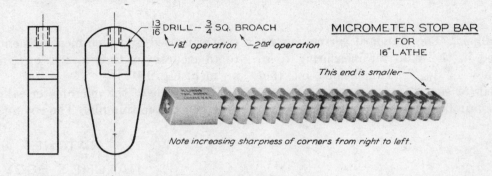

FIG. 150. A BROACHING JOB AND THE BROACH USED

carborundum. Grinding machines are either *cylindrical grinders*, Fig. 149, for grinding cylindrical and conical parts, or *surface grinders* for grinding flat surfaces. Cylindrical grinding machines are built so that the grinding wheel is fed automatically toward the work, and provision is also made for movement of the grinding wheel parallel to the center line of the work. The grinding wheel and the work rotate in opposite directions.

For rough grinding, the depth of cut may vary from 0.001″ to 0.004″. For finishing, the depth of cut may vary from 0.00025″ to 0.0005″. On the blueprint a surface to be ground is designated in the edge view of that surface with the note "grind" or the symbol G on the line.

already made in the piece by drilling, punching, or coring.

117. Jigs and Fixtures. *Jigs* and *fixtures* are specialized auxiliary devices used to extend the effectiveness on a specific job of a general-purpose machine tool. A *jig* is a device which holds the work and guides the tool, and is ordinarily not fixed rigidly to the machine. The most common example is a *drilling jig*, which holds successive duplicate pieces in exactly the same way and guides the drills to the correct locations, Fig. 142.

A *fixture* is rigidly fixed to the machine, becoming in fact an extension of it, and holds the work in position for the cutting tools without necessarily acting as a guide for them.

CHAPTER XI

READING MICROMETER CALIPER AND HEIGHT GAGE

118. Spring Caliper. The standard *spring caliper* is commonly used in the shop for measuring to a maximum accuracy of 1/64″. Dimensions on the blueprint intended for such measurements are given in common whole numbers and fractions.

caliper is used by which measurements may be made to an accuracy of thousandths or ten-thousandths of an inch, Fig. 151.

The spindle of the micrometer caliper, Fig. 151, is attached to the thimble. The covered portion of the

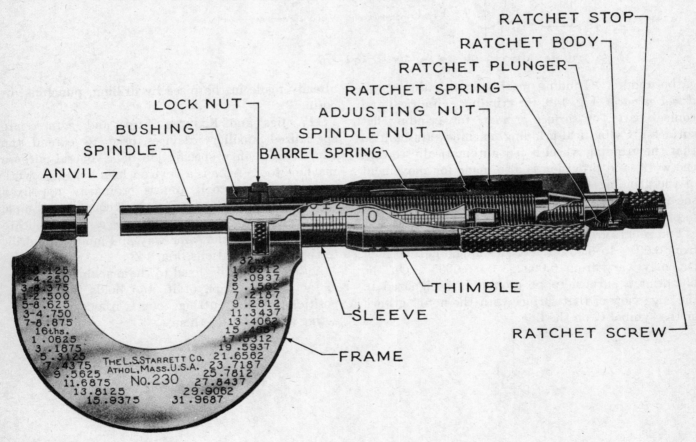

FIG. 151. THE MICROMETER CALIPER

119. Micrometer Caliper. Because almost every blueprint reader in the shop has to know how to read a *micrometer caliper* in connection with decimal dimensions on the blueprints, this chapter has been included here as a service to the industries.

Where greater accuracy is required and where dimensions are given in decimal form, the micrometer

spindle is threaded to fit threads inside of the sleeve, which is attached to the frame. When the thimble is turned, the space between the contact face at the end of the spindle and the face of the anvil is either increased or decreased, depending on which way the thimble is turned. Since there are forty threads to the inch on the spindle, one complete and exact revolution of the thimble and spindle moves the spindle and thimble longitudinally $\frac{1}{40}$ inch. The decimal equivalent of $\frac{1}{40}$ is twenty-five thousandths (0.025).

120. Reading to One-Thousandth of an Inch. The measurement of the opening between the contact faces of the anvil and the spindle is recorded on the sleeve and the thimble. Each small space on the sleeve represents one complete revolution of the thimble, or 0.025 inch. The space between 0 and 1 represents four $\frac{1}{40}$ths of an inch or 0.100 inch.

with the longitudinal line of the sleeve, Fig. 154, the reading is in ten-thousandths of an inch. The micrometer is first read in thousandths. In Fig. 154 thousandths of an inch are read $0.400 + 2$ times $0.025 + 0.018 + = 0.468 +$. The full reading is more than 0.468 but less than 0.469, making the correct reading be in ten-thousandths of an inch. The ten-thousandths are read on a special scale called the *vernier* on the sleeve. The ten spaces between the longitudinal lines of Fig. 154 are equal to nine spaces on the thimble. The difference between

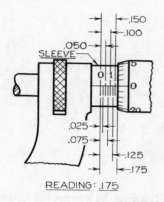

FIG. 152. READING THE SLEEVE

READING: .175

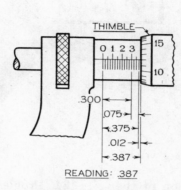

FIG. 153. READING THE THIMBLE

READING: .387

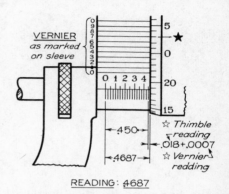

FIG. 154. READING THE VERNIER

READING: .4687

When the micrometer caliper is closed, the spindle touches the anvil and the beveled end of the thimble is in line with the zero (0) on the scale of the sleeve. If the thimble is turned counterclockwise one complete revolution, the opening between the anvil and spindle will be $\frac{1}{40}$th or 0.025 inch; for two revolutions, the opening will be $\frac{2}{40}$ths or 0.050 inch; three revolutions (0.075); four revolutions (0.100), etc. (See Fig. 152.)

Since one revolution represents 0.025 of an inch, one twenty-fifth ($\frac{1}{25}$) of one revolution of the thimble represents 0.001 of an inch. The beveled surface around the thimble has been divided and marked into twenty-five equal divisions with each representing 0.001 of an inch. The correct thimble reading is the one which is in line with the longitudinal line of the scale on the sleeve. The reading of Fig. 153 is $0.300 + 3$ times $0.025 + 0.012 = 0.387$ inch.

The full inch portion of a dimension is determined by the size of the micrometer caliper. A 4- to 5-inch caliper will measure all dimensions between 4 and 5 inches. The micrometer scale measures only the decimal portion of a dimension, or measurements of 1 inch or less.

121. Reading to Tenth-Thousandths of an Inch. When a marker of the thimble does not coincide

the width of one of the ten spaces and one of the nine spaces represents one-tenth of a division on the thimble or $\frac{1}{10,000}$th (0.0001) of an inch. To read in ten-thousandths observe the line on the sleeve which coincides with a marker on the thimble. The number of the line on the *sleeve* is the number of ten-thousandths. (Disregard the marker number of the coinciding marker on the thimble.) The complete reading of Fig. 154 is $0.400 + 2$ times $0.025 + 0.018 + 0.0007 = 0.4687$.

122. Height Gage, with Vernier. The *height gage* with vernier reads to thousandths of an inch, Fig. 155. The graduations on the bar are in fortieths ($\frac{1}{40}$) or 0.025 (25 thousandths) of an inch. Every fourth division is numbered and represents a tenth ($\frac{1}{10}$) of an inch ($4 \times 0.025 = 0.100$).

The bar reading is based on the reading of the bar which is in line with the zero of the vernier. In Fig. 155 the bar reading is $2 + 0.400 + 2 \times 0.025 + = 2.450 +$. The zero mark of the vernier is beyond the 2.450 mark and short of the 2.475 mark. The fourteenth division of the vernier coincides with a division of the bar.

The fourteenth division represents in thousandths of an inch the distance the zero mark of the vernier is beyond the 2.450 division of the bar. The reading therefore is $2 + 0.400 + 2 \times 0.025 + 0.014 = 2.464$. In reading thousandths the number of the division

The thimble is read as usual. Some depth gages have extension bars for depths greater than one inch.

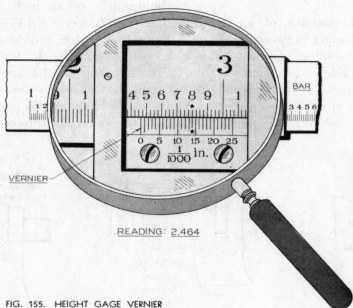

FIG. 155. HEIGHT GAGE VERNIER

on the bar opposite the fourteenth division of the vernier is disregarded. A magnifying glass should be used in reading the vernier, as shown.

123. Micrometer Depth-Gage Readings. The portion of the scale on the sleeve which is *covered* by the thimble is the correct reading of the sleeve as it applies to the depth of a groove, hole, and so on.

124. Problems in Reading Micrometer Caliper and Height Gage. An exercise in reading the micrometer caliper is given in sheet J–1. Underneath each figure the whole numbers, if any, are given; and the student is to supply the decimal readings.

An exercise in reading the height gage and depth gage is given in sheet J–2.

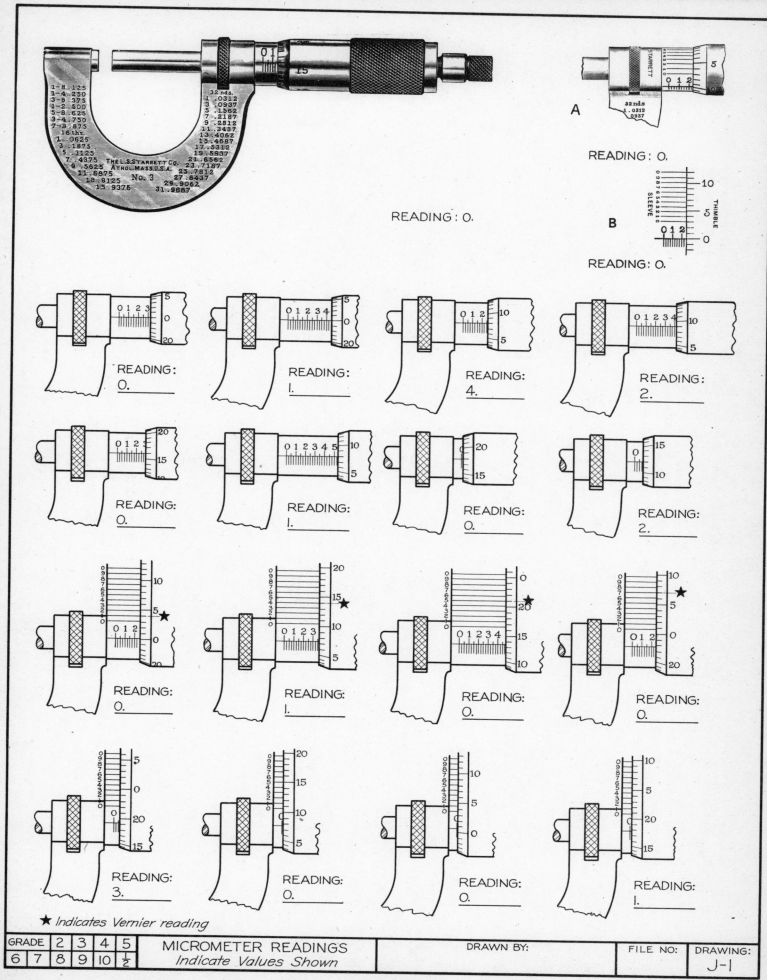

READING: 0.

A

READING: 0.

B

READING: 0.

READING: 0.

READING: 1.

READING: 4.

READING: 2.

READING: 0.

READING: 1.

READING: 0.

READING: 2.

READING: 0.

READING: 1.

READING: 0.

READING: 0.

READING: 3.

READING: 0.

READING: 0.

READING: 1.

★ *Indicates Vernier reading*

GRADE	2	3	4	5
	6	7	8	9	10	½

MICROMETER READINGS
Indicate Values Shown

DRAWN BY:

FILE NO:

DRAWING:
J-1

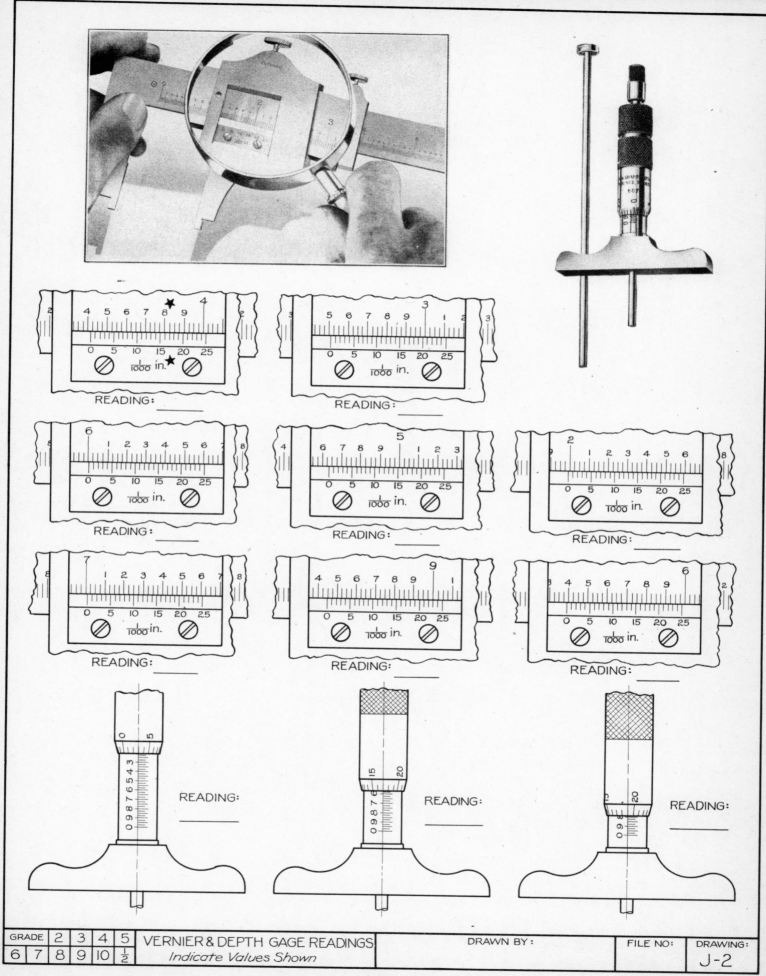

READING: ____

READING: ____

READING: ____

READING: ____

READING: ____

READING: ____

READING: ____

READING: ____

READING: ____

READING: ____

READING: ____

GRADE	2	3	4	5	VERNIER & DEPTH GAGE READINGS	DRAWN BY:	FILE NO:	DRAWING:
	6	7	8	9	10	½	*Indicate Values Shown*			J-2

CHAPTER XII

FIRST-ANGLE DRAWINGS

125. The Universal Language. One of the unique characteristics of working drawings is the fact that they may be read and understood by engineers and machinists in all parts of the world; that is, the shape description, or meaning of lines and views, can be understood by all. Of course, the dimensions might have to be converted from the inch system to the metric system or vice versa; but this is easy with a conversion table. Also some translation of notes may be required, but often their use indicates the import of the wording. Some languages are similar enough to English so that no difficulty is encountered in translation. In other cases a foreign-language dictionary may be necessary.

Many drawings from England have been received in this country because of our industrial position as the "Arsenal of Democracy." Almost all industrial concerns dealing in foreign trade have foreign drawings in their files or encounter them in their dealings. In many cases these drawings are redrawn according to the American system, but often, to save time the foreign prints are actually used in our shops. In any event the blueprint reader should know something about these foreign prints.

126. First-Angle Drawings. The method of graphic representation is not exactly the same in North America as in most of the rest of the world. In the United States and Canada and to some extent in England *third-angle projection* is used, while in nearly all other countries *first-angle projection* is used. However, the only difference between the two systems, as far as the blueprint reader is concerned, is in the arrangement of the views. The views in themselves are the same in both systems.

The theorists in projection originally conceived of three planes intersecting each other at right angles, Fig. 156: the *vertical* plane, which always remains stationary; the *horizontal* plane, which always revolves downward in front as shown by the arrows; and the *profile* plane, which revolves away from the

object, as indicated. The object is considered to be located in one of the four "angles" produced by the intersection of the vertical and horizontal planes, and its views obtained by dropping perpendiculars from the object to the planes of projection. In Fig. 156 the object is shown in the first angle.

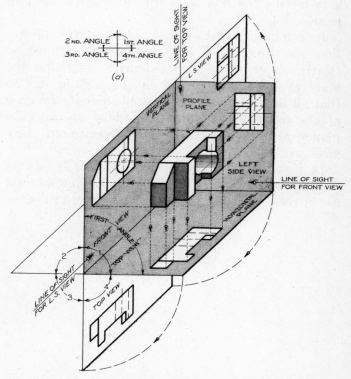

FIG. 156. PICTORIAL REPRESENTATION OF FIRST-ANGLE PROJECTION

If the object is placed in the third angle, it will be seen that this produces the arrangement of views discussed in preceding chapters. The top view will be projected on the horizontal plane above the object, the front view will be projected on the vertical plane in front of the object, and the side view will be projected on the profile plane at the side of the object. When the three planes are revolved, the views will fall in their natural positions; that is, the top view will be over the front view, the left side view will be to the left of the front view. and so on. See Fig. 157.

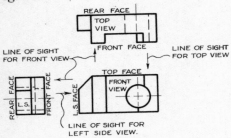

FIG. 157. THIRD–ANGLE PROJECTION

If the object is considered in the first angle, Figs. 156 and 158, it will be seen that the top view falls under the front view, and the left side view falls to the right of the front view. The arrangement of views is in a sense the reverse of that for third-angle projection, Fig. 157.

In comparing first-angle and third-angle projection, the direction of sight for each view must be clearly understood. In third-angle projection the observer is always "on the outside, looking in," so that all lines of sight are directed through the glass planes and to the object. The views on the glass planes are those seen by the observer in these positions.

In first-angle projection, the observer is always "on the inside, looking out," so that all lines of sight are directed through the object, and then to the glass

planes. The views as seen by the observer in these positions are the views projected to the glass planes. When the planes are revolved in the conventional manner, the views fall as shown in Figs. 156 and 157. In order to understand clearly the direction of viewing the object, a careful study of the lines of sight in Figs. 157 and 158 should be made. It should be noted that the views are identical in both figures, but that they are differently arranged.

127. First-Angle Problems. All of the problems on sheet K–1 are first-angle drawings. The student will be interested in the sources of these problems and also in the unusual types of finish marks. In Problem 1 the directions of sight are indicated. The top view is to be drawn under the front view, as seen

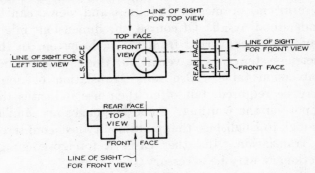

FIG. 158. FIRST–ANGLE PROJECTION

in the direction indicated by the arrows. In the remaining problems the student is to establish his points of view and directions of sight.

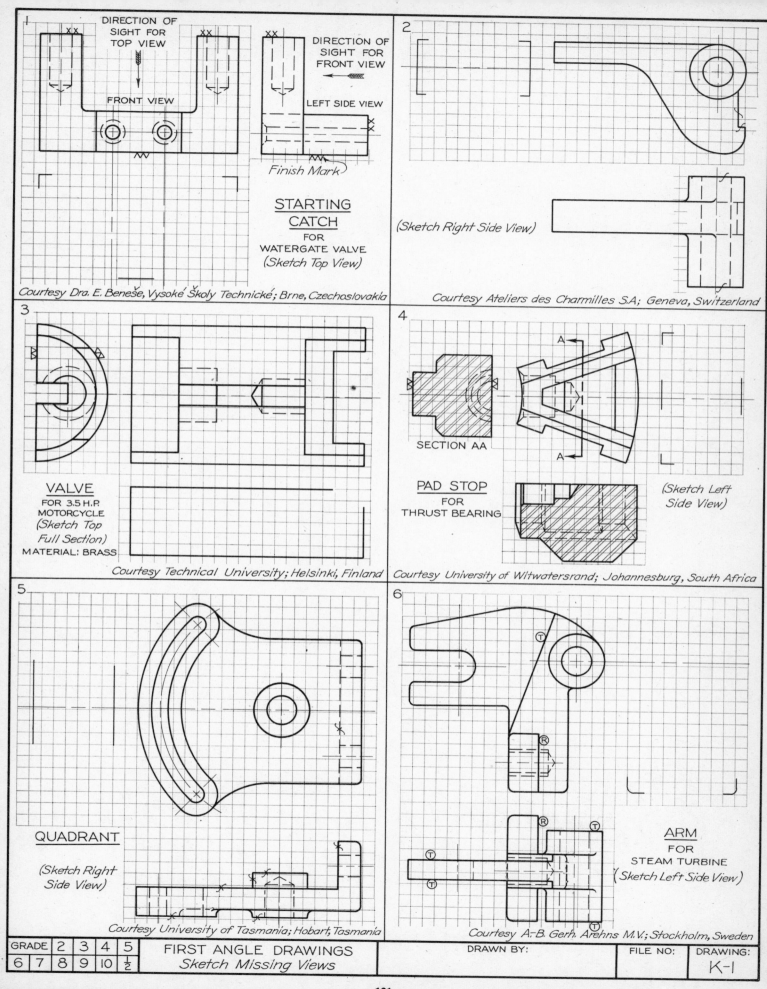

1

DIRECTION OF
SIGHT FOR
TOP VIEW

XX

XX

XX

DIRECTION OF
SIGHT FOR
FRONT VIEW

FRONT VIEW

LEFT SIDE VIEW

XX

Finish Mark

STARTING
CATCH
FOR
WATERGATE VALVE
(Sketch Top View)

Courtesy Dra. E. Beneše, Vysoké Školy Technické; Brne, Czechoslovakia

2

(Sketch Right Side View)

Courtesy Ateliers des Charmilles S.A; Geneva, Switzerland

3

VALVE
FOR 3.5 H.P.
MOTORCYCLE
(Sketch Top
Full Section)
MATERIAL: BRASS

Courtesy Technical University; Helsinki, Finland

4

A

A

SECTION AA

PAD STOP
FOR
THRUST BEARING

(Sketch Left
Side View)

Courtesy University of Witwatersrand; Johannesburg, South Africa

5

QUADRANT

(Sketch Right
Side View)

Courtesy University of Tasmania; Hobart, Tasmania

6

T

R

R

T

T

T

T

ARM
FOR
STEAM TURBINE
(Sketch Left Side View)

Courtesy A-B. Gerh. Arehns M.V.; Stockholm, Sweden

GRADE	2	3	4	5	FIRST ANGLE DRAWINGS	DRAWN BY:	FILE NO:	DRAWING:
	6	7	8	9	10	½	*Sketch Missing Views*			K-1

CHAPTER XIII

RIGHT-HAND AND LEFT-HAND DRAWINGS

128. Functioning Pairs of Machine Parts. It is quite common in machine design to make certain individual parts of a machine to function in pairs, which are usually placed opposite each other. These are usually placed symmetrically with relation to a principal axis on center line of the machine. For example, in an airplane landing gear, the wheel

Some concerns follow the practice of drawing the R.H. part, others the L.H. part, while still others give either part, carefully labeled. Only a few companies furnish drawings of both L.H. and R.H. parts. Usually, therefore, the patternmaker or machinist must visualize the opposite part, and he may need to make a freehand sketch of it. No one

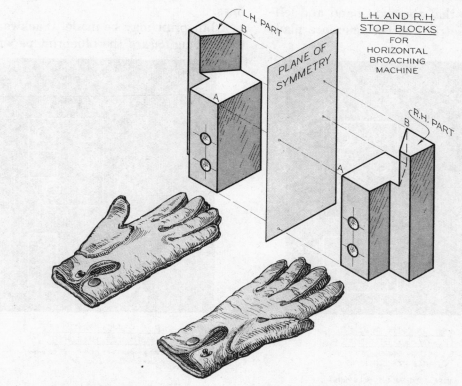

FIG. 159. SYMMETRY OF L.H. AND R.H. PARTS

assembly on the right of the pilot, or center line of the fuselage, is called *right-hand* or R.H. assembly and each of the detail parts is also called an R.H. part. Likewise, the corresponding parts on the left are *left-hand* and are designated L.H.

In industry it is common practice to give a detail drawing of one of the pairs and merely specify by a note that the *opposite* is required.

should think for a moment that an L.H. part is simply an R.H. part turned around. Unless it is a very simple symmetrical shape, such as a cube or cylinder, the two shapes will be different in a special way.

129. Symmetry. The idea of symmetrical pairs is illustrated in Fig. 159, where the two opposite parts are thought of as being symmetrical with respect to a reference plane between them. Every point in the R.H. part is exactly opposite the corresponding point in the L.H. part, and the same distance from the

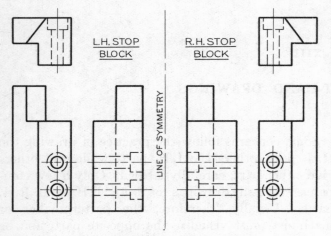

FIG. 160. L.H. AND R.H. DRAWINGS OF STOP BLOCK

reference plane. Note that the right-hand and left-hand gloves are symmetrical to the reference plane in the same way.

and are called R.H. and L.H. arbitrarily as they seem natural to the designer of the machine.

It will be seen in Fig. 160 that *drawings* of R.H. and L.H. parts are symmetrical with respect to a line of symmetry which can be drawn between them. Again, every point in one drawing has a corresponding point exactly opposite and at the same distance from the line of symmetry.

A drawing of an opposite part is a "mirror image" of the drawing of the part which the draftsman made, and the blueprint reader can check his sketch of the opposite part by holding the blueprint before a mirror and comparing the image with the sketch. The lettering in the mirror image will, of course, be "backward." The same result may be obtained by holding the blueprint to the light and looking through it from the back. If held against a window pane, the opposite part may be sketched on the back of the blueprint without any change of visibility of lines.

A blueprint may be made "backwards" by facing the tracing *toward* the blueprint paper and exposing

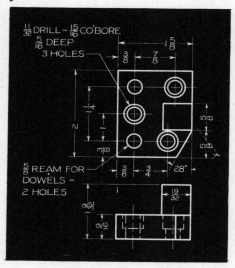

L.H. PUNCH AND DIE
FORMING BRACKET
AS USED IN PRODUCTION OF
CRADLE TELEPHONE

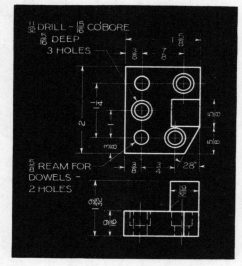

R.H. PUNCH AND DIE
FORMING BRACKET
(*Mirror view of left hand part, or view
as seen through back of blueprint.*)

FIG. 161. MIRROR VIEW OF BLUEPRINT

It is interesting to note that if the L.H. part were placed in any other position with respect to the plane of symmetry, the corresponding R.H. part will be exactly the same *shape* as before. The two parts can never change their shape. It is also interesting to note that if the observer should take up his position at the back so that the R.H. part becomes, to him, the L.H. part, the L.H. part becomes to him the R.H. part. The parts are always opposite in shape,

it in that position. The lettering will be backward, but the views will be the views of the opposite part, Fig. 161.

130. L.H. and R.H. Problems. Two problems are included here, on sheet L–1, but opposite parts may be sketched by the student from any of the problems in this book. On sheet L–1, the vertical lines in the two problems are to be used as "lines of symmetry."

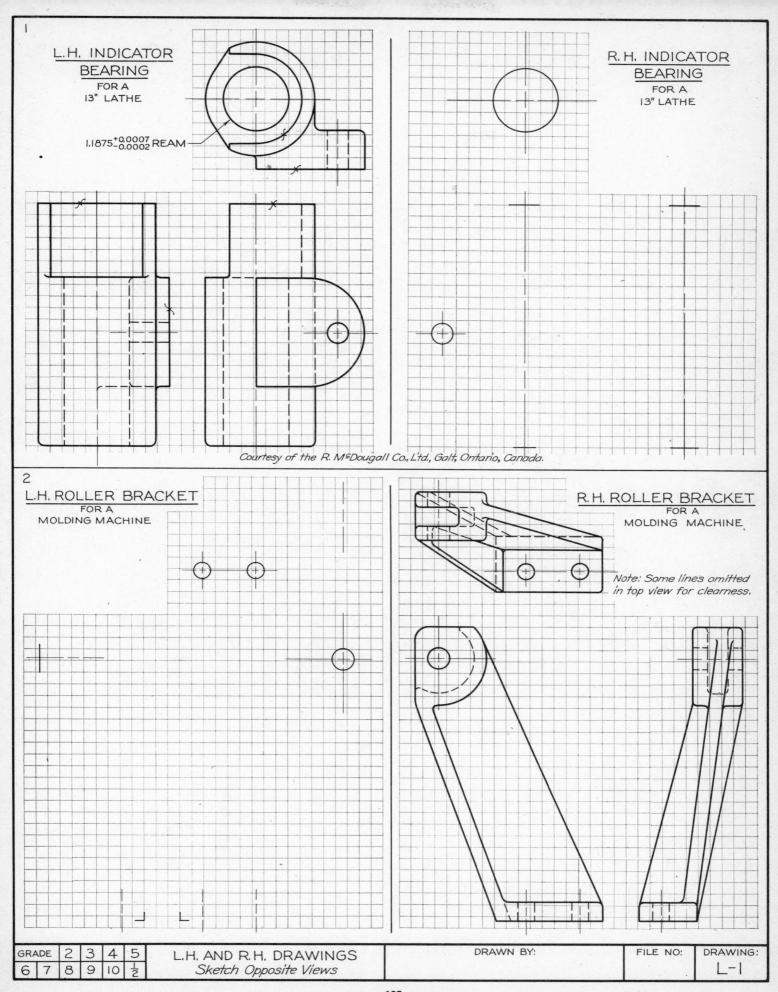

1

L.H. INDICATOR BEARING
FOR A 13" LATHE

1.1875 $^{+0.0007}_{-0.0002}$ REAM

R.H. INDICATOR BEARING
FOR A 13" LATHE

Courtesy of the R. M\(^c\)Dougall Co., L'td., Galt, Ontario, Canada.

2

L.H. ROLLER BRACKET
FOR A MOLDING MACHINE

R.H. ROLLER BRACKET
FOR A MOLDING MACHINE

Note: Some lines omitted in top view for clearness.

GRADE	2	3	4	5	L.H. AND R.H. DRAWINGS	DRAWN BY:	FILE NO:	DRAWING:
6	7	8	9	10	½	*Sketch Opposite Views*			L-1

CHAPTER XIV

WELDING REPRESENTATION

131. Welding in Industry. In the past decade welding has made great strides in machine manufacturing. Many parts which formerly were made by casting have been redesigned and are now constructed by welding. In general, casting is more suitable where a great many duplicate parts are needed, and welding is often best for special work or where few similar parts are required.

In welding, great flexibility of design is possible. Portions of a complicated part may be machined separately and welded together later. A high-grade piece of metal may be welded to a less expensive material, thus producing a further saving of cost.

132. Processes. Welding methods may be classified as *fusion* or *nonpressure processes*, and *pressure processes*. The nonpressure processes include *arc*

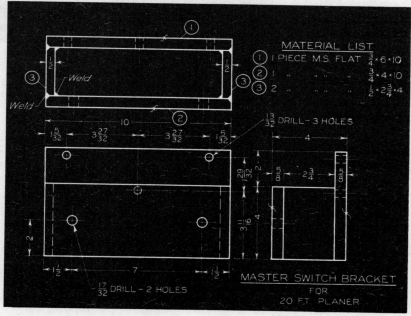

FIG. 162. A SIMPLE WELDED PART

Welding eliminates expensive patterns and the storage space necessary to keep them. Ordinarily a part can be welded in less time than it would take to make the pattern. Standard rolled stock, such as plate, round, and square bar stock, and structural steel shapes (angles, I-beams, channels) are used in welding, and these also reduce the cost. A welded part of such materials will actually be stronger than the cast iron. Further, the wall thickness may be reduced greatly, thus reducing the weight of the part — an objective usually to be desired.

welding and *gas welding*. In pressure welding mechanical pressure is exerted between the parts welded. In *resistance welding*, a pressure process, the heat for the weld is obtained from the resistance to the flow of an electric current, and mechanical pressure is used to unite the parts.

To weld two pieces of metal together, the contact surfaces must be heated to a fusion temperature; then with the aid of a flux and a welding rod of special material to furnish additional metal, the metals flow together, making a permanent junction.

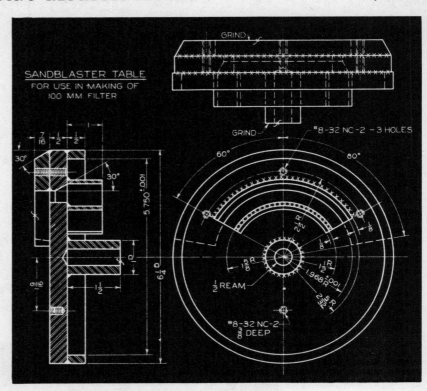

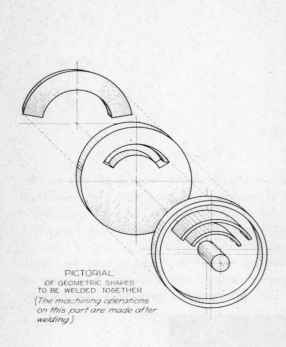

PICTORIAL
OF GEOMETRIC SHAPES
TO BE WELDED TOGETHER
(The machining operations
on this part are made after
welding.)

FIG. 163. A TYPICAL WELDED MACHINE PART

The weld may actually be stronger than the adjoining materials, if care and skill are exercised in making the weld.

133. Visualizing from a Welding Drawing. A welding drawing, though it is of a detail part, is in reality an assembly drawing, for it is composed of

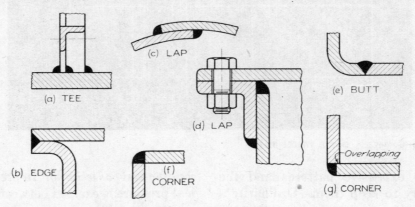

FIG. 164. TYPES OF WELDED JOINTS

numerous geometric shapes which are welded together rather than fastened with screws, bolts, or rivets. The sizes of the individual pieces are frequently given in table form as shown in Fig. 162. In parts 1 and 2, ¾" stock was used so there would be material to remove in the finishing operations required. In the top view are shown, by means of

solid triangles, the end views of the eight welds. This method of indicating welds is commonly used by many companies.

If Fig. 162 were a drawing of a solid casting, the two vertical inside solid lines in the right side view would be hidden lines and only the outline of the view would be shown with solid lines. Also, in the top view, between parts 2 and 3, the two short solid lines would be eliminated. Therefore in welded drawings the individual plates and shapes are shown together as in an assembly drawing, with lines of separation between adjacent parts to indicate clearly the separate pieces to be welded together.

134. Sectional Views in Welding Drawings. A three-view welding drawing for a sandblaster table is shown in Fig. 163. To the left is a pictorial drawing (not a part of the welding drawing) which shows the several pieces used to build up this part. In a sectional view of a welded part the section lines for adjacent pieces are drawn in opposite directions, as in ordinary assembly drawings. The machining may be done before or after the welding operations as the varying conditions may require. Another symbol commonly used to represent welds is illustrated in this drawing, in which the welds are represented by rows of X's.

135. Types of Welded Joints. A welded joint may be open or closed; that is, there may or may not be a small space between adjoining pieces during welding.

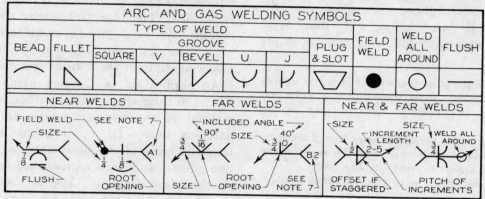

FIG. 165. STANDARD WELDING SYMBOLS

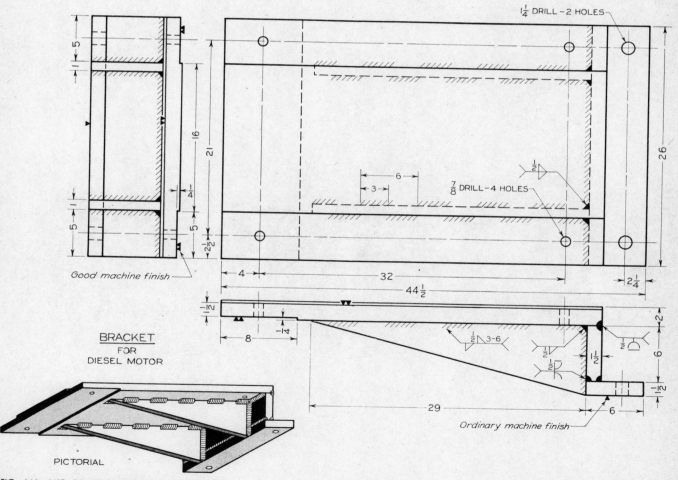

FIG. 166. USE OF STANDARD WELDING SYMBOLS

There are five general types of welded joints: *tee, lap, butt, edge,* and *corner,* all of which are shown in Fig. 164.

The four basic types of arc and gas welds are *bead,* used for building up surfaces, *fillet, groove* (square, or V, or bevel, or U, or J), *plug,* and *slot.*

136. Standard Symbols. In October, 1940, the American Welding Society recommended a new set of welding symbols and these were adopted by the American Standards Association, Fig. 165. With reference to this figure the following conditions are indicated:

1. Welds parallel to the plane of the paper or nearly so, with faces toward reader are near welds, those with faces away from reader are far welds. (Use sufficient views to make meaning clear.)

2. Welds in section or end views with faces toward the arrow are near welds, those with faces away from the arrow are far welds. (Use sufficient arrows to make locations clear.)

3. When one member only is to be grooved, arrow points to that member.

4. Near and far welds are same size unless otherwise shown.

5. Symbols apply between abrupt changes in direction of weld, or as dimensioned.

6. All welds are continuous and of user's standard proportions and all except V and bevel groove welds are closed unless otherwise shown.

7. Tail of arrow used for specification reference.

As yet, relatively few industrial concerns have adopted these symbols, the majority using simple representations, as in Figs. 162 and 163, and other variations. The blueprint reader should familiarize himself with these symbols, and if he comes in contact with drawings using this system he should make a special study of the subject from handbooks.

An application of the new symbols is shown in Fig. 166, together with another commonly used method of representing welds, namely, the short hatching lines. In practice, the welding symbols take the place of the short hatching lines and other line effects, and both representations do not appear on the same drawing. Also included is a pictorial drawing showing the assembly of the pieces and the application of the welds.

CHAPTER XV

GEARS

137. Transmission of Power by Gears. The power of a revolving shaft may be transmitted to another by a pair of pulleys and a belt, by a pair of cylinders or cones touching each other, or by gears.

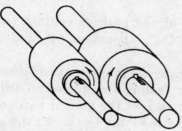

FIG. 167. ROLLING CYLINDERS

The rolling cylinders of Fig. 167 can transmit only a relatively small amount of power from one shaft to the other through the friction between the cylinders. With a series of indentations in and adjacent projections added to each cylinder, Fig. 168, much more power can be transmitted. The shafts will, of course, rotate in opposite directions. The smaller of the pair of gears is called a *pinion*, and the larger is called a *gear*. The basic cylinders on which the indentations and projections are made are called *pitch cylinders* (P.C.), Fig. 168. The diameter of the pitch circle is called *pitch diameter* (P.D.). The shape and size of these indentations and projections which form what are called *gear teeth* have developed into considerable design. The first gear teeth were very crude in design; in fact they were wood pegs and are in use today in Mexico and elsewhere on water wheels. The standard gear-tooth shape is based on the mathematical curve — the involute. The cycloid is occasionally used.

The shaft to which the power is being transmitted may rotate at the same number of revolutions per minute (RPM) or faster or slower than the one transmitting the power. This depends on the ratio of the pitch diameters of the two mating gears. If the two pitch diameters are the same, both shafts revolve at the same speed. If the diameter of one gear is twice that of the other, the shaft with the smaller gear will revolve twice as fast as the larger gear.

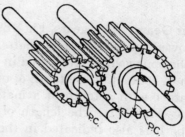

FIG. 168. GEARS

In shifting gears in an automobile, the driver is merely changing gear ratios for variations in speed and power. For the same RPM of the motor the car will move fastest in high gear and slowest in low gear. The ratio of the gears involved in the high gear position is smallest, while the ratio for low gear is largest.

FIG. 169. SPUR GEARS

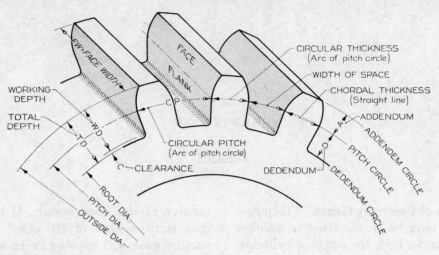

FIG. 170. GEAR TOOTH TERMINOLOGY

138. Spur Gears. Spur gears, Fig. 169, are used to transmit power between parallel shafts. The terminology of the spur gear is illustrated in Fig. 170.

The path of contact of the tooth of one gear while it is in contact with a tooth of a mating gear is a straight line, Fig. 171. The length of this contact along the path is also indicated in the illustration. The angle which this path of contact makes with a line perpendicular to a straight line connecting the centers of the gears may be varied but in so doing the size of the tooth also varies. The most commonly

used angle of the path of contact (called *pressure angle*) is $14\frac{1}{2}°$, though $17\frac{1}{2}°$ and $20°$ are also used.

Table I gives the symbol, a word description of the formula for finding the numerical values, and the formula for each of the several parts of the gear as regards the size of the teeth and the gears' various diameters. Variations of gear data as are commonly given are used as problem material in Problem Sheet M–1. All the numerical values may be obtained by substitution of the given data in the proper

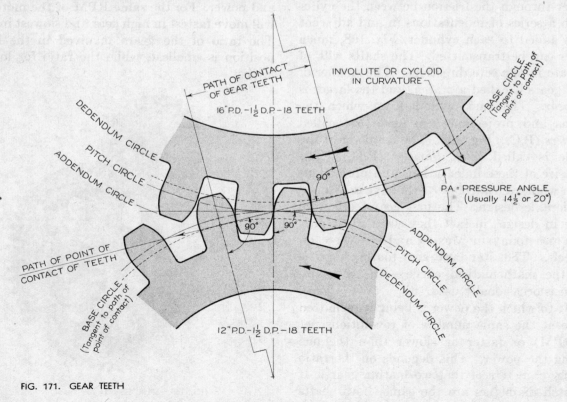

FIG. 171. GEAR TEETH

TABLE I

SPUR GEARS FOR PARALLEL SHAFTS. INVOLUTE TOOTH. $14\frac{1}{2}°$ PRESSURE ANGLE

Nomenclature	Symbol	Description of Formula	Formula
Number of teeth	N	Multiply diametral pitch by pitch diameter	$N = DP \times PD$
Pitch diameter	PD	Divide number of teeth by diametral pitch	$PD = \dfrac{N}{DP}$
Diametral pitch	DP	Divide number of teeth by pitch diameter	$DP = \dfrac{N}{PD}$
Circular pitch	CP	Divide 3.1416 by diametral pitch	$CP = \dfrac{3.1416}{DP}$
Addendum	A	Divide 1 by diametral pitch or circular pitch by 3.1416	$A = \dfrac{1}{DP} = \dfrac{CP}{3.1416}$
Dedendum	D	Add addendum plus clearance	$D = A + C$
Clearance	C	Divide 0.157 by diametral pitch or circular pitch by 20.	$C = \dfrac{0.157}{DP} = \dfrac{CP}{20}$
Working depth	WD	Multiply addendum by 2	$WD = 2A$
Total depth	TD	Divide 2.157 by diametral pitch or add addendum and dedendum	$TD = \dfrac{2.157}{DP} = A + D$
Outside diameter	OD	Pitch diameter plus 2 times addendum	$OD = PD + 2A$
Root diameter	RD	Pitch diameter minus 2 times dedendum	$RD = PD - 2D$
Circular thickness	$Ci.T$	Divide circular pitch by 2 or 1.5708 by diametral pitch	$Ci.T = \dfrac{CP}{2} = \dfrac{1.5708}{DP}$
Chordal thickness (used in measuring tooth size)	$Ch.T$	Multiply pitch diameter by sine of angle of 90° divided by number of teeth	$Ch.T = PD \times \sin\left(\dfrac{90°}{N}\right)$
Corrected addendum (used in measuring tooth size)	CA	Add addendum and ½ pitch diameter and subtract the product of ½ pitch diameter and cos of angle of 90° divided by number of teeth	$CA = A + \dfrac{PD}{2} - \dfrac{PD}{2}\cos\left(\dfrac{90°}{N}\right)$

formulas of this table, and on certain occasions the results of some formulas are used in other formulas.

The corrected addendum is necessary for accurately machined gears. Figure 172 illustrates the use of this value in measuring a gear tooth for size.

In checking the size of gear teeth for correct size, there are two important measurements to use; they are the chordal thickness and corrected addendum. The chordal thickness, as shown in Fig. 170, is the chord which subtends the arc of the circular thickness. It is necessary to measure chordal thickness rather than circular thickness because the gear-tooth vernier caliper measures only straight line distances, Fig. 172. Table I gives the formula for computing the chordal thickness.

The gear-tooth vernier caliper also measures the distances from the outside diameter portion of a gear tooth to the chordal-thickness straight line and not the arc of the circular thickness. The addendum is measured to the arc; therefore there needs to be a small correction factor, Fig. 172. The formula for the corrected addendum is given in Table I. The bar of the gear-tooth vernier caliper is set for the

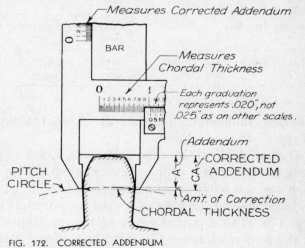

FIG. 172. CORRECTED ADDENDUM

TABLE II

BEVEL GEARS WITH SHAFTS AT RIGHT ANGLES. INVOLUTE TOOTH. $14\frac{1}{2}°$ PRESSURE ANGLE

Nomenclature	Symbol	Description of Formula	Formula
Number of teeth	N	Multiply diametral pitch by pitch diameter	$N = DP \times PD$
Pitch diameter	PD	Divide number of teeth by diametral pitch	$PD = \dfrac{N}{DP}$
Diametral pitch	DP	Divide number of teeth by pitch diameter	$DP = \dfrac{N}{PD}$
Circular pitch	CP	Divide 3.1416 by diametral pitch	$CP = \dfrac{3.1416}{DP}$
Addendum	A	Divide 1 by diametral pitch	$A = \dfrac{1}{DP}$
Dedendum	D	Divide 1.157 by diametral pitch	$D = \dfrac{1.157}{DP}$
Pitch cone angle of pinion	PCA pinion	Divide number of teeth of pinion by number of teeth of gear. Find angle which corresponds with the above resultant in table of natural tangents.	Tan PCA pinion $= \dfrac{N \text{ pinion}}{N \text{ gear}}$
Pitch cone angle of gear	PCA gear	Divide number of teeth of gear by number of teeth of pinion. Find angle which corresponds with above resultant in table of natural tangents.	Tan PCA gear $= \dfrac{N \text{ gear}}{N \text{ pinion}}$
Pitch cone radius	PCR	Divide pitch diameter by two times sin PCA. Find sin PCA in table of natural sines.	$PCR = \dfrac{PD}{2 \sin PCA}$
Addendum angle	AA	Divide addendum by pitch cone radius. Find angle which corresponds with above resultant in table of natural tangents.	Tan $AA = \dfrac{A}{PCR}$
Dedendum angle	DA	Divide dedendum by pitch cone radius. Find angle which corresponds with above resultant in table of natural tangents.	tan $DA = \dfrac{D}{PCR}$
Cutting angle	CA	Subtract dedendum angle from pitch cone angle	$CA = PCA - DA$
Face angle	FA	Subtract the sum of pitch cone angle and addendum angle from 90°	$FA = 90° - (PCA + AA)$
Angular addendum	AAd	Multiply addendum by natural cosine of pitch cone radius	$AAd = A \cos PCR$
Outside diameter	OD	Sum of pitch diameter and two times angular addendum	$OD = PD + 2\,AAd$
Apex distance	AD	Multiply one-half of outside diameter by natural tangent of face angle	$AD = \dfrac{OD}{2} \times \tan FA$

corrected addendum, and then the chordal thickness of the tooth is measured.

It should be noted that each graduation of the gear-tooth vernier caliper represents 0.020 of an inch and not 0.025 as on other verniers.

An industrial drawing of a spur gear is shown in Fig. 173. The standard conventional representation of the gear teeth is used in this illustration. A light solid line represents the outside diameter and a dotted line represents the root diameter. A circular centerline represents the pitch circle.

The Rockwell C–33–37 is the name of the method and the values to be obtained on the hardness tester for the proper hardness of the surfaces of the gear teeth. If a tooth is too soft, it will wear too fast; and if too hard, it is likely to be brittle and will chip.

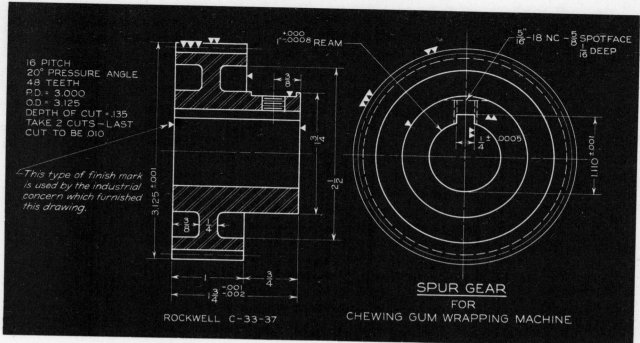

16 PITCH
20° PRESSURE ANGLE
48 TEETH
P.D. = 3.000
O.D. = 3.125
DEPTH OF CUT = .135
TAKE 2 CUTS – LAST
CUT TO BE .010

This type of finish mark is used by the industrial concern which furnished this drawing.

ROCKWELL C–33–37

SPUR GEAR
FOR
CHEWING GUM WRAPPING MACHINE

FIG. 173. TYPICAL SPUR GEAR DRAWING

139. Bevel Gears. Bevel gears, Fig. 174, are used to transmit power between shafts whose axes intersect, though not necessarily at right angles. Since in most instances the angle between the shafts is 90°, it will be the only angle considered here.

FIG. 174. BEVEL GEARS

If the two shafts are to have the same speed, the gears will be of the same size and are given the special name of *miter gears*.

The design of a pair of bevel gears is based on a pair of cones with vertexes touching and in rolling contact with each other. The gear teeth are formed by cutting into these cones and adding projections. These cones will be the pitch cones of the gears.

An industrial miter gear drawing is shown in Fig. 175. The standard conventional representations are used.

The necessary formulas, their word descriptions, and symbols are given in Table II for the entire nomenclature of bevel gears.

140. Other Gears. There are other types of gears, such as helical and herringbone gears, worm gears, and hypoid gears, but space does not permit their inclusion here. A complete knowledge of gearing is a study in itself, and it is anticipated that this brief treatment will be sufficient for a student to recognize gears on drawings and to read the drawings intelligently.

141. Problems in Gears. Sheet M–1 provides six possible assignments in calculating the various elements of spur gears and bevel gears. The blank spaces in the columns are to be filled in with the correct answers in each case. These values are found by substituting known values in the formulas given in Table I, page 193, and Table II, page 194.

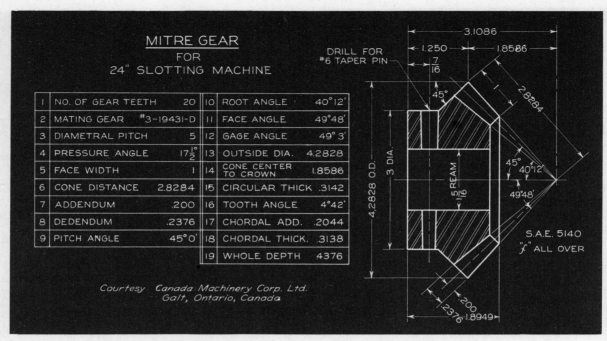

FIG. 175. TYPICAL BEVEL GEAR DRAWING

The following data appears within the figure:

MITRE GEAR
FOR
24" SLOTTING MACHINE

1	NO. OF GEAR TEETH	20	10	ROOT ANGLE	40°12'
2	MATING GEAR	#3-19431-D	11	FACE ANGLE	49°48'
3	DIAMETRAL PITCH	5	12	GAGE ANGLE	49°3'
4	PRESSURE ANGLE	17½°	13	OUTSIDE DIA.	4.2828
5	FACE WIDTH	1	14	CONE CENTER TO CROWN	1.8586
6	CONE DISTANCE	2.8284	15	CIRCULAR THICK.	.3142
7	ADDENDUM	.200	16	TOOTH ANGLE	4°42'
8	DEDENDUM	.2376	17	CHORDAL ADD.	.2044
9	PITCH ANGLE	45°0'	18	CHORDAL THICK.	.3138
			19	WHOLE DEPTH	.4376

Courtesy Canada Machinery Corp. Ltd.
Galt, Ontario, Canada

INVOLUTE TOOTH	SPUR GEARS			$14\frac{1}{2}°$ PRESSURE ANGLE		
	PROBLEM 1		PROBLEM 2		PROBLEM 3	
	GEAR	PINION	GEAR	PINION	GEAR	PINION
NUMBER OF TEETH	42	20	60	18		
PITCH DIAMETER			10	3	12	7
DIAMETRAL PITCH	2	2			3	3
CIRCULAR PITCH						
ADDENDUM						
DEDENDUM						
CLEARANCE						
WORKING DEPTH						
TOTAL DEPTH						
OUTSIDE DIAMETER						
ROOT DIAMETER						
CIRCULAR THICKNESS						
CHORDAL THICKNESS						

INVOLUTE TOOTH	BEVEL GEARS			$14\frac{1}{2}°$ PRESSURE ANGLE		
	PROBLEM 1		PROBLEM 2		PROBLEM 3	
	GEAR	PINION	GEAR	PINION	GEAR	PINION
NUMBER OF TEETH	50	30	92	20		
PITCH DIAMETER			11.5	2.5	17	3
DIAMETRAL PITCH	10	10			7	7
CIRCULAR PITCH						
ADDENDUM						
DEDENDUM						
PITCH CONE ANGLE						
PITCH CONE RADIUS						
ADDENDUM ANGLE						
DEDENDUM ANGLE						
CUTTING ANGLE						
FACE ANGLE						
ANGULAR ADDENDUM						
OUTSIDE DIAMETER						
APEX DISTANCE						

Use Formulas in Articles 139 and 140 in Computing Problems

GRADE	2	3	4	5	GEAR PROBLEMS	DRAWN BY:	FILE NO:	DRAWING:
	6	7	8	9	10	$\frac{1}{2}$	*Solve Assigned Problems*			M-1

CHAPTER XVI

COMMERCIAL BLUEPRINTS

142. Study of Industrial Drawings. While it is very important for the blueprint reader to obtain a thorough knowledge of the fundamental principles of drawing — especially of multiview projection — he cannot become proficient in reading blueprints until he has actually read a large number of typical prints. It is for that reason that this book would not be complete without a representative series of prints, which are worth considerable study on the part of the student.

These prints are exact reproductions of blueprints actually in use in a number of well-known manufacturing plants. Permission has been given by the industrial concerns to add the symbols necessary in asking questions about the drawings. They were carefully selected to bring out a variety of principles and practices with which the student should be familiar. No print should be passed by until the student understands everything on it, down to the most minute detail. He may, and if necessary he should, call on his instructor, or some other person who is experienced, to answer some of his questions.

He should not stop with these prints, but should seize every opportunity which presents itself to study blueprints carefully. After considerable practice, the student who persists will find that no blueprint is a stranger to him, but instead it conveys clear and unmistakable instructions to him for the construction of some part.

On sheet N–1a is given a dimensioned assembly of a fixture. The student is to sketch necessary views of assigned parts on sheet N–1b, and dimension fully.

For the blueprint reading exercises that follow, answer sheets are provided in which the student is to answer the questions briefly. On a basis of 100 per cent, each question is valued at four.

See Appendixes V and VI, pages 236 and 238, for definitions of unfamiliar words and for abbreviations used on blueprints.

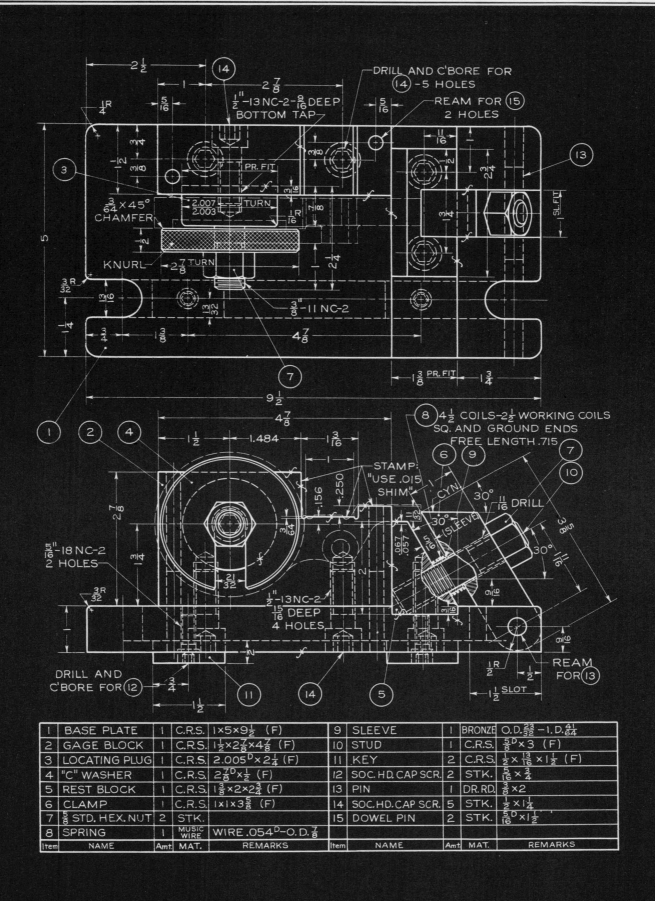

Item	NAME	Amt.	MAT.	REMARKS	Item	NAME	Amt.	MAT.	REMARKS
1	BASE PLATE	1	C.R.S.	$1 \times 5 \times 9\frac{1}{2}$ (F)	9	SLEEVE	1	BRONZE	O.D. $\frac{23}{32}$ – I.D. $\frac{41}{64}$
2	GAGE BLOCK	1	C.R.S.	$1\frac{1}{2} \times 2\frac{7}{8} \times 4\frac{7}{8}$ (F)	10	STUD	1	C.R.S.	$\frac{5}{8}D \times 3$ (F)
3	LOCATING PLUG	1	C.R.S.	$2.005D \times 2\frac{1}{4}$ (F)	11	KEY	2	C.R.S.	$\frac{1}{2} \times \frac{13}{16} \times 1\frac{1}{2}$ (F)
4	"C" WASHER	1	C.R.S.	$2\frac{7}{8}D \times \frac{1}{2}$ (F)	12	SOC. HD. CAP SCR.	2	STK.	$\frac{5}{16} \times \frac{3}{4}$
5	REST BLOCK	1	C.R.S.	$1\frac{3}{8} \times 2 \times 2\frac{3}{4}$ (F)	13	PIN	1	DR. RD.	$\frac{3}{8} \times 2$
6	CLAMP	1	C.R.S.	$1 \times 1 \times 3\frac{5}{8}$ (F)	14	SOC. HD. CAP SCR.	5	STK.	$\frac{1}{2} \times 1\frac{1}{4}$
7	$\frac{5}{8}$ STD. HEX. NUT	2	STK.		15	DOWEL PIN	2	STK.	$\frac{5}{16}D \times 1\frac{1}{2}$
8	SPRING	1	MUSIC WIRE	WIRE .054D – O.D. $\frac{7}{8}$					

Make sketches on Sheet N-1b

DETAIL SKETCHING
Sketch Views of Assigned Parts, and Dimension Fully

DRAWN BY:

FILE NO:

DRAWING:
N-1a

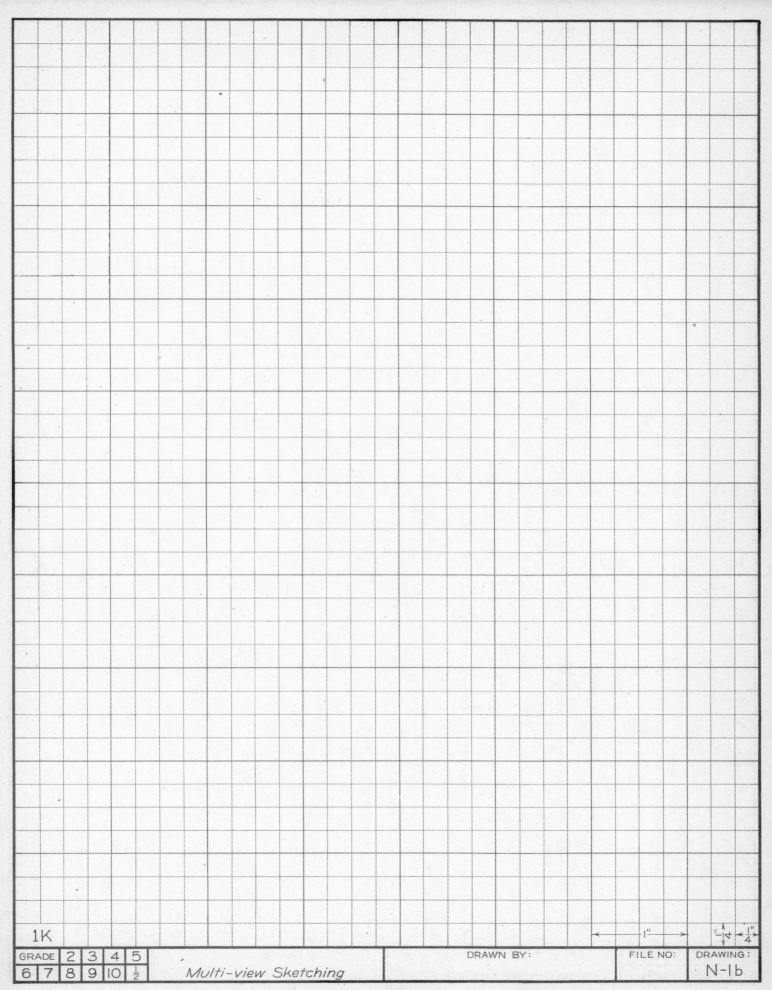

1K

GRADE	2	3	4	5		DRAWN BY:		FILE NO:	DRAWING:
6	7	8	9	10	½	*Multi-view Sketching*			N-1b

Multi-view Sketching

N-1b

Multi-view Sketching

DRAWN BY:

FILE NO:

DRAWING:

N-1b

#1

13" LATHE HEADSTOCK DRIVE SHAFT BEARING

	Answers
1. What is the part number?	
2. What scale is the drawing?	
3. Who made the drawing?	
4. What material is specified?	
5. In what town is the factory located?	
6. What bushing is specified for the lower large hole?	
7. What is the basic size of this hole?	
8. What is the tolerance on this hole?	
9. What is the smallest permissible size of this hole?	
10. How many tapped holes are there?	
11. What size tap drill is used on the longer tapped hole?	
12. How deep is the tap on this hole?	
13. How deep is the tapered portion of tapered hole?	
14. Why are the ¼" dowel holes not located?	
15. How many drill holes are there?	
16. How long is the piece?	
17. How high is the piece?	
18. How many finished plane surfaces are there?	
19. Why are the holes Ⓐ omitted in the side view?	
20. What is the diameter Ⓑ ?	
21. What variation is permitted on all dimensions given in plain whole numbers and fractions?	
22. What is the radius of the boss on the front of the object?	
23. Name operation to produce 1.625" and 1.3125" holes	
24. When is the operation to be performed?	
25. What is the geometric name of the tapered hole?	

Sketch on back of this sheet, full size, Section **A–A** and bottom view of object.

GRADE	2	3	4	5	**BLUEPRINT READING**	NAME:	FILE NO.:	DRAWING
6	7	8	9	10	½	*Answer Questions Briefly*			4428–D

1K

1" ↕1"/4 ←1"/4→

206

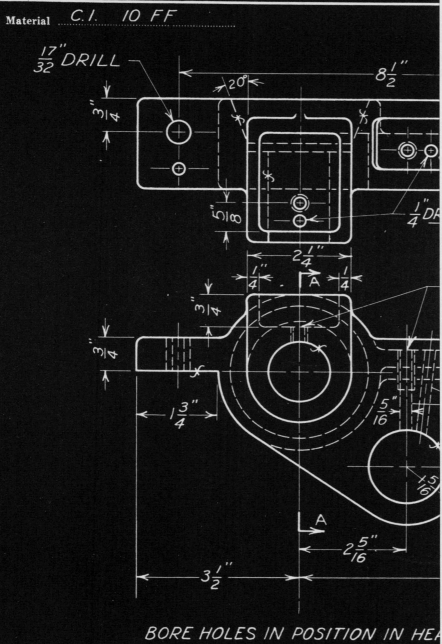

Material ....C.I.....10 FF.........

$\frac{17}{32}$" DRILL

$\frac{3}{4}$"

20°

$8\frac{1}{2}$"

$\frac{5}{8}$"

$\frac{1}{4}$" DR

$2\frac{1}{4}$"

$\frac{1}{4}$"   A $\frac{1}{4}$"

$\frac{3}{4}$"

$\frac{3}{4}$"

$1\frac{3}{4}$"

$\frac{5}{16}$"

$\frac{5}{16}$

A

$2\frac{5}{16}$"

$3\frac{1}{2}$"

BORE HOLES IN POSITION IN HEA

2
SIDE HEAD VERTICAL ADJUSTING GEAR CASE (R.S. HD.)

	Answers
1. On what machine is this part used?	
2. On which side of the machine is it used?	
3. Who made the drawing?	
4. What material is used?	
5. How is surface (1) finished?	
6. What is dimension (2) ?	
7. What is dimension (3) (common fractions)?	
8. What is (4) used for?	
9. What part goes in hole (5) ?	
10. Is surface (6) rough or finished?	
11. What is hole (7) used for?	
12. What part goes into hole (8) ?	
13. What is dimension (9) ?	
14. What is dimension (10) ?	
15. What is dimension (11) (common fractions)?	
16. How is hole (12) produced?	
17. Name the tool and its size for hole (12)	
18. What is the tolerance on dimension (14) ?	
19. What is wall-thickness (16) in fractions of an inch?	
20. What does **R** mean at (18) ?	
21. What part goes in hole (19) ? Spell it out.	
22. What is dimension (20) ?	
23. What is dimension (21) ?	
24. How many hex. head cap screws must be ordered?	
25. What is the total height of the object?	

Sketch on back of this sheet, full size, Sections **A–A** and **B–B.**

GRADE	2	3	4	5	**BLUEPRINT READING**	NAME:	FILE NO.:	DRAWING
6	7	8	9	10	½	*Answer Questions Briefly*			LM–352–A

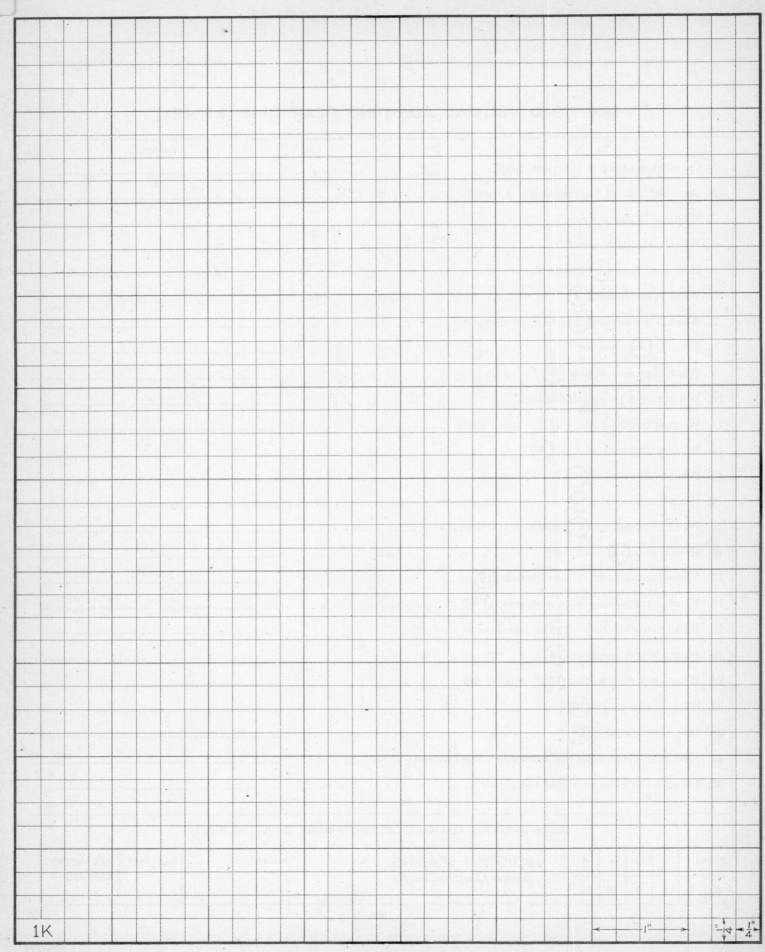

1K

|←—— 1" ——→| |←¼"→|←¼"→|

208

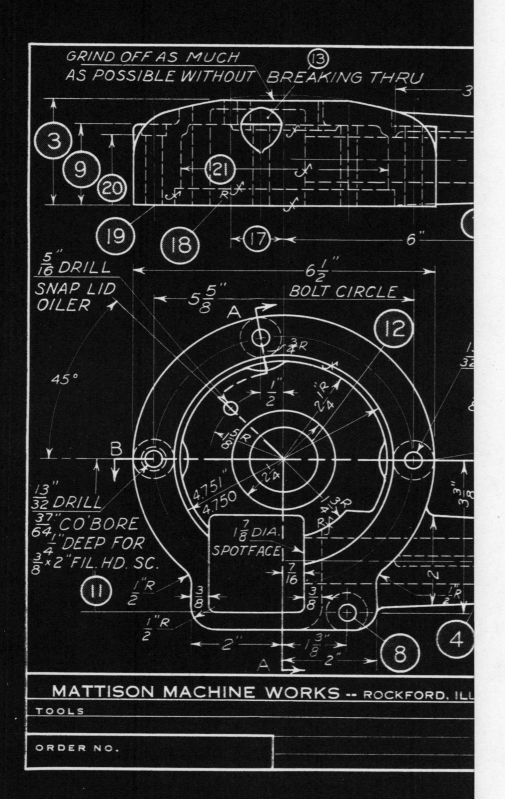

GRIND OFF AS MUCH
AS POSSIBLE WITHOUT BREAKING THRU

GRIND OFF AS MUCH AS POSSIBLE WITHOUT BREAKING THRU

$\frac{5}{16}"$ DRILL
SNAP LID
OILER

$6\frac{1}{2}"$
BOLT CIRCLE

$5\frac{5}{8}"$

45°

$\frac{13}{32}"$ DRILL
$\frac{37}{64}"$ CO'BORE
$\frac{1}{4}"$ DEEP FOR
$\frac{3}{8}" \times 2"$ FIL. HD. SC.

4.751"
4.750

$1\frac{7}{8}$ DIA.
SPOTFACE

MATTISON MACHINE WORKS -- ROCKFORD, ILL

TOOLS

ORDER NO.

#3
SPRING DISC CASE

	Answers
1. On what machine is this used?	
2. When was hole (A) added to the drawing?	
3. What treatment is specified for corner (B) ?	
4. How deep is the spotface?	
5. What is the largest key which could be used in the keyway?	
6. Who made this drawing?	
7. Who checked the drawing?	
8. If "belt drive" is ordered, what should be done?	
9. How many grease cups will be used?	
10. What size tap drill will be used for the grease-cup holes?	
11. How many threads per inch for the grease-cup holes?	
12. What form of threads for the grease-cup holes?	
13. How deep is the counterbored hole?	
14. What diameter is the counterbored hole?	
15. What is dimension (C) ?	
16. What is angle (D) ?	
17. How many cylindrical finished surfaces are there, not counting drilled or counterbored holes?	
18. What is dimension (E) ?	
19. This piece is a part of what mechanism?	
20. What kind of section is this?	
21. Need a new pattern be made?	
22. What is the diameter of the #7 drill?	
23. Is the dotted line behind the cutting plane of much aid to you in the reading of the drawing?	
24. What is dimension (F) ? (To nearest $\frac{1}{32}''$)	
25. What is maximum of dimension (G) ? (In decimals)	

Sketch on back of this sheet, full size, a back view (Sec. is L.S. view).

GRADE	2	3	4	5	BLUEPRINT READING	NAME:	FILE NO.:	DRAWING
6	7	8	9	10	½	*Answer Questions Briefly*			Y68838

1K

1"

1"
4

TAIL BLOCK

	Answers
1. What are letters **A** and **B,** in the margin, used for?	
2. What was dimension 3½ at (A), originally?	
3. What was dimension 0.125 at (B) originally?	
4. What machine is the *tail block* used on?	
5. What subassembly is the *tail block* used on?	
6. In general, what do the small solid triangles indicate?	
7. How many of this piece are needed?	
8. What drawing number is on the drawing which replaces this one?	
9. What drill jig is called for?	
10. What diameter is the cored hole?	
11. What is the pattern number?	
12. What is the first operation called for?	
13. Why are ends of ⁵⁄₁₆ drill hole plugged?	
14. What are the ⅛″ pipe tapped holes used for?	
15. How will hole (C) be located?	
16. How many threads per inch for hole (D) ?	
17. How deep is the threaded portion of (E) ?	
18. What size tap drill is used for hole (F) ?	
19. How deep is the threaded portion of (D) ?	
20. Why are grooves cut in bottom of *ways?*	
21. What operations are used to produce the ways?	
22. Theoretically, what is wrong with lines (G) ?	
23. What is represented at (H) ?	
24. What is dimension (J) ?	
25. How is large hole to be bored?	

Sketch on back of this sheet, half size, the bottom view as seen in direction of arrow **K.**

GRADE	2	3	4	5	BLUEPRINT READING	NAME:	FILE NO.:	DRAWING
6	7	8	9	10	½	*Answer Questions Briefly*			5686

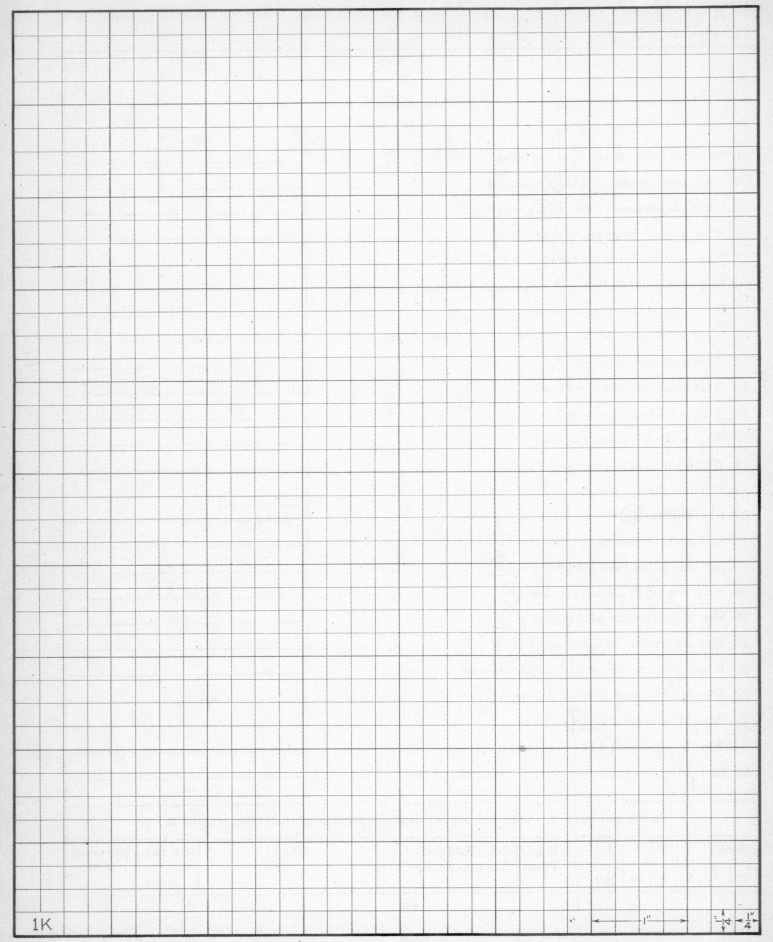

1K

1"   1"/4   1"/4

#5

PUMP BODY

	Answers
1. How are finished surfaces indicated?	
2. What is the over-all height?	
3. What material is called for?	
4. What drawing does this take the place of?	
5. Where will this piece be used?	
6. What was this *pump body* originally made to be used on?	
7. What tolerance is permissible on fractional dimensions not otherwise specified?	
8. What "lot" was this piece first used on?	
9. What operation is specified for surface (A)?	
10. Theoretically what did draftsman do wrong at (B) ?	
11. What does the number at (C) mean?	
12. What is "unorthodox" about the draftsman's fractions?	
13. What special accuracy requirement is specified for surface (D) ?	
14. How far apart are holes (E) ?	
15. How far are holes (E) from the top surface of the object?	
16. What are holes (E) used for?	
17. What is dimension (G) ?	
18. What is shown at (H) ?	
19. How many threads per inch for hole (K) ?	
20. Why is hole (K) not located on the drawing?	
21. How deep is tap drill hole for (K) ?	
22. How is cylindrical surface (N) produced?	
23. What is dimension (O) ?	
24. What is dimension (P) ?	
25. How is hole (R) to be made?	

Sketch the top view of the object, full size, on back of this sheet.

GRADE	2	3	4	5	BLUEPRINT READING	NAME:	FILE NO.:	DRAWING
6	7	8	9	10	½	*Answer Questions Briefly*			106-634

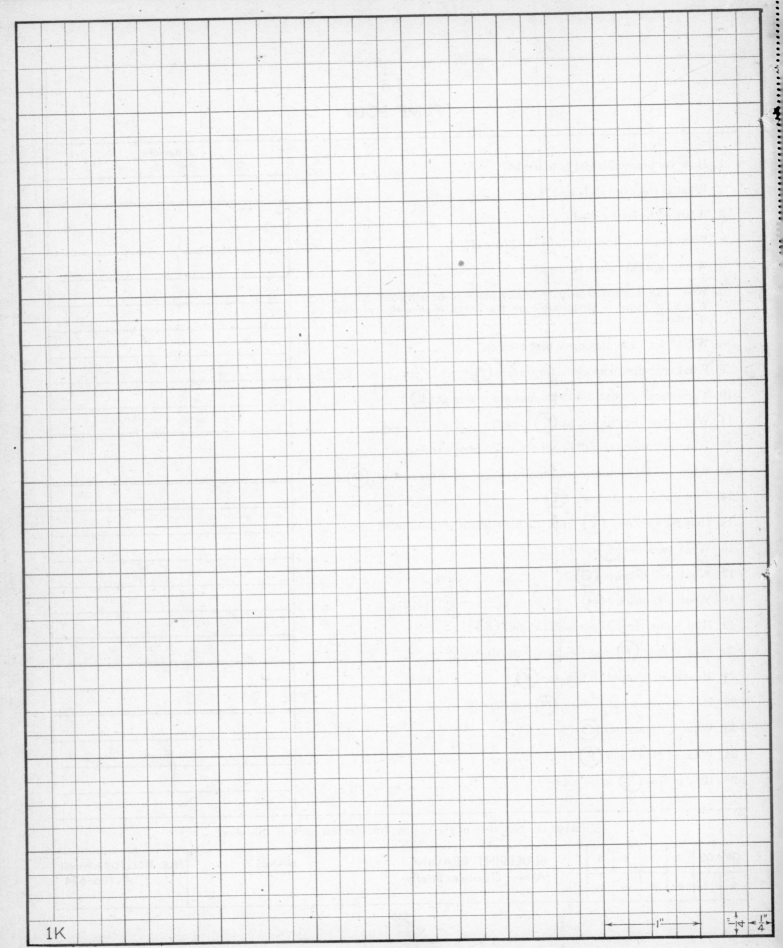

1K

1"

3/4

1"/4

Ⓐ

Ⓔ

Ⓓ

Ⓑ

$\frac{9}{16}$ $1\frac{1}{2}$ DEEP $\frac{3}{8}$ -16 NC TAP

SC · LOCATE FROM 106-572

LLOĪ
LLOĪ ERIAL—

HYDRAULIC IRON

	JOB ORDER No.	

RSEDES	SUPERSEDED BY	MATERIAL
LL FR 569		

#6
SWIVEL WORM WHEEL BRACKET

	Answers
1. Why is drawing number bottom-side-up in lower left corner?	
2. Have there been any changes made on this drawing?	
3. What does "HEX" at (A) mean?	
4. What does "7" mean at (B) ?	
5. What does "2" mean at (C) ?	
6. What does "RM" mean at (D) ?	
7. When is operation for diameter at (E) performed?	
8. What is the pattern number?	
9. How are the six ⅜″ tapped holes on large flange located?	
10. Why are the six ⅜″ tapped holes located in this manner?	
11. What is diameter (F) ?	
12. How many ribs are there? How thick are they?	
13. What is radius (G) ?	
14. What kind of machining is indicated at (H) ?	
15. What is indicated by dashed lines at (J) ?	
16. What diameter is spotface at (K) ?	
17. This bracket is for what kind of gear?	
18. What are the nominal outside diameters of the bearings for the worm? . . .	
19. What is the maximum permissible limit on the dimension at (L) ?	
20. What is the diameter of hole at (M)?	
21. How many holes require the same drill as (M)?	
22. What is the order number?	
23. Is this piece to be heat treated?	
24. What is dimension (O)?	
25. The worm gear could not be, for clearance, of a larger diameter than . . .	

Sketch on back of this sheet, full size, Section **C–C**.

GRADE	2	3	4	5	BLUEPRINT READING	NAME:	FILE NO.:	DRAWING
6	7	8	9	10	½	*Answer Questions Briefly*			7C570

1K

1"

1"/4   1"/4

216

MATERIAL	PATTERN NO.	DRAWING NO.				
C.I.	7P570	7C570				

PART NAME

VORM WHEEL BRACKET

OL CORPORATION, ROCHESTER, N.Y.

B   WORKS

OR PLATE DRILL

ORDER NO. E-4875

BORE WHEN ASB.

WITH #7A465

$\frac{11}{16}$ DR. ÷ $1\frac{1}{8}$ S'FACE

7 HOLES

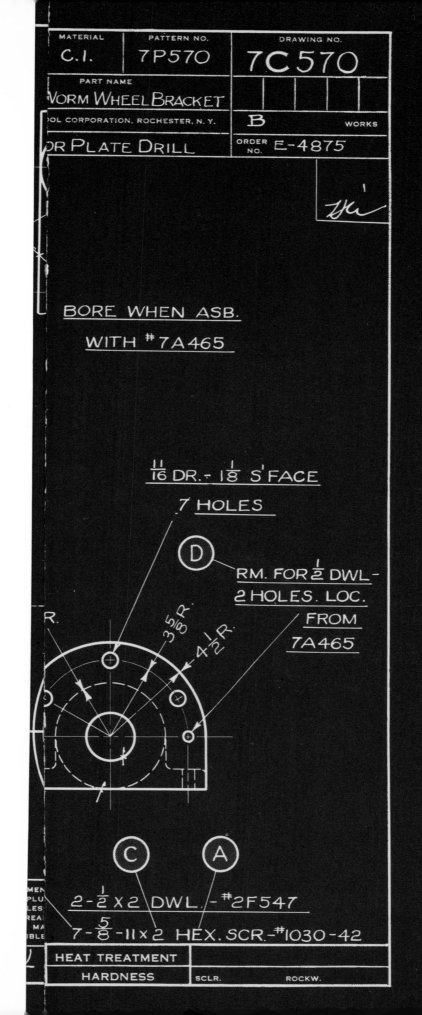

Ⓓ

RM. FOR $\frac{1}{2}$ DWL -

2 HOLES. LOC.

FROM

7A465

$3\frac{5}{8}$R.

$4\frac{1}{2}$R.

Ⓒ   Ⓐ

2-$\frac{1}{2}$×2 DWL.-#2F547

7-$\frac{5}{8}$-11×2 HEX. SCR.-#1030-42

HEAT TREATMENT		
HARDNESS	SCLR.	ROCKW.

7
PUMP CONTROL LEVER

	Answers
1. What does the symbol at (A) mean?	
2. What machine was this piece first used on?	
3. What scale is the drawing?	
4. What kind of surface is specified for (B) ?	
5. What is radius (C) ?	
6. What is radius (D) ?	
7. What is the diameter and depth of drill at (F) ?	
8. Is (H) a rough or finished surface?	
9. What material is specified?	
10. Who was the checker on this drawing?	
11. What type of fit is specified for hole (J) ?	
12. What part goes into hole (J) ?...........................	
13. How is hole (J) to be made?	
14. What kind of surface is (K) ?	
15. How is slot at (L) made?	
16. What is dimension (M)? (Common fractions)	
17. What is dimension (O)?	
18. What thread series is specified for hole (N) ?	
19. What is the decimal value of (P) ?(See table, Appendix, p. 235)	
20. What is dimension (Q)?	
21. What machine is used to produce cyl. surface (U) ?........	
22. What does the numeral 2 mean at (R) ?	
23. How deep is counterbore (S) ?	
24. How many threads per inch for (T) ?......................	
25. How many times is the #10–32 tap used on this piece?	

Taking the left view on the sheet as the front view, sketch on back of this sheet, full size, the bottom view. In addition, sketch, full size, auxiliary Section **A–A**.

GRADE	2	3	4	5	**BLUEPRINT READING**		NAME:		FILE NO.:	DRAWING
6	7	8	9	10	½	*Answer Questions Briefly*				39077

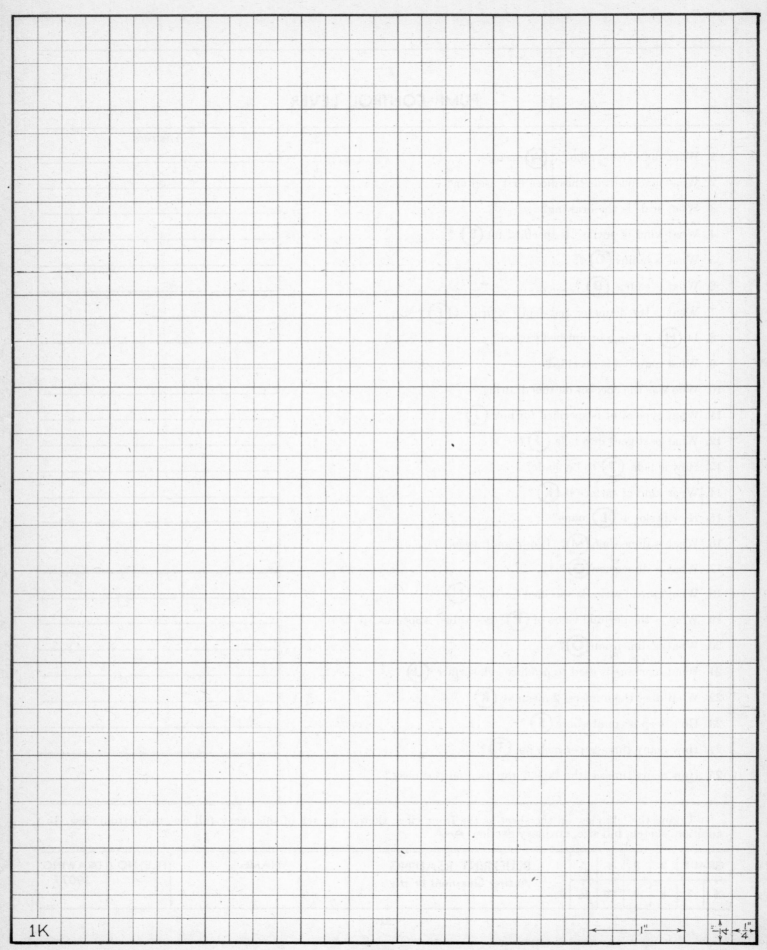

1K

218

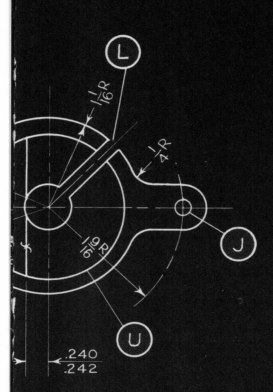

LGEAR CO., MILWAUKEE, WIS.

.341 IN³/REV. PUMP

CONTROL LEVER

. IRON | DATE 1-13-42 | TYPE

CH. Ca.
APP. E. H.

39077

#8

FUEL OIL FILTER COVER

	Answers
1. What kind of rough workpiece was used?	
2. What do you think **MD** in part number means?	
3. How many spotfaces are there?	
4. How deep are spotfaces required?	
5. What does symbol (E) mean?	
6. What does symbol (F) mean?	
7. What is dimension (H)?	
8. How is space (J) produced?	
9. How much is dimension (K) ?	
10. What scale is the drawing?	
11. What heat treatment is specified, if any?	
12. What machines is the piece used on?	
13. If a dimension is apparently incorrect, what are you supposed to do about it?	
14. Who made this drawing?	
15. When was the drawing completed?	
16. How many threads per inch for hole (L) ?	
17. What is dimension (M)?	
18. What is the largest drill used on this job?	
19. What is the outside diameter of the L.H. thread?	
20. What class fit is specified for this L.H. thread?	
21. What was dimension (G) originally?	
22. What is dimension (N) ?	
23. Why is the hole representing the ¼ pipe tap larger than ¼″?	
24. What is the meaning of the ³⁄₃₂″ in connection with some of the finish marks?	
25. How much tolerance is allowable on the machine dimensions?	

Sketch on back of this sheet, full size, Sections **B–B** and **C–C**.

GRADE	2	3	4	5	**BLUEPRINT READING**	NAME:	FILE NO.:	DRAWING
					Answer Questions Briefly			MD1170
6	7	8	9	10	½			

1K

$\leftarrow$ 1" $\rightarrow$ $\frac{1"}{4}$ $\frac{1"}{4}$

220

Central Missouri State University

Central Missouri State University, located in Warrensburg, meets the expectations of a wide variety of students. The location offers the best of both worlds — "small town" friendly flavor, yet within easy access to the activities and advantages of a large urban area. The 1,002-acre campus and 414 full-time faculty members serve the needs of over 9,000 students who are currently seeking educational degrees at CMSU.

At CMSU you will find many top-notch courses with a faculty/student ratio of 1:18, abundant campus involvement opportunities, comfortable living lifestyles and all at a very affordable cost. The best way for you to learn that Central Missouri State University is for you is to arrange a visit to see and experience for yourself.

Any questions concerning the content herein or the department in general should be addressed to:

Dr. William A. Downs, Chair
Department of Graphics, G-206A
Central Missouri State University
Warrensburg, MO 64093
(816) 429-4727

photos by Jerry Schmidt

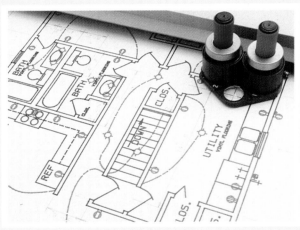

AIDD — Student Organization

Many of the drafting students are members of the CMSU student chapter of the American Institute for Design and Drafting. This organization is designed to give students an opportunity to explore the field of drafting while they make new and supportive friendships. The AIDD members work together to schedule field trips to area industries, to invite guest speakers to the campus, and to attend local, state, and national conventions. Not only do these students learn many extras, they are also meeting many people currently in the drafting industry — this certainly helps them when finding that first job after graduation! But don't forget the fun side, too; making new friends and becoming more active is part of a university experience.

Drafting Courses At CMSU

Orientation to Graphics
Fundamentals of Drafting
Machine Drafting
Technical Illustration
Descriptive Geometry
Structural Drafting
Introduction to Computer Aided Drafting
Production Design Drafting
Machine Design
Civil Drafting
Architectural Drawing
Computer Drafting Systems
Drafting Reproduction
Architectural Drawing — Commercial
Industrial Design
Computer Drafting & Design
Computer Graphics
Special Projects in Graphics
Special Problems in Graphics

Drafting Programs & Careers

Drafting Technology is a four-year baccalaureate program designed to prepare individuals for technical positions leading into management opportunities in industries. Graduates of this program have a broad-based background in drafting and can elect a specialized area of drafting if they choose.

A student has two options for the two-year associate of science degree. **Industrial Design Drafting Technology** prepares personnel for the mechanical drafting facets of industry, while **Architectural Drafting Technology** allows the individual specialized instruction to enter the architectural drafting field.

Positions that graduates of these programs currently hold include: Technicians, Drafters, Illustrators, Designers, Checkers, Senior Drafters, Detail Drafters, Structural Detailers, Patent Drafters, CAD Technicians, Architectural Drafters, Tool and Design Drafters, Layout Drafters, Civil Drafters, and Administrative and Supervisory positions.

The three gentlemen pictured below (left to right) are employed at Stahl Special Company. Ron Zara is Manager of Manufacturing (Mechnical Technology graduate, 1973); Arnold Deevers, Engineering Technician (Drafting Technology graduate, 1985); and Walter Link, Manager of Production (Drafting Technology graduate, 1973).

#9

CONTROL VALVE

	Answers
1. Who made the tracing?	
2. Who checked the drawing? . . . . , ...	
3. What material is specified?	
4. What is the meaning of H.T. at (A)?	
5. How much variation is permitted for fractional dimensions?	
6. What tool is used at (B) ?	
7. What is dimension (C) ?	
8. What is diameter (D) ?	
9. What tool is used at (E) ?	
10. What are two holes (F) used for?	
11. To what does extension line (G) lead?	
12. What is angle (H) ?	
13. What is dimension (J) ?	
14. Why is radius (K) not shown?	
15. What heat treatment is specified?	
16. What does R.C. 58–60 at (L) mean?	
17. How deep is hole (M)?	
18. Why is dimension (N) not given?	
19. Referring to (O), is this a true ellipse?	
20. How deep is depression at (P) ?	
21. How does this company indicate difference in degree of finish?	
22. What are the diameters of the two holes at (Q)?	
23. What is the maximum permitted total length? (Decimals)	
24. How is surface (R) to be produced?	
25. What is the minimum permissible dimension (S) ?	

Sketch on back of this sheet, full size, Sections **C–C**, **D–D**, **E–E**, and **F–F**.

GRADE	2	3	4	5	BLUEPRINT READING	NAME:	FILE NO.:	DRAWING
	6	7	8	9	10	½	*Answer Questions Briefly*			42X–1121A

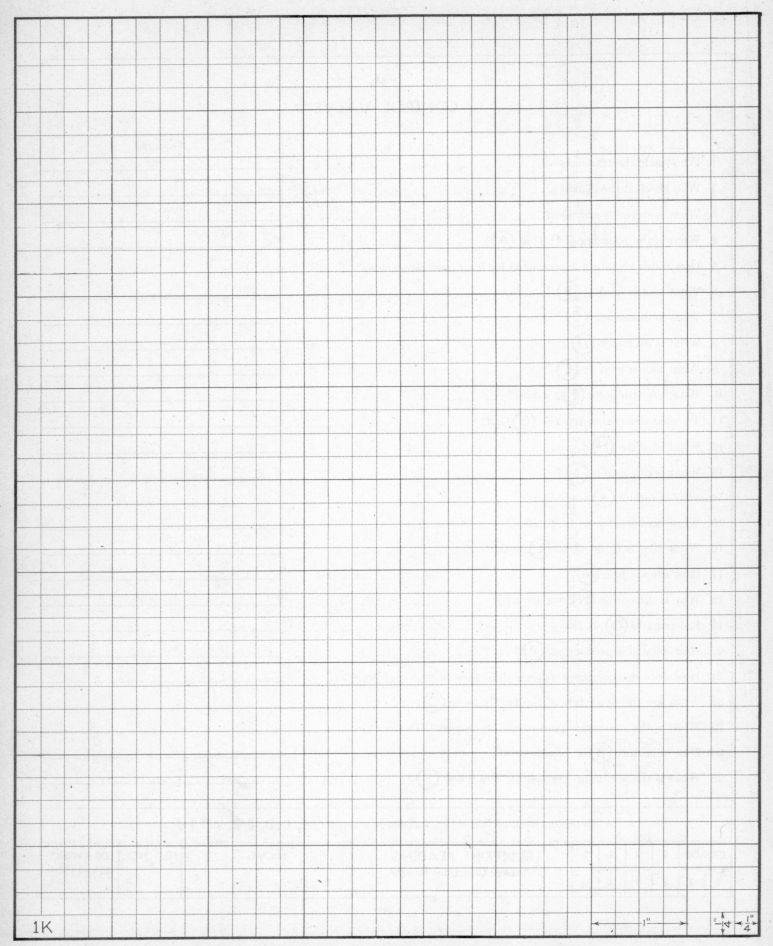

1K

1"

1"/4 1"/4

222

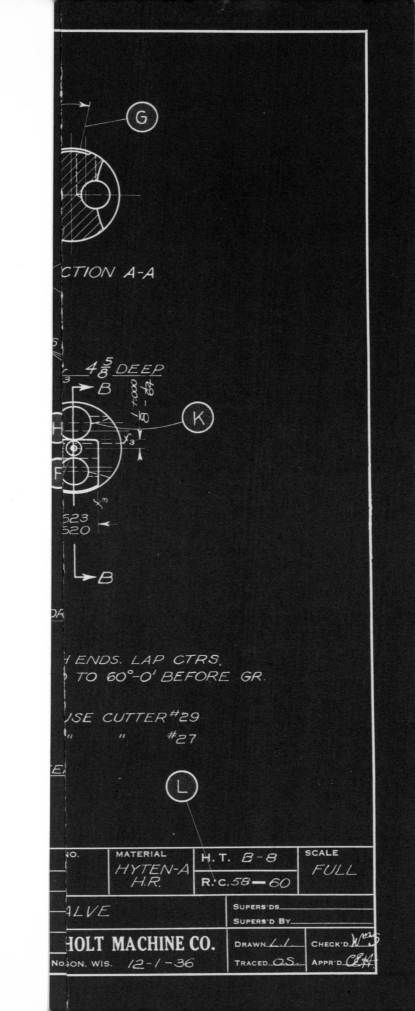

G

CTION A-A

$4\frac{5}{8}$ DEEP

B

K

623
520

B

H ENDS. LAP CTRS.
TO 60°-0' BEFORE GR.

USE CUTTER #29
"   "   #27

L

NO.	MATERIAL	H.T. B-8	SCALE
	HYTEN-A H.R.	R.C. 58 — 60	FULL
ALVE		SUPERS'DS	
		SUPERS'D BY	

HOLT MACHINE CO.

	DRAWN L.L.	CHECK'D
NoSON. WIS. 12-1-36	TRACED O.S.	APPR'D

#10

UPPER BRACKET

	Answers
1. On what machine is this piece used?	
2. What do the letters **D, T** and **C** at (A) mean?	
3. What maximum decimal size can (B) be and still be O.K.?	
4. How many of these pieces are required?	
5. What material is specified?	
6. What do you think C.I.G. means here?	
7. What is dimension (C) ?	
8. How is hole (D) to be made?	
9. What is tap drill size of hole (E) ?	
10. How many times will this same drill be used on this job?	
11. What is dimension (F) ?	
12. What is dimension (G) ?	
13. Why is the pipe tap (H) drawn larger than ⅛"?	
14. To what dimension does note (J) refer?	
15. What does line (K) represent?	
16. To what dimension does note (L) refer?	
17. What is dimension (M) ?	
18. What is dimension (N) ?	
19. What does "normalize" at (O) mean?	
20. How is opening (P) produced?	
21. What is hole (Q) to be used for?	
22. What does U.S.S. mean, at (R) ?	
23. How much are the thread lengths in the four holes at (S) ?	
24. This piece can be packed in a box whose minimum inside dimensions are what?	
25. What is dimension (T) ?	

Sketch on back of this sheet, full size, Section **A–A.**

GRADE	2	3	4	5	BLUEPRINT READING	NAME:	FILE NO.:	DRAWING
6	7	8	9	10	½	*Answer Questions Briefly*			52995

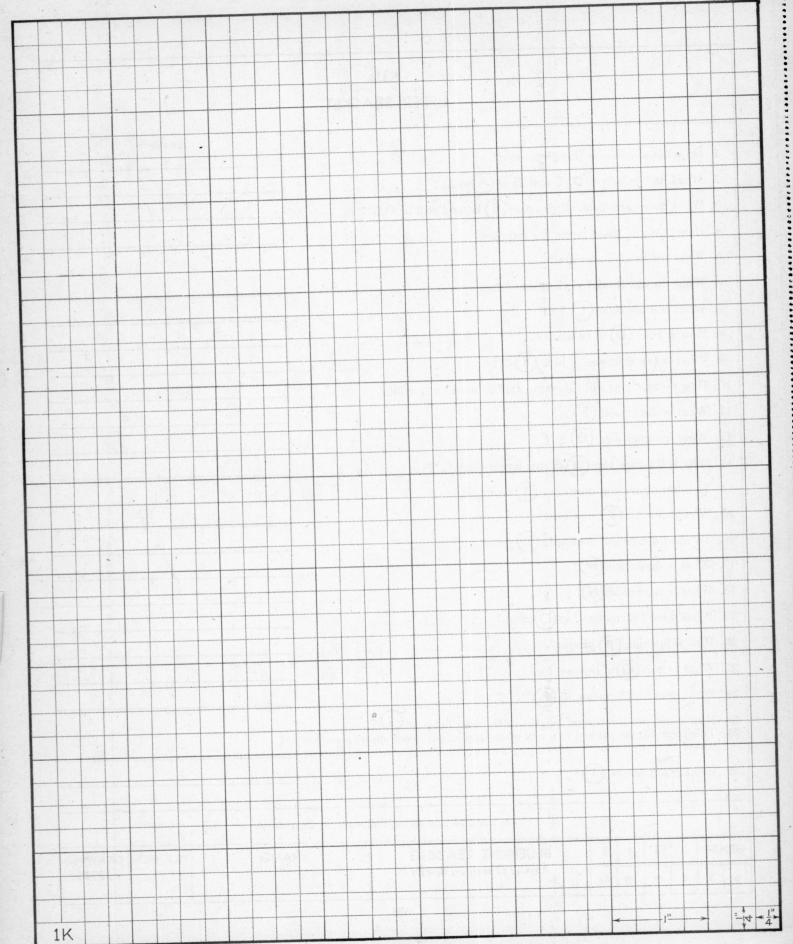

1K

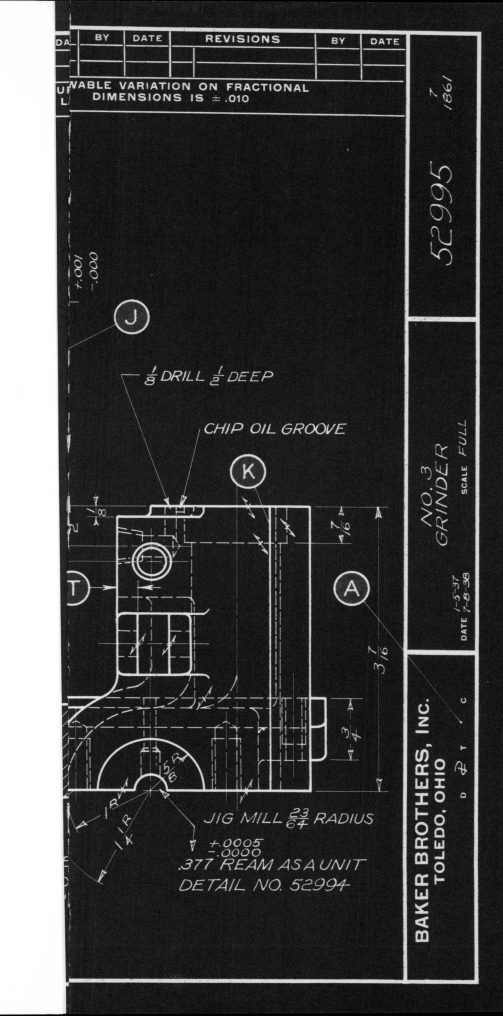

BAKER BROTHERS, INC.
TOLEDO, OHIO

NO. 3
GRINDER

SCALE FULL

DATE 1-5-37
7-8-38

52995

7
1861

	BY	DATE	REVISIONS	BY	DATE
DA					

...WABLE VARIATION ON FRACTIONAL
...L DIMENSIONS IS ± .010

+.001
-.000

J

$\frac{1}{8}$ DRILL $\frac{1}{2}$ DEEP

CHIP OIL GROOVE

K

$\frac{1}{8}$

$\frac{7}{16}$

T

A

$3\frac{7}{16}$

$\frac{3}{4}$

$\frac{5}{8}$ R

1 R

1 R

$1\frac{1}{4}$

JIG MILL $\frac{23}{64}$ RADIUS

+.0005
-.0000
.377 REAM AS A UNIT
DETAIL NO. 52994

11

REAR–END HEAD

	Answers
1. For what machine was this piece originally made?	
2. What material is specified?	
3. Which views are not in their normal positions?	
4. What does **BOT.** at Ⓐ mean?	
5. What does **SP.F** at Ⓑ mean?	
6. How deep is the tap drill at Ⓒ ?	
7. What is chamfer angle Ⓓ ?	
8. What does letter **P** at Ⓔ mean?	
9. What is radius of circle Ⓕ ?	
10. What diameter is hole Ⓖ ?	
11. How many pipes will be screwed into this piece when assembled?	
12. What is diameter of hole Ⓗ ?	
13. What is depth of hole Ⓗ ?	
14. What is dimension Ⓙ ?	
15. What is dimension Ⓚ ?	
16. What size drill was used at Ⓜ ?	
17. How far apart are the holes at Ⓝ ?	
18. What kind of fit is specified for hole Ⓗ ?	
19. What piece fits with hole Ⓗ in assembly?	
20. At what temperature will normalizing be done?	
21. What does machinist do with lettering at Ⓞ ?	
22. What was dimension Ⓟ originally?	
23. What does **B.C.** at Ⓠ mean?	
24. What does **C'T'B'R** at Ⓡ mean?	
25. What does **2** at Ⓣ mean?	

Sketch on back of this sheet, full size, Sections **C–C** and **D–D.**

GRADE	2	3	4	5	**BLUEPRINT READING**	NAME:	FILE NO.:	DRAWING
6	7	8	9	10	½	*Answer Questions Briefly*			38745

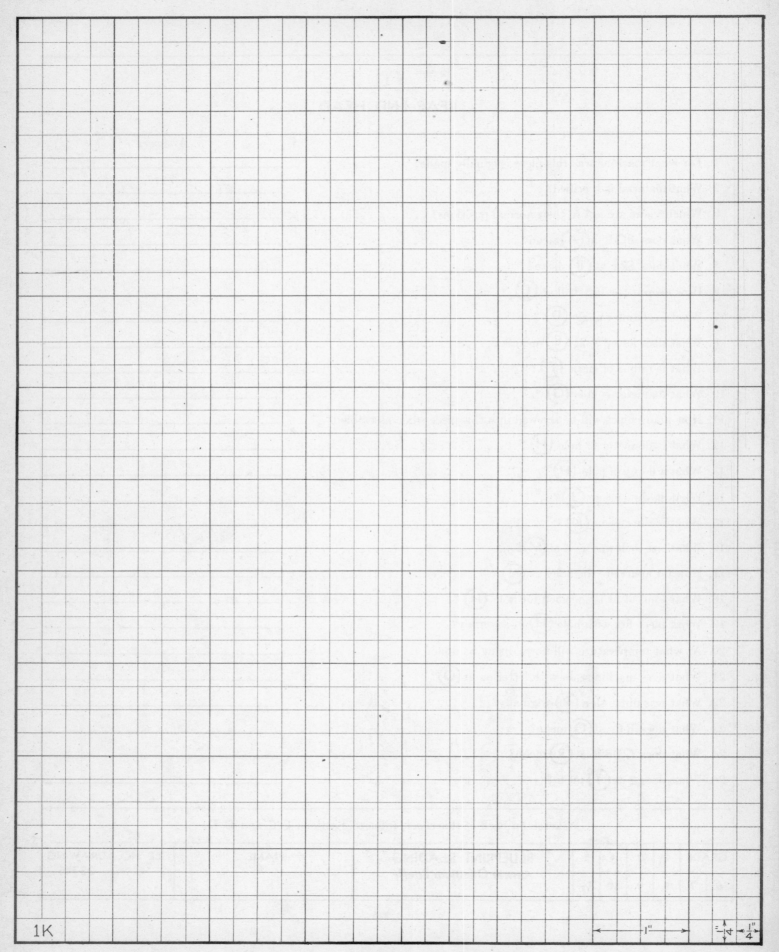

1K

226

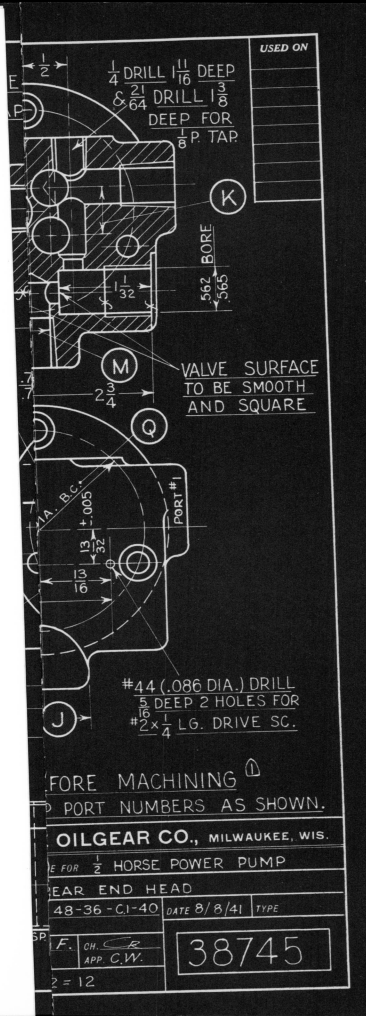

$\frac{1}{4}$ DRILL $1\frac{11}{16}$ DEEP

& $\frac{21}{64}$ DRILL $1\frac{3}{8}$

DEEP FOR

$\frac{1}{8}$ P. TAP.

K

.562 BORE .565

M

$2\frac{3}{4}$

$1\frac{1}{32}$

VALVE SURFACE
TO BE SMOOTH
AND SQUARE

Q

PORT #1

DIA. B.C.

$\frac{13}{32} \pm .005$

$\frac{13}{16}$

J

#44 (.086 DIA.) DRILL
$\frac{5}{16}$ DEEP 2 HOLES FOR
#2 × $\frac{1}{4}$ LG. DRIVE SC.

FORE MACHINING ①

P PORT NUMBERS AS SHOWN.

OILGEAR CO., MILWAUKEE, WIS.

E FOR $\frac{1}{2}$ HORSE POWER PUMP

EAR END HEAD

48-36-C.1-40	DATE 8/8/41	TYPE

F. | CH. CR
APP. C.W.

38745

2 = 12

12

HEAD BLOCK FRAME

	Answers
1. Who made the drawing?	
2. What scale was used?	
3. How many pieces are required?	
4. What material is specified?	
5. What pattern is to be used?	
6. What assembly is this piece used on?	
7. What are the two grooves at (A) used for?	
8. How are the two grooves at (A) produced?	
9. What does symbol at (B) mean?	
10. How is space (C) produced?	
11. What is true radius of arc (D) ?	
12. What is true dimension (E) ?	
13. What is hole (F) used for?	
14. What is (G) used for?	
15. What do cross-lines mean at (H) ?	
16. How many threads per inch does hole (G) have?	
17. What is true dimension of (J) ?	
18. What is the total over-all height of the piece?	
19. What is angle (K) ?	
20. What diameter is slot (L) ?	
21. Have there been any changes on this drawing?	
22. What does (M) represent?	
23. What is (M) used for?	
24. What is the diameter of (N) ?	
25. What size of drill is used at (O) ?	

Sketch on back of this sheet, half size, Section A–A.

GRADE	2	3	4	5	BLUEPRINT READING	NAME:	FILE NO.:	DRAWING
6	7	8	9	10	½	*Answer Questions Briefly*			B–114–1

1K

13
FEED WORM HOUSING

	Answers
1. On what machine is this piece used?	
2. Who was the draftsman?	
3. What scale was used?	
4. How many pieces are required?	
5. What material is specified?	
6. Who made alteration (B) ?	
7. What alteration did he make?	
8. How many core boxes are required?	
9. What is space (G) used for?	
10. What does FF, as at (H) , mean?	
11. What special tool is used for hole (J) ?	
12. What does O.D. at (K) mean?	
13. How many threads per inch are used for hole (L) ?	
14. What is diameter of boss (M) ?	
15. What is diameter of counterbore (N) ?	
16. What is depth of counterbore (N) ?	
17. What does number 5 at (O) mean?	
18. What was original radius of arc at (P) ?	
19. What does abbreviation MILL. FIXT. at (Q) , mean?	
20. What is hole (R) used for?	
21. What material is the bushing at (S) made of?	
22. What fit is specified between bushing and hole?	
23. What diameter is counterbore (T) ?	
24. What fits into this counterbore?	
25. What size of tap drill is used in hole at (V) ?	

Sketch on back of this sheet, half size, Section **C–C.**

GRADE	2	3	4	5	**BLUEPRINT READING**	NAME:	FILE NO.:	DRAWING
6	7	8	9	10	½	*Answer Questions Briefly*			$\frac{710}{500}$ / 3

1K

230

APPENDIX

APPENDIX

I. TECHNICAL LETTERS

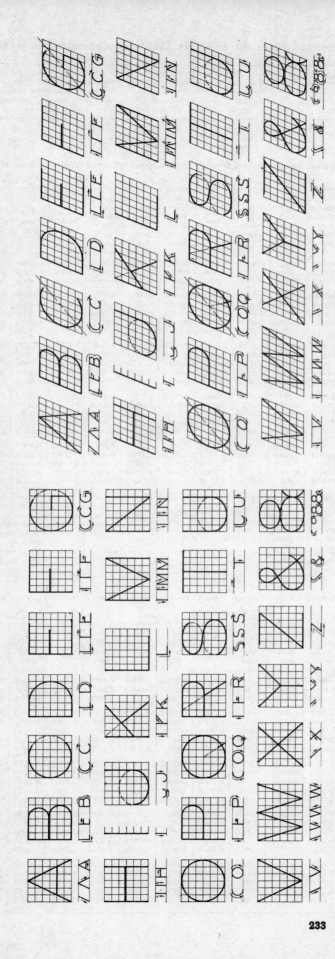

FIG. 176. VERTICAL CAPITAL LETTERS

FIG. 177. INCLINED CAPITAL LETTERS

FIG. 179. INCLINED NUMERALS AND FRACTIONS

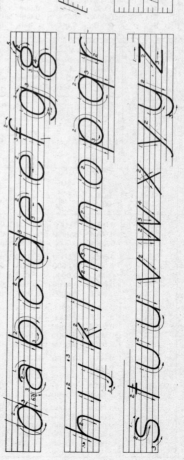

FIG. 178. INCLINED LOWER CASE LETTERS

Class 1 — Loose Fit Large allowance; interchangeable. Provides for considerable freedom — accuracy not essential.
Class 2 — Free Fit Liberal allowance; interchangeable. For running fits, 600 r.p.m. or over, and journal pressures 600 lb. per sq. in. or over.
Class 3 — Medium Fit Medium allowance; interchangeable. For running fits under 600 r.p.m.; journal pressures less than 600 lb. per sq. in. Also sliding fits.
Class 4 — Snug Fit Zero allowance; interchangeable. Closest fit assembled by hand; requires precision. No perceptible shake permitted.

Nominal Size — For basic size, change nominal size to decimal equivalent.

From	to, and including	Class 1 Hole (+ Add)	Class 1 Hole (Use basic)	Class 1 Shaft (− Subtract)	Class 1 Shaft (− Subtract)	Class 2 Hole (+ Add)	Class 2 Hole (Use basic)	Class 2 Shaft (− Subtract)	Class 2 Shaft (− Subtract)	Class 3 Hole (+ Add)	Class 3 Hole (Use basic)	Class 3 Shaft (− Subtract)	Class 3 Shaft (− Subtract)	Class 4 Hole (+ Add)	Class 4 Hole (Use basic)	Class 4 Shaft (Use basic)	Class 4 Shaft (− Subtract)
0	3/16	0.001	0.000	0.001	0.002	0.0007	0.0000	0.0004	0.0011	0.0004	0.0000	0.0002	0.0006	0.0003	0.0000	0.0000	0.0002
3/16	5/16	0.002	0.000	0.001	0.003	0.0008	0.0000	0.0006	0.0014	0.0005	0.0000	0.0004	0.0009	0.0004	0.0000	0.0000	0.0003
5/16	7/16	0.002	0.000	0.001	0.003	0.0009	0.0000	0.0007	0.0016	0.0006	0.0000	0.0005	0.0011	0.0004	0.0000	0.0000	0.0003
7/16	9/16	0.002	0.000	0.002	0.004	0.0010	0.0000	0.0009	0.0019	0.0006	0.0000	0.0006	0.0012	0.0005	0.0000	0.0000	0.0003
9/16	11/16	0.002	0.000	0.002	0.004	0.0011	0.0000	0.0010	0.0021	0.0007	0.0000	0.0007	0.0014	0.0005	0.0000	0.0000	0.0003
11/16	13/16	0.002	0.000	0.002	0.004	0.0012	0.0000	0.0012	0.0024	0.0007	0.0000	0.0007	0.0014	0.0005	0.0000	0.0000	0.0004
13/16	15/16	0.002	0.000	0.002	0.004	0.0012	0.0000	0.0013	0.0025	0.0008	0.0000	0.0008	0.0016	0.0006	0.0000	0.0000	0.0004
15/16	1 1/16	0.003	0.000	0.003	0.006	0.0013	0.0000	0.0014	0.0027	0.0008	0.0000	0.0009	0.0017	0.0006	0.0000	0.0000	0.0004
1 1/16	1 3/16	0.003	0.000	0.003	0.006	0.0014	0.0000	0.0015	0.0029	0.0008	0.0000	0.0010	0.0018	0.0006	0.0000	0.0000	0.0004
1 3/16	1 3/8	0.003	0.000	0.003	0.006	0.0014	0.0000	0.0016	0.0030	0.0009	0.0000	0.0010	0.0019	0.0006	0.0000	0.0000	0.0004
1 3/8	1 5/8	0.003	0.000	0.003	0.006	0.0015	0.0000	0.0018	0.0033	0.0009	0.0000	0.0012	0.0021	0.0007	0.0000	0.0000	0.0005
1 5/8	1 7/8	0.003	0.000	0.004	0.007	0.0016	0.0000	0.0020	0.0036	0.0010	0.0000	0.0013	0.0023	0.0007	0.0000	0.0000	0.0005
1 7/8	2 1/8	0.003	0.000	0.004	0.007	0.0016	0.0000	0.0022	0.0038	0.0010	0.0000	0.0014	0.0024	0.0008	0.0000	0.0000	0.0005
2 1/8	2 3/8	0.003	0.000	0.004	0.007	0.0017	0.0000	0.0024	0.0041	0.0010	0.0000	0.0015	0.0025	0.0008	0.0000	0.0000	0.0005
2 3/8	2 3/4	0.003	0.000	0.005	0.008	0.0018	0.0000	0.0026	0.0044	0.0011	0.0000	0.0017	0.0028	0.0008	0.0000	0.0000	0.0005
2 3/4	3 1/4	0.004	0.000	0.005	0.009	0.0019	0.0000	0.0029	0.0048	0.0012	0.0000	0.0019	0.0031	0.0009	0.0000	0.0000	0.0006
3 1/4	3 3/4	0.004	0.000	0.006	0.010	0.0020	0.0000	0.0032	0.0052	0.0012	0.0000	0.0021	0.0033	0.0009	0.0000	0.0000	0.0006
3 3/4	4 1/4	0.004	0.000	0.006	0.010	0.0021	0.0000	0.0035	0.0056	0.0013	0.0000	0.0023	0.0036	0.0010	0.0000	0.0000	0.0006
4 1/4	4 3/4	0.004	0.000	0.007	0.011	0.0021	0.0000	0.0038	0.0059	0.0013	0.0000	0.0025	0.0038	0.0010	0.0000	0.0000	0.0007
4 3/4	5 1/2	0.004	0.000	0.007	0.011	0.0022	0.0000	0.0041	0.0063	0.0014	0.0000	0.0026	0.0040	0.0010	0.0000	0.0000	0.0007
5 1/2	6 1/2	0.005	0.000	0.008	0.013	0.0024	0.0000	0.0046	0.0070	0.0015	0.0000	0.0030	0.0045	0.0011	0.0000	0.0000	0.0007
6 1/2	7 1/2	0.005	0.000	0.009	0.014	0.0025	0.0000	0.0051	0.0076	0.0015	0.0000	0.0033	0.0048	0.0011	0.0000	0.0000	0.0008
7 1/2	8 1/2	0.005	0.000	0.010	0.015	0.0026	0.0000	0.0056	0.0082	0.0016	0.0000	0.0036	0.0052	0.0012	0.0000	0.0000	0.0008

Class 5 — Wringing Fit Zero to negative allowance; selective assembly. Also known as "tunking fit" — practically metal-to-metal. Not interchangeable.
Class 6 — Tight Fit Slight negative allowance; selective assembly. Light pressure to assemble — in more or less permanent form.
Class 7 — Medium Force Fit Negative allowance; selective assembly. Considerable pressure to assemble — in permanent form.
Class 8 — Heavy Force & Shrink Fit Considerable negative allowance; selective assembly. For steel holes where metal can be stressed to elastic limit.

Nominal Size — For basic size, change nominal size to decimal equivalent.

From	to, and including	Class 5 Hole (+ Add)	Class 5 Hole (Use basic)	Class 5 Shaft (+ Add)	Class 5 Shaft (Use basic)	Class 6 Hole (+ Add)	Class 6 Hole (Use basic)	Class 6 Shaft (+ Add)	Class 6 Shaft (+ Add)	Class 7 Hole (+ Add)	Class 7 Hole (Use basic)	Class 7 Shaft (+ Add)	Class 7 Shaft (+ Add)	Class 8 Hole (+ Add)	Class 8 Hole (Use basic)	Class 8 Shaft (+ Add)	Class 8 Shaft (+ Add)
0	3/16	0.0003	0.0000	0.0002	0.0000	0.0003	0.0000	0.0003	0.0000	0.0003	0.0000	0.0004	0.0001	0.0003	0.0000	0.0004	0.0001
3/16	5/16	0.0004	0.0000	0.0003	0.0000	0.0004	0.0000	0.0005	0.0001	0.0004	0.0000	0.0005	0.0001	0.0004	0.0000	0.0007	0.0003
5/16	7/16	0.0004	0.0000	0.0003	0.0000	0.0004	0.0000	0.0005	0.0001	0.0004	0.0000	0.0006	0.0002	0.0004	0.0000	0.0008	0.0004
7/16	9/16	0.0005	0.0000	0.0003	0.0000	0.0005	0.0000	0.0006	0.0001	0.0005	0.0000	0.0008	0.0003	0.0005	0.0000	0.0010	0.0005
9/16	11/16	0.0005	0.0000	0.0003	0.0000	0.0005	0.0000	0.0007	0.0002	0.0005	0.0000	0.0008	0.0003	0.0005	0.0000	0.0011	0.0006
11/16	13/16	0.0005	0.0000	0.0004	0.0000	0.0005	0.0000	0.0007	0.0002	0.0005	0.0000	0.0009	0.0004	0.0005	0.0000	0.0013	0.0008
13/16	15/16	0.0006	0.0000	0.0004	0.0000	0.0006	0.0000	0.0008	0.0002	0.0006	0.0000	0.0010	0.0004	0.0006	0.0000	0.0015	0.0009
15/16	1 1/16	0.0006	0.0000	0.0004	0.0000	0.0006	0.0000	0.0009	0.0003	0.0006	0.0000	0.0011	0.0005	0.0006	0.0000	0.0016	0.0010
1 1/16	1 3/16	0.0006	0.0000	0.0004	0.0000	0.0006	0.0000	0.0009	0.0003	0.0006	0.0000	0.0012	0.0006	0.0006	0.0000	0.0017	0.0011
1 3/16	1 3/8	0.0006	0.0000	0.0004	0.0000	0.0006	0.0000	0.0009	0.0003	0.0006	0.0000	0.0012	0.0006	0.0006	0.0000	0.0019	0.0013
1 3/8	1 5/8	0.0007	0.0000	0.0005	0.0000	0.0007	0.0000	0.0011	0.0004	0.0007	0.0000	0.0015	0.0008	0.0007	0.0000	0.0022	0.0015
1 5/8	1 7/8	0.0007	0.0000	0.0005	0.0000	0.0007	0.0000	0.0011	0.0004	0.0007	0.0000	0.0016	0.0009	0.0007	0.0000	0.0025	0.0018
1 7/8	2 1/8	0.0008	0.0000	0.0005	0.0000	0.0008	0.0000	0.0013	0.0005	0.0008	0.0000	0.0018	0.0010	0.0008	0.0000	0.0028	0.0020
2 1/8	2 3/8	0.0008	0.0000	0.0005	0.0000	0.0008	0.0000	0.0014	0.0006	0.0008	0.0000	0.0019	0.0011	0.0008	0.0000	0.0031	0.0023
2 3/8	2 3/4	0.0008	0.0000	0.0005	0.0000	0.0008	0.0000	0.0014	0.0006	0.0008	0.0000	0.0021	0.0013	0.0008	0.0000	0.0033	0.0025
2 3/4	3 1/4	0.0009	0.0000	0.0006	0.0000	0.0009	0.0000	0.0017	0.0008	0.0009	0.0000	0.0024	0.0015	0.0009	0.0000	0.0039	0.0030
3 1/4	3 3/4	0.0009	0.0000	0.0006	0.0000	0.0009	0.0000	0.0018	0.0009	0.0009	0.0000	0.0027	0.0018	0.0009	0.0000	0.0044	0.0035
3 3/4	4 1/4	0.0010	0.0000	0.0066	0.0000	0.0010	0.0000	0.0020	0.0010	0.0010	0.0000	0.0030	0.0020	0.0010	0.0000	0.0050	0.0040
4 1/4	4 3/4	0.0010	0.0000	0.0007	0.0000	0.0010	0.0000	0.0021	0.0011	0.0010	0.0000	0.0033	0.0023	0.0010	0.0000	0.0055	0.0045
4 3/4	5 1/2	0.0010	0.0000	0.0007	0.0000	0.0010	0.0000	0.0023	0.0013	0.0010	0.0000	0.0035	0.0025	0.0010	0.0000	0.0060	0.0050
5 1/2	6 1/2	0.0011	0.0000	0.0007	0.0000	0.0011	0.0000	0.0026	0.0015	0.0011	0.0000	0.0041	0.0030	0.0011	0.0000	0.0071	0.0060
6 1/2	7 1/2	0.0011	0.0000	0.0008	0.0000	0.0011	0.0000	0.0029	0.0018	0.0011	0.0000	0.0046	0.0035	0.0011	0.0000	0.0081	0.0070
7 1/2	8 1/2	0.0012	0.0000	0.0008	0.0000	0.0012	0.0000	0.0032	0.0020	0.0012	0.0000	0.0052	0.0040	0.0012	0.0000	0.0092	0.0080

| Size | Threads per Inch | | | Outside Diameter Inches | Pitch Diameter Inches | Root Diameter Inches | Tap Drill Approx. 75% Full Thread | Decimal Equivalent of Tap Drill |
	NC (National Coarse)	NF (National Fine)	NS (National Special)					
0	....	80	....	.0600	.0519	.0438	3/64	.0469
1		....	56	.0730	.0614	.0498	54	.0550
1	64	....	....	.0730	.0629	.0527	53	.0595
1	....	72	....	.0730	.0640	.0550	53	.0595
2	56	....		.0860	.0744	.0628	50	.0700
2	....	64	....	.0860	.0759	.0657	49	.0730
3	48		....	.0990	.0855	.0719	47	.0785
3	....	56		.0990	.0874	.0758	45	.0820
4	....	....	32	.1120	.0917	.0714	45	.0820
4			36	.1120	.0940	.0759	44	.0860
4	40	....		.1120	.0958	.0795	43	.0890
4	....	48	....	.1120	.0985	.0849	42	.0935
5	....		36	.1250	.1070	.0889	40	.0980
5	40	....	....	.1250	.1088	.0925	38	.1015
5	....	44	....	.1250	.1102	.0955	37	.1040
6	32		....	.1380	.1177	.0974	35	.1065
6	....		36	.1380	.1200	.1019	34	.1110
6	....	40	....	.1380	.1218	.1055	33	.1130
8	....	....	30	.1640	.1423	.1207	30	.1285
8	32			.1640	.1437	.1234	29	.1360
8	....	36		.1640	.1460	.1279	29	.1360
8	....	....	40	.1640	.1478	.1315	28	.1405
10	24	....	....	.1900	.1629	.1359	25	.1495
10		....	28	.1900	.1668	.1436	23	.1540
10			30	.1900	.1684	.1467	22	.1570
10	....	32	....	.1900	.1697	.1494	21	.1590
12	24		....	.2160	.1889	.1619	16	.1770
12	....	28		.2160	.1928	.1696	14	.1820
12	....		32	.2160	.1957	.1754	13	.1850
1/4	20		....	.2500	.2175	.1850	7	.2010
1/4	....	28		.2500	.2268	.2036	3	.2130
5/16	18		....	.3125	.2764	.2403	F	.2570
5/16	....	24		.3125	.2854	.2584	I	.2720
3/8	16	....		.3750	.3344	.2938	5/16	.3125
3/8	....	24		.3750	.3479	.3209	Q	.3320
7/16	14		....	.4375	.3911	.3447	U	.3680
7/16	....	20		.4375	.4050	.3726	25/64	.3906
1/2	13	....		.5000	.4500	.4001	27/64	.4219
1/2	....	20		.5000	.4675	.4351	29/64	.4531
9/16	12	....		.5625	.5084	.4542	31/64	.4844
9/16	....	18		.5625	.5264	.4903	33/64	.5156
5/8	11	....		.6250	.5660	.5069	17/32	.5312
5/8	....	18		.6250	.5889	.5528	37/64	.5781
3/4	10			.7500	.6850	.6201	21/32	.6562
3/4	....	16		.7500	.7094	.6688	11/16	.6875
7/8	9	....		.8750	.8028	.7307	49/64	.7656
7/8		14		.8750	.8286	.7822	13/16	.8125
7/8	....		18	.8750	.8389	.8028	53/64	.8281
1	8	....	....	1.0000	.9188	.8376	7/8	.8750
1	....	14	....	1.0000	.9536	.9072	15/16	.9375
1 1/8	7	....		1.1250	1.0322	.9394	63/64	.9844
1 1/8	....	12		1.1250	1.0709	1.0168	1 3/64	1.0469
1 1/4	7		....	1.2500	1.1572	1.0644	1 7/64	1.1094
1 1/4	....	12		1.2500	1.1959	1.1418	1 11/64	1.1719
1 3/8	6	....		1.3750	1.2667	1.1585	1 7/32	1.2187
1 3/8	....	12		1.3750	1.3209	1.2668	1 19/64	1.2969
1 1/2	6	....		1.5000	1.3917	1.2835	1 11/32	1.3437
1 1/2	....	12		1.5000	1.4459	1.3918	1 27/64	1.4219
1 3/4	5	....		1.7500	1.6201	1.4902	1 9/16	1.5625
2	4 1/2	....	....	2.0000	1.8557	1.7113	1 25/32	1.7812
2 1/4	4 1/2		....	2.2500	2.1057	1.9613	2 1/32	2.0313
2 1/2	4		....	2.5000	2.3376	2.1752	2 1/4	2.2500
2 3/4	4		....	2.7500	2.5876	2.4252	2 1/2	2.5000
3	4		....	3.0000	2.8376	2.6752	2 3/4	2.7500

IV. DECIMAL EQUIVALENTS

Fraction	Decimal	Fraction	Decimal	Fraction	Decimal	Fraction	Decimal
1/64	.015625	17/64	.265625	33/64	.515625	49/64	.765625
1/32	.03125	9/32	.28125	17/32	.53125	25/32	.78125
3/64	.046875	19/64	.296875	35/64	.546875	51/64	.796875
1/16	.0625	5/16	.3125	9/16	.5625	13/16	.8125
5/64	.078125	21/64	.328125	37/64	.578125	53/64	.828125
3/32	.09375	11/32	.34375	19/32	.59375	27/32	.84375
7/64	.109375	23/64	.359375	39/64	.609375	55/64	.859375
1/8	.125	3/8	.375	5/8	.625	7/8	.875
9/64	.140625	25/64	.390625	41/64	.640625	57/64	.890625
5/32	.15625	13/32	.40625	21/32	.65625	29/32	.90625
11/64	.171875	27/64	.421875	43/64	.671875	59/64	.921875
3/16	.1875	7/16	.4375	11/16	.6875	15/16	.9375
13/64	.203125	29/64	.453125	45/64	.703125	61/64	.953125
7/32	.21875	15/32	.46875	23/32	.71875	31/32	.96875
15/64	.234375	31/64	.484375	47/64	.734375	63/64	.984375
1/4	.25	1/2	.5	3/4	.75	1	1.

V. ABBREVIATIONS ON BLUEPRINTS

Abbr.	Meaning	Abbr.	Meaning
A–C	Alternating current	CAL.	Calculated
ACT.	Actual	CARB.	Carburize
ADJ.	Adjustable	CAST.	Casting
AL.	Aluminum	C'BORE	Counterbore
ALL.	Alloy	CBR.	Counterbore
AM.	American	C.I.G.	Cast iron, gray
AM. NAT.	American National	CIR.	Circular
A.N.	Army & Navy	CO'BORE	Counterbore
A.P.I.	American Petroleum Institute	COL.	Column
APP.	Approved (by)	C'T'BORE	Counterbore
APPROX.	Approximately	C'T'R'BORE	Counterbore
ASB	Assembly	C to C	Center to center
A.S.A.	American Standards Association	CH.	Checked (by)
A.S.M.E.	American Society of Mechanical Engineers	C.H.	Case harden
A.S.T.E.	American Society of Tool Engineers	CHAMF.	Chamfer
A.S.T.M.	American Society of Testing Materials	CHFR.	Chamfer
ASS'Y	Assembly	CH'M'F'R	Chamfer
ATTACH.	Attachment	CK.	Checked (by)
AUX.	Auxiliary	C.L.	Center line (also ℄)
AWG.	American Wire Gage	CONN.	Connecting
BABB.	Babbitt	COP.	Copper
BB.	Ball bearing	C.P.	Circular pitch
B.C.	Bolt circle	C.R.S.	Cold rolled steel
BHN	Brinell Hardness Number	C'SINK	Countersink
BLDG.	Building	CSK.	Countersink
B/M	Bill of Materials	CTR.	Center
BOT.	Bottom	C'T'SINK	Countersink
BP.	Blueprint	CU.	Cubic
BR.	Brass	CYAN.	Cyanide
BRG.	Bearing	CYL.	Cylindrical
BRKT.	Bracket	D.	Diameter
BRO.	Bronze	D–C	Direct current
B & S	Brown & Sharpe	D. CASTING	Die casting
BUSH.	Bushing	DEG.	Degrees (also °)
BUT. HD.	Button head	DET.	Detail
BWG.	Birmingham Wire Gage	DIA.	Diameter (also ϕ)
BZ.	Bronze	DIAG.	Diagonal
C	Center	DIAM.	Diameter

DIM.	Dimension		MACH.	Machine
D.F.	Drive fit or drop forged		MACH. ST.	Machine steel
D.F.S.	Drop-forged steel		MALL. I.	Malleable iron
DP.	Deep		MAT.	Material
D.P.	Dowel pin or diametral pitch		MAT'L	Material
DR.	Drawn or drawing		MAX.	Maximum
D.R.	Drill rod		MFG.	Manufacturing
DRG.	Drawing		M.I.	Malleable iron
DRWG.	Drawing		MIN.	Minimum
DTL.	Detail		MOD.	Model
DWG.	Drawing		M.S.	Machine steel
DWL.	Dowel		N	National (form of thread)
EA.	Each		NAT.	National
E.F.	Extra Fine		NAT'L	National
ELEV.	Elevation		N.C.	National Coarse
ENG.	Engineering		N.F.	National Fine
EQ.	Equal		NO.	Number (also #)
EST.	Estimated		NORM.	Normalize
EXT.	External or exterior		N.P.T.	National Pipe Thread
ƒ	Finish		O.C.	On center
F.A.O.	Finish all over		O.D.	Outside diameter
FDRY.	Foundry		O.H.	Open hearth
F.F.	File finish		OPP.	Opposite
FIN.	Finish		ORD.	Order
FILL.	Fillister		OX.	Oxidize
F.I.R.	Full indicator reading		P	Pitch
FIXT.	Fixture		PAT.	Patent
FL.	Flat		PATT.	Pattern
FORG.	Forging		PC.	Piece, and pitch circle
F.S.	Full size; Forged steel		P.D.	Pitch diameter
FT.	Foot, feet (also ')		P.F.	Press fit
G	Grind		PHOS. BRO.	Phosphor bronze
GA.	Gage		P.I.	Per inch
GAL.	Gallon		PL.	Plate
G.I.	Galvanized iron		PT.	Point, or pint
GR.	Grind		P & W	Pratt & Whitney
GRO.	Groove		POL.	Polish
H	H-beam		QUAN.	Quantity
HD.	Head		R.	Radius
HDN.	Harden		RAD.	Radius
HEX.	Hexagon		R.C.	Rockwell "C" Scale
HOR.	Horizontal		RD.	Round
H.P.	Horsepower (also HP)		REF.	Reference
H.R.	Hot rolled		REQ.	Required
H.R.S.	Hot rolled steel		REQ'D	Required
H.S.S.	High-speed steel		REV.	Revision or revolution
H.S. ST.	High-speed steel		RG.	Rough
H.T.	Heat treat		R.F.	Rough finish, and running fit
H. TR.	Heat treat		R.H.	Right hand
I	I-beam		ROCK.	Rockwell
IN.	Inch (also ")		RM.	Ream
INCL.	Inclined or included		RPM.	Revolutions per minute
I.D.	Inside diameter		RPS.	Revolutions per second
KW.	Kilowatt		S	Steel
L	Angle		S.A.E.	Society of Automotive Engineers
LB.	Pound (also #)		SEC.	Section
LG.	Long		ST. C.	Steel casting
L.H.	Left hand		SCL.	Scleroscope
LOC.	Locate		SCR.	Screw
LUB.	Lubricate		S'FACE	Spotface

SKT.	Socket	TH'D	Thread
SPEC.	Special, or specification	THRU	Through
SP. FACE	Spotface	TOL.	Tolerance
SN. F.	Snug fit	T.P.	Taper pin
SOCK.	Socket	T.P.I.	Threads per inch
SPG.	Spring	TR.	Tracing, or traced
SPH.	Spherical	T.S.	Tool steel, and tensile strength
SQ.	Square	⊔	Channel
ST.	Steel	U.S.F.	United States Form (Threads)
STA.	Station	U.S.S.	United States Standard
STD.	Standard	V	Finish
STL.	Steel	VERT.	Vertical
STK.	Stock	WDRF.	Woodruff (key)
STR.	Straight	W.F.	Working fit
SURF.	Surface	WF	Wide flange (structural)
S.W.	Spot weld	W.I.	Wrought iron
SYM.	Symbol, or symmetrical	WT.	Weight
T	T-beam, or teeth	YD.	Yard
TAN.	Tangent	Z	Z-beam

VI. DEFINITIONS OF SYMBOLS AND SHOP TERMS USED ON BLUEPRINTS

SYMBOLS

And	&	Center Line	₵	Feet (or minutes)	'	Number, or pounds	#	Perpendicular	⊥
Angle	∟	Diameter	φ	Horsepower	HP	Parallel	‖	Square feet	□'
At	@	Degrees	°	Inches	"	Per	/	Square inches	□"

ADDENDUM — Radial distance from pitch circle to top of tooth.

ALLEN SCREW — Special set screw or cap screw with hexagonal socket in head.

ALLOWANCE — Minimum clearance between mating parts.

ALLOY — A combination of two or more metals — usually a fine metal with a baser metal.

ANNEAL — To heat and cool gradually metals or other materials, to reduce brittleness and increase ductility.

ARC–WELD — To weld by electric arc, in which the work is usually the positive terminal.

BABBITT — A soft alloy for bearings, mostly of tin, with small amounts of copper and antimony.

BASIC — The exact theoretical size from which limit dimensions are figured. See page 142.

BEARING — A supporting member for a rotating shaft.

BOLT CIRCLE — A circle on a drawing, or scribed on a workpiece, containing the centers of holes about a common center.

BORE — To cut a large hole with a boring bar; in lathe, drill press, or boring mill; relatively very accurate. See pages 139 and 169.

BOSS — A cylindrical projection on a casting or forging.

BRASS — An alloy of copper and zinc.

BRAZE — To join with hard solder of brass and zinc.

BROACH — To enlarge a hole, usually changing its shape, by means of a broach (a serrated rod) forced through the hole. See page 171.

BRONZE — An alloy composed of eight or nine parts of copper and one part of tin.

BUFF — To polish or finish on a buffing wheel composed of fabric and carrying abrasive powders.

BURNISH — To polish or finish by pressure upon a smooth rolling or sliding tool.

BUSHING — A replaceable lining or sleeve for a bearing.

CAM — A rotating member for changing circular motion to reciprocating motion.

CARBURIZE — To heat a low carbon steel to about 2000° F. in contact with carbonaceous material (which adds carbon to the surface of the steel), and to cool slowly, in preparation for heat treatment.

CASEHARDEN — To harden the outer surface of a carburized steel by heating and then quenching.

CASTELLATE — To form like a castle, as a castellated nut or shaft.

CHAMFER — To bevel an edge.

CHAPLET — A support for a core.

CHASE — To cut threads with an external cutting tool. See page 167.

CHEEK — The middle portion of a three-piece flask.

CHILL — To harden the outer surface of cast iron by quick cooling, as in a metal mold.

CHIP — To cut metal away with a cold chisel.

CHUCK — A mechanism for holding a rotating tool or workpiece.

CIRCULAR PITCH	Distance along pitch circle from a point on one tooth to the corresponding point on the next tooth.
COLD ROLLED STEEL	Open hearth or Bessemer steel with 0.12% to 0.20% carbon which has been rolled while cold to produce a smooth, quite accurate stock.
COLLAR	A round flange or ring fitted on a shaft to prevent relative sliding.
COLORHARDEN	Same as caseharden, except to a relatively shallow depth, usually for appearance only.
COPE	The upper portion of a flask. See page 157.
CORE	To form a hollow portion in a casting by using a dry-sand core or green-sand core in a mold. See page 157.
CORE PRINT	A projection on a pattern which forms an opening in the sand to hold the end of a core. See page 158.
COUNTERBORE	To enlarge a hole for a part of its length, usually with a *counterbore* tool. See page 138.
COUNTERSINK	To cut a conical enlargement at the end of a hole, usually with a *countersink* tool. See page 138.
CROWN	A raised contour, as on the surface of a pulley.
CRUST	The hard surface on a casting.
CYANIDE	To surface-harden steel by heating in contact with a cyanide salt, followed by quenching.
DEDENDUM	The radial distance from pitch circle to bottom of tooth space.
DEVELOPMENT	Drawing of surface of an object unfolded or rolled out on a plane.
DIAMETRAL PITCH	A ratio equal to number of teeth per inch of pitch diameter.
DIE	A hardened metal piece shaped to cut or form a required shape in a sheet of metal by pressing it against another mating die. Also for cutting small threads and is in a sense the opposite to a tap.
DIE CASTING	The process of forcing molten metal under pressure into metal dies or molds, producing a very accurate and smooth casting.
DIE STAMPING	The process of cutting or forming a piece of sheet metal with a die.
DOG	A small auxiliary clamp for preventing work from rotating with respect to the face plate of the lathe.
DOWEL	A cylindrical pin, used chiefly for preventing relative sliding of two contacting surfaces.
DRAFT	The tapered shape of a pattern which facilitates withdrawal from the sand; or on a forging to permit easy withdrawal of the dies.
DRAG	The lower portion of a flask.
DRAW	To stretch or otherwise deform a piece of metal. Also, to temper steel.

DRILL	To cut a cylindrical hole with a drill. A *blind hole* does not go through the piece.
DRIVE FIT	A fit between mating parts in which interference of metal necessitates the use of moderate force to assemble.
DROP FORGE	To form a piece while hot between dies in a drop hammer or with great pressure.
FACE	To finish a surface at right angles, or nearly so, to the center line of rotation on a lathe.
FEATHER	A key, sunk partly in a shaft and partly in the hub, permitting the hub to slide lengthwise of the shaft.
FILE	To finish or smooth with a file.
FILLET	An interior rounded intersection between two surfaces. See page 158.
FIN	A thin extrusion of metal formed at the intersection of two dies or sand molds.
FIT	Relative size of mating parts. See page 141.
FIXTURE	A special device for holding the work in a machine tool, but not *guiding* the tool.
FLANGE	A relatively thin rim around a piece.
FLASH	Same as fin.
FLUTE	Groove as on twist drills, reamers, taps, etc.
FOLLOW BOARD	A recessed molding board, permitting the pattern to lie in it to the parting line and obviating the need for a sand parting.
FORCE FIT	Same as drive fit.
FORGE	To force metal while hot to assume a desired shape by hammering or pressing.
FUSION WELDING	Welding by fusing welding material, together with the parts to be welded, into a solid mass.
GALVANIZE	To cover a surface with a thin layer of molten alloy composed mainly of zinc to prevent rusting.
GATE	The opening in a sand mold at the bottom of the "sprue" through which the molten metal enters the mold.
GITS OILER	Oil cup produced by Gits Bros.
GRADUATE	To set off accurate divisions on a dial or scale.
GRIND	To remove metal by means of an abrasive wheel, as carborundum; used chiefly where accuracy is important.
HYTEN–A	A trade name for a special steel.
INTERCHANGE–ABLE	Refers to a part which has been made to fixed limit dimensions so it will fit any mating part similarly manufactured.
INTERFERENCE	A fit between mating parts in which the female member is smaller than the male member.
JIG	A device for guiding a tool in cutting a piece; usually it also holds the work in position.
JOURNAL	Portion of rotating shaft supported by a bearing.
KERF	Groove or cut made by a saw.

KEY — A small piece of metal sunk partly into both shaft and hub to prevent relative rotation.

KEYSEAT — A recess to hold a key in a fixed position, as a Woodruff keyseat. See page 128.

KEYWAY — A recess permitting a key to slide lengthwise.

KLOZURE — Trade name for end cover or housing for ball or roller bearings.

KNURL — To impress a design of dents in a turned surface with a knurling tool, to produce a better hand grip.

LAND — The raised portion between flutes on twist drills, reamers, taps, etc.

LAP — To obtain a very accurate finish by sliding contact with a *lap*, or piece of wood, leather, or soft metal impregnated with abrasive powder.

LUG — An irregular (not cylindrical, as a boss) projection of metal.

MALLEABLE CASTING — A casting which has been made less brittle and tougher by annealing.

MILL — To remove material by means of a rotating milling cutter or a milling machine.

MOLD — The body of sand or other material which gives shape to material poured into it.

MOLDING BOARD — A base upon which the flask may rest.

MONEL METAL — An alloy composed of 67% nickel, 28% copper and 5% cobalt and iron; practically rustproof.

NECK — To cut a groove around a cylindrical piece, itself called a *neck*.

NORMALIZE — To heat steel above its upper critical temperature and cool in air.

OILITE — A trade name for a bearing.

PACK–HARDEN — Carburizing followed by casehardening.

PAD — A slight projection, usually to provide a bearing surface around a hole or group of holes. Distinguished from boss by being very shallow, and not necessarily cylindrical.

PARTING LINE — The line around a pattern marking the contact between the two surfaces of the mold.

PATTERN — A model, usually of wood, used in forming a mold for casting.

PEEN — To hammer into shape with a *peen* of a ball-peen hammer.

PICKLE — To clean forgings or castings in dilute sulphuric acid.

PITCH CIRCLE — An imaginary circle corresponding to the circumference of the friction gear from which spur gear was derived. See page 191.

PLANE — To remove material by means of the planer. See page 169.

PLANISH — To impart a planished surface to sheet metal by hammering with a smooth-surfaced hammer.

PLUG WELD — A fusion weld produced through an open hole in one piece to form a "plug."

POLISH — To produce a highly finished or polished surface by friction in which a very fine abrasive is used.

PROFILE — To cut any desired outline by moving a small rotating cutter — usually with a master template as a guide.

PUNCH — To cut openings of a desired shape with a rigid tool having the same shape by pressing the tool through the work.

RACK — A straight piece with gear teeth in a straight line, to engage with teeth in a gear wheel.

RAMMING — Process of forcing sand around a pattern. See page 157.

REAM — To enlarge a finished hole slightly, to give it greater accuracy, with a reamer. See page 138.

RELIEF — An offset of surfaces to provide clearance for machining.

RESISTANCE WELDING — Welding by sending an electric current through the joint of the parts to be welded, under pressure.

RISER — A vertical opening in the sand of a mold to allow metal to rise and air to escape.

RIVET — To connect with rivets or to clench over the end of a pin by hammering.

ROUND — An exterior rounded intersection of two surfaces.

SANDBLAST — To blow sand at high velocity with compressed air against castings or forgings to clean them.

SCALE — The hard crystalline surface of a casting.

SCLEROSCOPE — An instrument for measuring the hardness of metals.

SCRAPE — To remove metal by scraping with a hand tool (scraper) usually to fit a bearing.

SEAM WELD — A resistance weld continued along a seam.

SHAKE — Movement of pattern from side-to-side before removing pattern from the sand.

SHAPE — To remove metal on a *shaper*. See page 168.

SHEAR — To cut metal by means of shearing with two blades sliding together.

SHERARDIZE — To galvanize a piece with a coating of zinc by heating it in a drum with zinc powder, 575° to 850° F.

SHIM — A thin piece of metal or other material used as a spacer in adjusting two parts.

SHRINK FIT — An extremely tight fit obtained by heating the outer member and assembling the parts before cooling.

SLOT WELD — A fusion weld produced through a slot in one member.

SOAKING — Keeping steel at a fixed heat until the piece is uniformly heated throughout.

SOLDER	To join with solder, usually composed of lead and tin.
SPIN	To give form to sheet metal by pressing it with a smooth tool against a rotating form.
SPLINE	A keyway (or sometimes, a key). Usually used in connection with a series of such keyways around a shaft.
SPOTFACE	To produce a round "spot" or bearing surface around a hole, usually with a *spotfacer*. The spotface may cover the top of a boss, or may be sunk into a surface.
SPOT–WELD	A resistance weld at a point or "spot."
SPRUE	A hole in the sand leading to the "gate," which leads to the mold, through which the metal enters.
STEEL CASTING	Like cast-iron casting except that in the furnace scrap steel has been added. The carbon content is 0.25% to 0.65%.
SWAGE	To hammer metal into shape while it is held over a *swage*, or die, which fits in a hole in the *swage block*, or anvil.
SWEAT	To fasten metal together by the use of solder between the pieces and the application of pressure and heat.
TAP	To cut relatively small internal threads with a *tap*. See page 138.

TAPER	A uniform and gradual decrease in cross section, as of a shaft, or a socket.
TAPER PIN	A small rounded tapered pin for fastening, usually to prevent a collar from rotation on a shaft.
TAPER REAMER	A tapered reamer for producing accurate tapered holes.
TEMPER	To heat-treat steel to bring it to a desired hardness.
TEMPLATE OR TEMPLET	A guide or pattern used to mark out the work, guide the tool in cutting it, or check the finished product.
TOLERANCE	Total amount of variation permitted in limit dimensions of a part.
TUMBLE	To clean rough castings or forgings in a revolving drum filled with scrap metal, by friction.
TURN	To finish a surface more or less parallel to the center line of rotation on a lathe.
UNDERCUT	A recessed cut, or cut with inwardly sloping sides.
UPSET	To form a head or enlarged end on a bar by pressure between dies.
VENTS	Small openings in the sand to permit escape of gases in molding.
WELD	Uniting metal pieces by pressure or fusion welding processes.

VII. VISUAL AIDS FOR CLASSES IN BLUEPRINT READING

A. FILMS

(All are 16 mm., and can be rented for nominal charges)

Title	Length	Source
1. *Auxiliary Views*	1 reel, silent	Purdue University Purdue Research Foundation Lafayette, Indiana
2. *Behind the Shop Drawing*	800 ft., sound	Jam Handy Corporation 2900 East Grand Blvd. Detroit, Michigan
3. *Development of Surfaces*	1 reel, silent	Purdue University Purdue Research Foundation Lafayette, Indiana
4. *Drafting Tips*	1037 ft., sound	Pennsylvania State College Central Extension Office State College, Pennsylvania
5. *The Draftsman*	400 ft., sound	Iowa State College Department of Visual Education Ames, Iowa
6. *Graphic Representation of Machine Operations*	2 reels, silent	Massachusetts Institute of Technology Division of Visual Education Cambridge, Massachusetts
7. *Height Gages and Standard Indicators*	450 ft., sound	Bell & Howell Company 1801 West Larchmont Avenue Chicago, Illinois
8. *Intersections of Surfaces*	1 reel, silent	Purdue University Purdue Research Foundation Lafayette, Indiana
9. *Instrumental Drawing*	700 ft., in color, silent	Illinois Institute of Technology Technical Drawing Department 3300 South Federal Street Chicago, Illinois
10. *Laying Out Small Castings*	575 ft., sound	Bell & Howell Company 1801 West Larchmont Avenue Chicago, Illinois
11. *Machining a Tool Steel V-Block*	750 ft., sound	Bell & Howell Company 1801 West Larchmont Avenue Chicago, Illinois
12. *Orthographic Projection*	2 reels, silent	Purdue University Purdue Research Foundation Lafayette, Indiana
13. *Pictorial Drawing*	1 reel, silent	Purdue University Purdue Research Foundation Lafayette, Indiana
14. *Precision Layout and Measuring*	1 reel, sound	University of Illinois Visual Aids Service Urbana, Illinois
15. *Sectional Views*	1 reel, silent	Purdue University Purdue Research Foundation Lafayette, Indiana
16. *Shop Drawing*	1 reel, sound	Bell & Howell Company 1801 West Larchmont Avenue Chicago, Illinois
17. *Shop Work*	2 reels, silent	Purdue University Purdue Research Foundation Lafayette, Indiana

B. SLIDE FILMS
(2 × 2 mm.)

Eighteen strip films, covering such subjects as "Scales and Models," "T-Squares and Triangles," "Geometric Construction," and "Layout Work." Jam Handy Corporation, 2900 East Grand Blvd., Detroit, Michigan

C. FILM GUIDES

Bibliography of Visual Aids of Pre-Induction Training
  United States Office of Education
  Division of Visual Aids
  Washington, D. C.

Slide-Films and Motion Pictures to Help Instructors
  Jam Handy Corporation
  2900 East Grand Blvd.
  Detroit, Michigan

Bell & Howell Filmosound Library
  Bell & Howell Company
  1801 West Larchmont Avenue
  Chicago, Illinois

Directory of Technical Motion Pictures and Slide Films
  Illinois Institute of Technology
  Visual Education Department
  3300 South Federal Street
  Chicago, Illinois

Educational Films for Use in Industrial Educational Departments
  Marvel T. Moore
  Richmond Senior High School
  Richmond, Indiana

VIII. SELECTED BIBLIOGRAPHY FOR BLUEPRINT READING

BLUEPRINT READING

De Vette, W. A., and Kellogg, D. E., *Blueprint Reading for the Metal Trades*, 132 pp., The Bruce Publishing Company, Milwaukee, 1942.

Ihne, R. W., and Streeter, W. E., *Machine Trades Blueprint Reading*, 138 pp., American Technical Society, Chicago, 1942.

New York State Education Department (Bureau of Industrial and Technical Education), *Suggested Unit Course in Blueprint Reading for Beginners in Machine Shop Practice*, 68 pp., 1943; and *Suggested Unit Course in Advanced Blueprint Reading for Machine Trades* (Volumes I and II, 1942), both published by above department, Albany, N. Y.

Owens, A. A., and Slingluff, B. F., *How to Read Blueprints*, 204 pp., John C. Winston Company, Philadelphia, 1938.

Spencer, H. C., and Grant, H. E., *The Blueprint Language of the Machine Industries*, The Macmillan Company, New York, 1947.

ENGINEERING DRAWING

French, T. E., *Engineering Drawing*, 622 pp., McGraw-Hill Book Company, Inc., New York, 1941.

French, T. E., and Svensen, C. L., *Mechanical Drawing*, 300 pp., McGraw-Hill Book Company, Inc., New York, 1940.

Giesecke, F. E., Mitchell, A., and Spencer, H. C., *Technical Drawing*, 704 pp., The Macmillan Company, New York, 1940.

Henry Ford Trade School, *Applied Mechanical Drawing*, Henry Ford Trade School, Dearborn, Mich.

Luzadder, W. J., *Fundamentals of Engineering Drawing*, 568 pp., Prentice-Hall, Inc., New York, 1943.

Schumann, C. H., *Technical Drafting*, 793 pp., Harper & Brothers, New York, 1940.

Svensen, C. L., *Drafting for Engineers*, 554 pp., D. Van Nostrand Company, Inc., New York, 1935.

HAND BOOKS

Altz, A. J., *Chevrolet Draftsman's Handbook*, General Motors Corp., Detroit, Mich., 1941.

Colvin, F. H., and Stanley, F. A., *American Machinists' Handbook*, 1366 pp., McGraw-Hill Book Company, Inc., New York, 1940.

Kent, William, *Mechanical Engineer's Handbook*, in 2 volumes, I — Design Shop Practice, 1938; II — Power, 1936; John Wiley & Son, New York.

Lincoln Electric Company, *Procedure Handbook of Arc Welding and Design*, Cleveland, O., 1942.

Marks, L. S., *Mechanical Engineer's Handbook*, 2274 pp., McGraw-Hill Book Company, Inc., 1943.

Oberg, E., and Jones, F. D., *Machinery's Handbook*, 1815 pp., Industrial Press, New York, 1943.

MACHINE DRAWING

Felten, R. B., *Problems in Machine Drawing*, 186 pp., McGraw-Hill Book Company, Inc., New York, 1933.

Svensen, C. L., *Machine Drawing*, 248 pp., D. Van Nostrand Company, Inc., New York, 1933.

Tozer, E. F., and Rising, H. A., *Machine Drawing*, 317 pp., McGraw-Hill Book Company, Inc., New York, 1934.

RELATED SHOP BOOKS

American Standards, American Standards Association, 29 West 39th St., New York.

Boston, O. W., *Shop Processes*, 630 pp., John Wiley & Sons, Inc., New York, 1943.

Brown & Sharpe Handbook, 317 pp., Brown & Sharpe Mfg. Company, Providence, R. I., 1938.

Burghardt, H. D., *Machine Tool Operations*, in 2 volumes: I, 401 pp., II, 440 pp., McGraw-Hill Book Company, Inc., New York, 1936.

Campbell, H. L., *Metal Castings*, 318 pp., John Wiley & Sons, Inc., New York, 1936.

Clapp, W. H., and Clarke, D. S., *Engineering Materials and Processes*, 543 pp., International Textbook Company, Scranton, Pa., 1938.

Colvin, F. H., and Stanley, F. A., *Machine Tools and Their Operation*, in 2 volumes, McGraw-Hill Book Company, Inc., New York, 1922.

I.C.S. Staff, *Patternmaking*, 66 pp., International Textbook Company, Scranton, Pa., 1933.

Johnson, C. G., *Forging Practice*, 136 pp., American Technical Society, Chicago, 1939.

Jones, F. D., *Machine Shop Training Course*, in 2 volumes: I, 538 pp., II, 552 pp., Industrial Press, New York, 1941.

Stimpson, Gray, and Grennan, *Foundry Work*, 216 pp., American Technical Society, Chicago, 1939.

SHOP MATHEMATICS

Henry Ford Trade School, *Practical Shop Mathematics*, in 2 volumes, Henry Ford Trade School, Dearborn, Mich.

Keal, H. M., and Leonard, C. J., *Mathematics for Shop and Drawing Students*, 225 pp., John Wiley & Sons, Inc., New York, 1938.

Oberg, Erik, *Draftsman's Mathematical Manual*, 265 pp., Industrial Press, New York, 1941.

Thompson, J. E., *Mathematics for Self-Study*, in 5 volumes: Arithmetic, Algebra, Geometry, Trigonometry, and Calculus, D. Van Nostrand Company, Inc., New York, 1931.

Wolfe, J. H., and Phelps, E. R., *Practical Shop Mathematics*, Part I, Elementary, 349 pp.; Part II, Advanced, 318 pp., McGraw-Hill Book Company, Inc., New York, 1939.

TECHNICAL SKETCHING

Zipprich, A. E., *Freehand Drafting*, 149 pp., D. Van Nostrand Company, Inc., New York, 1943.

IX. PICTORIAL DRAWINGS FOR PROBLEM SHEETS

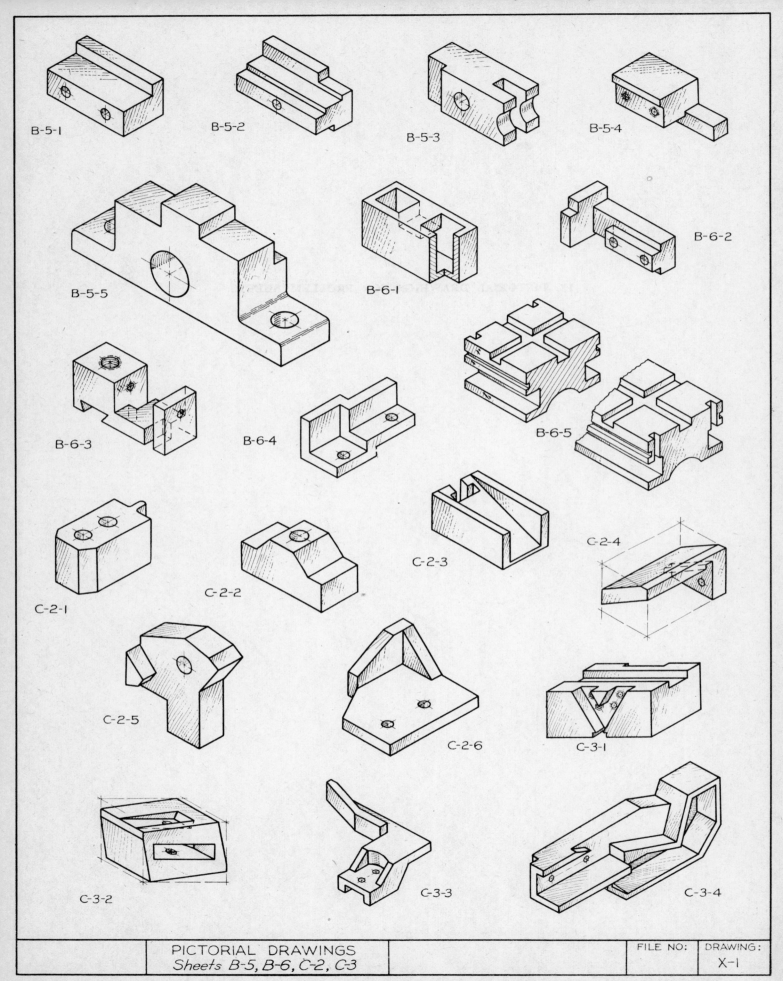

B-5-1
B-5-2
B-5-3
B-5-4
B-5-5
B-6-1
B-6-2
B-6-3
B-6-4
B-6-5
C-2-1
C-2-2
C-2-3
C-2-4
C-2-5
C-2-6
C-3-1
C-3-2
C-3-3
C-3-4

PICTORIAL DRAWINGS
Sheets B-5, B-6, C-2, C-3

FILE NO:

DRAWING:
X-1

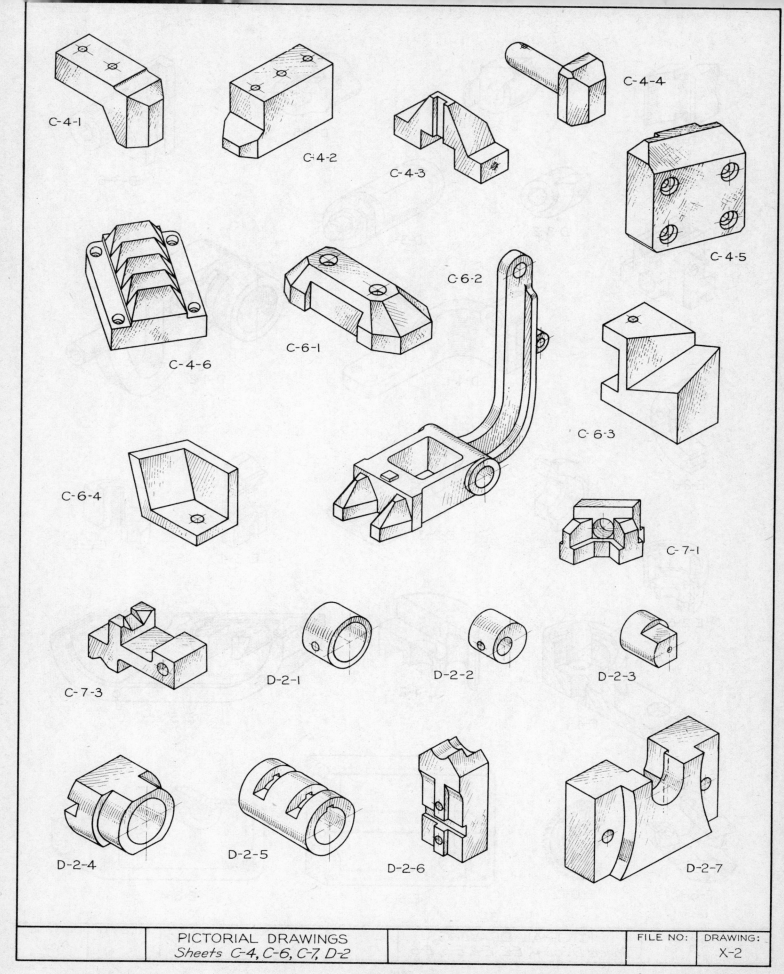

C-4-1

C-4-2

C-4-3

C-4-4

C-4-5

C-4-6

C-6-1

C-6-2

C-6-3

C-6-4

C-7-1

C-7-3

D-2-1

D-2-2

D-2-3

D-2-4

D-2-5

D-2-6

D-2-7

PICTORIAL DRAWINGS
Sheets C-4, C-6, C-7, D-2

FILE NO:

DRAWING:
X-2

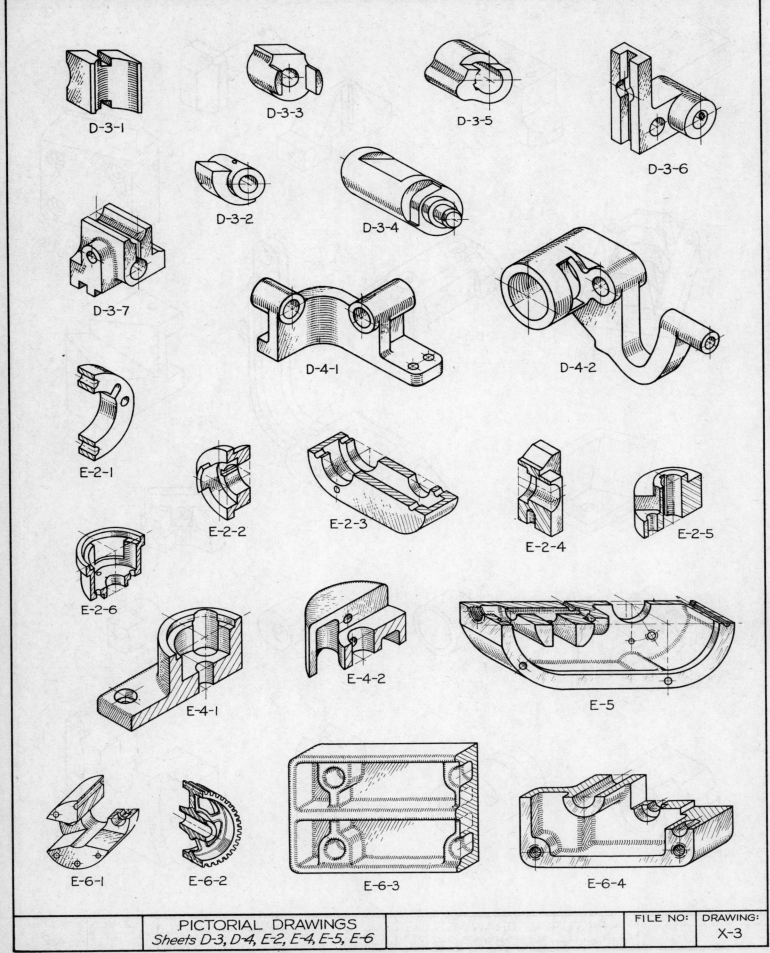

D-3-1

D-3-3

D-3-5

D-3-6

D-3-2

D-3-4

D-3-7

D-4-1

D-4-2

E-2-1

E-2-2

E-2-3

E-2-4

E-2-5

E-2-6

E-4-1

E-4-2

E-5

E-6-1

E-6-2

E-6-3

E-6-4

| PICTORIAL DRAWINGS
Sheets D-3, D-4, E-2, E-4, E-5, E-6 | | FILE NO: | DRAWING:
X-3 |

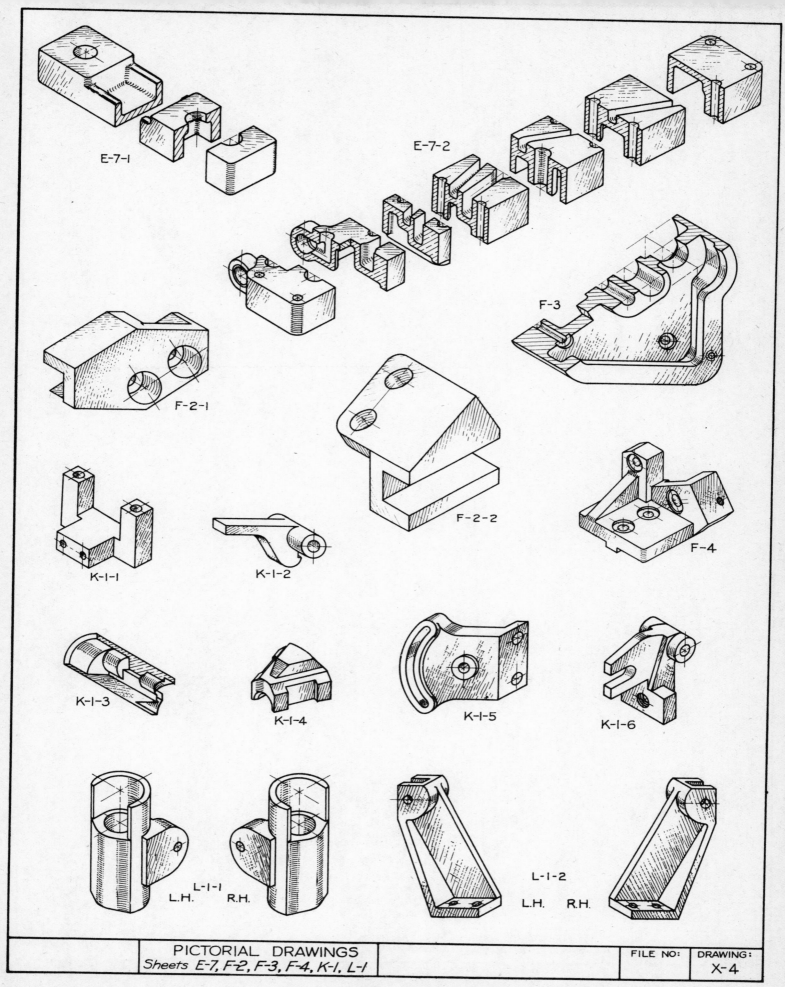

E-7-I

E-7-2

F-3

F-2-I

F-2-2

F-4

K-I-I

K-I-2

K-I-3

K-I-4

K-I-5

K-I-6

L-I-I
L.H.   R.H.

L-I-2
L.H.   R.H.

PICTORIAL DRAWINGS
Sheets E-7, F-2, F-3, F-4, K-1, L-1

FILE NO:

DRAWING:
X-4

INDEX

DATE DUE